Law and Ethics in Dentistry

Third Edition

Law and Ethics in Dentistry

Third Edition

John Seear LDS RCS(Eng)
Formerly Dental Secretary, The Medical Protection Society, London

Lynn Walters LDS RCS(Eng)
Deputy Secretary, Dental Protection Ltd, a division of The Medical Protection Society, London

WRIGHT

Wright
is an imprint of Butterworth–Heinemann Ltd
Halley Court, Jordan Hill, Oxford OX2 8EJ

 PART OF REED INTERNATIONAL P.L.C.

OXFORD LONDON GUILDFORD BOSTON MUNICH NEW DELHI
SINGAPORE SYDNEY TOKYO TORONTO WELLINGTON

First published 1975
Second edition 1981
Third edition 1991

British Library Cataloguing in Publication Data

Seear, John
  Law and ethics in dentistry.—3rd ed.
  1. Great Britain. Dental profession. Law
  I. Title   II. Walters, Lynn
  344.104413

ISBN 0-7236-0933-0

Library of Congress Cataloging-in-Publication Data

Seear, John.
  Law and ethics in dentistry/John Seear, Lynn Walters.—
3rd ed.
     p. cm.
  Includes index.
  ISBN 0-7236-1943-3
  1. Dental laws and legislation—Great Britain.
  2. Dental ethics.
  I. Walters, Lynn.   II. Title.
  [DNLM: 1. Ethics, Dental.   2. Legislation, Dental—
Great Britain.   WU50 S451L]
KD2965.D4S4   1991
344.41′0413—dc20
[344.104413]
DNLM/DLC
                              90-13065

Composition by Genesis Typesetting, Laser Quay, Rochester, Kent
Printed and bound by Hartnolls Ltd, Bodmin, Cornwall

Foreword

You may think that *Law and Ethics in Dentistry* is a prosaic title, but the fact that this is the third edition says something about the vital importance of the subject and the success of this book.

Lynn Walters, a senior member of the Secretariat of Dental Protection has, with the help of many other experts, thoroughly revised and expanded the previous edition written by John Seear.

The growth of environmental, employment and health legislation is creating a minefield for the practitioner. The continuing rise of consumerism and the attitude of the courts to patients' rights mean that professional attitudes must change. Some would say, 'Not before time'.

The general practice of dentistry is a complex meld of professional service, professional ethics and business acumen. The legal and ethical background and foreground which this book provides must be immensely helpful in getting the mix into balance.

I therefore urge practising dentists to read the work from beginning to end. They will find not only reinforcement of half-remembered knowledge but also much that is new. This has to be taken on board if service to patients is to be improved and the risk of litigation reduced.

Thanks to the General Dental Council's Recommendations on the Undergraduate Curriculum, the undergraduate cannot escape instruction on these topics. I know of no more concise and authoritiative work to provide support and amplification of the lecture course. Students and practitioners simply have to take time to come to grips with the constant flow of new legislation and changes in public attitudes.

This is a necessary book for all who are working or proposing to work in our profession in the United Kingdom, Ireland and most countries which substantially follow the British Legal system.

Sir Paul Bramley
Emeritus Professor of Dental Surgery
University of Sheffield

Preface

John Seear wrote the first edition of *Law and Ethics in Dentistry* in 1975. It was so well received by dental institutions and by individuals, both undergraduate and postgraduate, that in 1981 the second edition was published. John Seear retired from the dental secretariat of the Medical Protection Society in 1981 and it is likely that had he not done so the third edition would have been published considerably earlier.

I first became interested in the work of the Medical Protection Society in 1976, and was fortunate that this interest was nourished by John Seear's enthusiasm and total commitment to the concept of the Medical Protection Society and the implementation of its policies in the interests of members.

It did not initially seem too daunting a task to update the second edition; perhaps a few names and dates altered here and there. The eventuality however turned out to be entirely different. The contemplation of the constant flow of important new legislation and regulations has proved to be extremely frustrating both to myself and the publishers, with the result that the most important part of the exercise has been to decide when to call a halt to the updating and actually publish. It will be obvious to many readers that there are significant changes in the pipeline relating to the practice of dentistry especially in the UK that cannot be described in detail at the time of writing, hence the brief allusions thereto in the text. The aim, however, has been to try and present an update upon a complex subject in as readable a form as possible. I have tried to retain John Seear's free and easy style of narrative. I have not made changes to the text simply for the sake of change, and where a case history taken from a Medical Protection Society Annual Report, albeit of many years ago, is still relevant I have retained it.

To say thank you for advice and assistance freely given is very pleasurable, and I would like to place on record my grateful thanks to the Council of the Medical Protection Society for permission to quote case histories and to use other relevant material. My thanks go also to my colleagues at the Society, both dental and medical, for their ready assistance, to our solicitors Messrs Le Brasseurs, London; Messrs. Shepherd and Wedderburn, Edinburgh, and to our legal advisors beyond these shores: Messrs Carson & McDowell, Belfast; Messrs Hayes & Sons, Dublin; Messrs Johnson Stokes & Master, Hong Kong; Messrs Murphy & Dunbar, Singapore; Messrs P. S. Ranjan & Co., Kuala Lumpur; Messrs Robinson Cox & Co., Perth, Western Australia; Messrs Wallmans, Adelaide, South Australia; Messrs Phillips Fox, Melbourne; Messrs Minter Ellison, Sydney; Messrs Flower & Hart, Brisbane: Messrs Murdock, Clarke, Cosgrove & Drake, Hobart, Tasmania;

Messrs Waters, James & McCormack & Co., Darwin; and Messrs MacAlister, Mazengarb, Perry, Castle, Wellington, New Zealand. All of these have willingly and expertly assisted me through the years, together with the British, Irish, Hong Kong, Singapore, Malaysian, and New Zealand Dental Associations and the State Branches of the Australian Dental Association. The General Dental Council in London has given an enormous amount of practical help and advice, and that body together with the British Dental Association have graciously given permission for reproduction of certain material, as has the Department of Health via Her Majesty's Stationery Office.

Even a jack of all trades and master of none certainly could not produce a book of this nature without the advice and assistance of recognized experts in various fields. I have been fortunate to receive such advice and assistance from so many individuals and organizations that it is impossible to name them all. My gratitude has been expressed individually and I trust that they and all who read the book will find the result acceptable. It would, however, be wrong not to thank my wife Rosalyn, a general dental practitioner, my parents and my secretary Nasma Charania for putting up with me through thick and thin.

Finally, I would like to thank Professor Sir Paul Bramley for so kindly agreeing to write the Foreword to this edition.

L.W.

Contents

Chapter 1

The necessity for awareness

'What is my position in law?'
'How should I reply to this letter?'
'What attitude is the General Dental Council likely to take?'
'Is this libellous?'
'The police came to see me today . . .'
'Some solicitors want a report on this patient.'
'The Family Health Services Authority are accusing me of breaches of Terms of
    Service.'

Questions and statements similar to the above are frequently received at the offices
of the Protection/Defence organizations and often indicate a lack of awareness on
the part of dental practitioners of the law, the government and ethics of the
profession, the Terms of Service within the National Health Service and equivalent
schemes outside the United Kingdom, obligations to employers and staff and other
matters relevant to their professional life.

Many dental practitioners during the course of time have to face, and try to
resolve, problems ranging from such apparently mundane matters as complaints
regarding the fit or efficiency of dentures, to actions in law for negligence and
hearings by the General Dental Council in the United Kingdom or comparable
bodies overseas of alleged 'Serious professional misconduct'.

Certain incidents, especially some clinical ones, may be totally unavoidable,
others occur because of a failure to 'exercise reasonable skill and care'. Problems
also arise because of a lack of appreciation of the profession's code of ethics or of a
practitioner's legal commitments. Complications develop from what appear, when
viewed in retrospect, as acts of sheer stupidity. Obvious examples are those
instances where dentists have acted improperly or indecently with patients or staff.
We are all human, however, and as such have our failings, and thus Utopia will
doubtless remain undiscovered and uninhabited.

The dentist who can practise for a lifetime without meeting professional
problems apparently difficult of resolution is indeed fortunate and undoubtedly a
rarity. The writers, following many years in general dental practice and through
their subsequent appointments as a full-time Dental Secretaries to a Protection
Organization, are cognizant of numerous pitfalls and problems that their colleagues
in practice encounter and of matters on which the average practitioner appears to
have a lack of awareness.

Many of these are dealt with in this and subsequent chapters. In the circumstances it would seem only sensible to start at the beginning, which for the dentist is the moment immediately following his possession of a relevant qualification, that never-to-be-forgotten moment of exhilaration coupled often with a glorious session in the company of Bacchus.

The possession of a dental qualification is not necessarily a licence to practise dentistry. In most countries registration with an appropriate authority is essential. In some areas a foreign national may require a 'work permit' and may also have to pass a statutory examination. In the United Kingdom the General Dental Council, 37 Wimpole Street, London WIM 8DQ is the 'appropriate authority'.

The practice of dentistry in the United Kingdom

The Dentists Act 1984

The Dentists Act 1984 regulates the practice of dentistry in the United Kingdom. Section 37 of the Act, sub-section (1), reads:

> For the purposes of this Act, the practice of dentistry shall be deemed to include the performance of any such operation and the giving of any such treatment, advice or attendance as is usually performed or given by dentists; and any person who performs any operation or gives any treatment, advice or attendance on or to any person as preparatory to or for the purpose of or in connection with the fitting, insertion or fixing of dentures, artificial teeth or other dental appliances shall be deemed to have practised dentistry within the meaning of this Act.

Limitation

The practice of dentistry is limited by the Act to:

1. Registered dental practitioners.
2. Registered medical practitioners.
3. Enrolled dental auxiliaries.

(Dental work carried out by dental, medical or dental auxiliary students as part of their course of training is not regarded as the practice of dentistry for the purposes of the Act.)

The General Dental Council

This is a statutory body set up by the Dentists Act (1956) to regulate the practice of dentistry in the United Kingdom. The General Dental Council (GDC) is composed of 50 persons of whom 40 are registered dentists, three are members of the General Medical Council and seven (including one enrolled dental auxiliary) are not registered dentists.

Of the 40 registered dentists, in addition to the President, 18 are elected by registered dentists on a geographical basis (14 from England, the Isle of Man or the Channel Islands, two from Scotland and one each from Wales and Northern Ireland), two by the University of London, 15 by other Universities and Royal Colleges, and the remaining four are the chief dental officers (CDOs) of England,

Wales, Scotland and Northern Ireland. The three persons nominated by the General Medical council participate in educational matters only.

Six of the seven members who are not registered dentists are appointed by Her Majesty on the advice of her Privy Council. Of these, three are chosen for England and Wales, one for Scotland and one for Northern Ireland. Of the six, one must serve on the Preliminary Proceedings Committee and two each on the Professional Conduct Committee and Health Committee of the Council.

The President must be a registered dentist and is elected from and by the council.

The main functions of the GDC are registration, education, and conduct as related to dental practitioners and dental auxiliaries.

Registration

The Council has a duty to maintain the Dentists Register and the Rolls of Dental Auxiliaries. It is the responsibility of the Registrar of the Council to ensure the accuracy of the Register and the Rolls and in this respect he will remove the name of any dentist or dental auxiliary who fails to pay the annual retention fee when due. A dentist whose name has been removed from the register for the foregoing reason may have his/her name restored by making application to the GDC and by the payment of a restoration fee and the retention fee (currently £7 and £37 respectively).

Graduates and Licentiates of the Universities and Royal Colleges of the United Kingdom and the Republic of Ireland are registered on completion of the appropriate form and payment of the prescribed fee. Currently, there are transitional arrangements in force whereby up to January 1994 holders of primary dental degrees or diplomas awarded in the Republic of Ireland may register with the GDC without proving their nationality. Thereafter, dentists from the Republic of Ireland will register under the provisions of the EC Directives and must be nationals of a member state. The Council receives certified lists from the dental authorities of persons who pass their final examinations and is thus aware of those entitled to registration under this heading. The 1984 Dentists Act requires an applicant for registration to provide evidence of his/her identity, good character and good physical and mental health.

Nationals of Member States of the EC who hold an 'Appropriate European Diploma' are entitled to registration on presentation of documentary evidence in support of identity, academic attainment, good standing and good health, both physical and mental. The Registrar keeps a list of visiting EC practitioners. Such a practitioner may render dental services in the UK without being registered upon the presentation of the foregoing documentation and a written declaration giving particulars of the services to be provided and the period or periods in which he/she expects to render them. In the case of an emergency, an unregistered visiting EC dentist may treat a patient provided the appropriate declaration is submitted to the Registrar not more than 15 days thereafter. Disqualification in any EC member state will bar a dentist from registration in the UK.

Dentists holding a primary diploma awarded in Australia, New Zealand, Malta (prior to 1978), Singapore, Hong Kong and the Republic of South Africa are entitled to registration upon personal attendance at the offices of the Council and the production of their original diploma, together with evidence of good standing and good health and payment of the prescribed fee.

Statutory Examination

Dentists having qualifications other than those recognized as entitling the holder to registration may be admitted to the Register on passing the Statutory Examination arranged by the General Dental Council.

Temporary registration

Holders of a 'Recognized Overseas Diploma' may become temporarily registered to enable them to teach, do research work or obtain postgraduate instruction in certain approved hospital posts for a limited period. An applicant must attend at the offices of the Council with proof of identity (passport), his/her original qualifying degree or diploma (with certified true translation if not in English), evidence of good character, a necessary knowledge of English, good health both physically and mentally, and with evidence that an acceptable offer of employment has been made and its duration.

Additional qualifications

Many qualifications in addition to those giving entitlement to registration are recognized by the Council and may be entered against a practitioner's name in the Register following an appropriate application to the Council.

Such qualifications include, amongst others, higher degrees and diplomas granted by Universities and Royal Colleges in the United Kingdom, many Commonwealth countries and the Republic of Ireland. A list of these qualifications is obtainable from the General Dental Council and is published in the Dentists Register.

Work permits

It is important that overseas nationals (other than those from the EC) who wish to practise in the United Kingdom ensure they satisfy the Immigration Rules. It is not the intention of the authors to attempt to detail these rules, which are complicated, but a brief reference to them may be helpful.

The regulations governing entry to the United Kingdom and the control after entry of overseas nationals are described in the Immigration Act 1971, and in the current 'Statement of Changes in Immigration Rules', House of Commons Paper 169 (as amended) available from Her Majesty's Stationery Office, PO Box 659, London SE1, or through booksellers. The rules relating to doctors and dentists are contained in House of Commons Paper 293 which came into effect on 1 April 1985.

The general position under the Immigation Rules is that an overseas national (other than EC nationals) coming to work in the United Kingdom must have a work permit before setting out. The work permit holder presents the permit to the Immigration Officer on arrival and will normally be admitted for the period indicated on the permit. The permit holder will not be allowed to change job without the approval of the Department of Employment.

A dentist coming to the United Kingdom to set up in private practice must meet the requirements of the Immigration Rules which cover self-employed people. The relevant paragraphs of the rules state as follows:

Businessmen and self-employed persons

35. A passenger seeking admission for the purpose of establishing himself in the United Kingdom in business or in self-employment, whether on his own account or in partnership, must hold a current entry clearance issued for that purpose. A passenger who has obtained such an entry clearance should be admitted, subject to paragraph 13, for a period not exceeding 12 months with a condition restricting his freedom to take employment. For an applicant to obtain an entry clearance for this purpose he will need to satisfy the requirements of either paragraph 36 or paragraph 37. In addition he will need to show that he will be bringing money of his own to put into the business; that his level of financial investment will be proportional to his interest in the business; that he will be able to bear his share of the liabilities; that he will be occupied full-time in the running of the business; and that there is a genuine need for his services and investment. In no case should the amount of money to be invested by the applicant be less than £150 000 and evidence that this amount or more is under his control and disposable in the United Kingdom must be produced.

36. Where the applicant intends to take over, or join as a partner, an existing business, he will need, in addition to meeting the requirements of the preceding paragraph, to show that his share of the profits will be sufficient to maintain and accommodate him and his dependents. Audited accounts of the business for previous years must be produced to the entry clearance officer in order to establish the precise financial position, together with a written statement of the terms on which he is to enter or take over the business. There must be evidence to show that his services and investment will create new, paid, full-time employment in the business for persons already settled here. An entry clearance is to be refused if an applicant cannot satisfy all the relevant requirements of this or the preceding paragraph or where it appears that the proposed partnership or directorship amounts to disguised employment or where it seems likely that, to obtain a livelihood, the applicant will have to supplement his business activities by employment of any kind or by recourse to public funds.

37. If the applicant wishes to establish a new business in the United Kingdom on his own account or to be self-employed he will need to meet the requirements of paragraph 35 and satisfy the entry clearance officer that he will be bringing into the country sufficient funds of his own to establish an enterprise that can realistically be expected to maintain and accommodate him and any dependants without recourse to employment of any kind (other than his self-employment) or to public funds. He will need to show in addition that the business will provide new, paid, full-time employment in the business for persons already settled here. An entry clearance is to be refused if an applicant cannot satisfy all the requirements of this paragraph and of paragraph 35.

A dentist seeking entry into the United Kingdom for postgraduate training in hospital will not require a work permit, but will be required to satisfy the Immigration Officer of his/her eligibility for full or temporary registration with the General Dental Council, and that he/she intends to leave the United Kingdom upon completion of the training period. The total period which may be spent in the United Kingdom for the purpose of post-graduate training is four years.

Further information about work permits can be obtained from the Department of Employment, Overseas Labour Section, Caxton House, Tothill Street, London SW1 0NF.

Education

The Council's duty to maintain the Register requires it to supervise standards of dental education, and the Dentists Act 1984 gives the Council explicit responsibility for this supervision to relate to dental education 'at all its stages', thus incorporating postgraduate as well as undergraduate education. The Council determines minimum standards necessary for the efficient practice of dentistry, issues 'Recommendations Concerning the Dental Curriculum', arranges visitations to dental schools and examinations to ensure that minimum standards are maintained in the light of the 'Recommendations', and has the power to recommend the withdrawal of recognition of a qualification which it considers no longer secures possession of the requisite knowledge and skill.

Conduct

As the Council supervises the educational standards for entry to the Register, so it has a duty to remove from the Register those whose conduct, after investigation, shows they are not fit to remain on it.

A booklet entitled 'Professional Conduct and Fitness to Practice' is issued by the General Dental Council to all registered practitioners and is also published in the Dentists Register. It is reprinted on pages 7–16, in full, with the kind permission of the Council.

Appeal against disciplinary suspension or erasure

There is no right of appeal against a finding by the Professional Conduct Committee of 'guilty of serious professional misconduct'. There is, however, a right of appeal against the determination to suspend or erase from the Register. This has to be lodged with the Judicial Committee of the Privy Council within 28 days from the service of the notification of the determination of the Professional Conduct Committee. Immediate suspension from the Register does not deny the right of appeal but remains in force until either the 28 day limit to lodge an appeal expires or an appeal is decided. Appeals, when appropriate, may be carried out by a protection organization on behalf of its member.

Restoration after disciplinary suspension or erasure

Where the Professional Conduct Committee directs a dentist's name be suspended from the Register, it will be for a set period of time not exceeding 12 months, after which restoration is automatic.

Where the Professional Conduct Committee directs a dentist's name be erased from the Register, application for restoration to the Register cannot be made within 10 months from the date of erasure, or 10 months from the date of a previous application. Such applications are considered by the Professional Conduct Committee. The person involved is expected to explain his conduct in the interim and persuade the Committee that he will, in future, prove a satisfactory and respectable member of the profession. A person applying for restoration is now permitted to be represented by a legal adviser or friend during the hearing.

Professional Conduct and Fitness to Practise

1. The purpose of this booklet is to advise dentists about the statutory functions of the General Dental Council in relation to their professional conduct and fitness to practise. It describes the machinery by means of which the Council fulfils these functions and contains guidance on specific aspects of professional conduct and ethical practice. Dentists requiring further advice on any matter referred to in the booklet should consult their defence society or professional association.

Education
2. In connection with its statutory remit to promote high standards of dental education at all its stages, the Council has issued a Statement of Intent on Postgraduate Education. The statement is reproduced as an annexure to this pamphlet. All dentists have a duty to continue their professional education for the duration of their practising lives in the best interests of their patients. Dentists who fail to maintain and update their professional skills and who, as a result, provide treatment that falls short of the standard which the public and the profession have a right to expect may be liable to proceedings for misconduct.

Registration
3. Dentists should be aware that it is an offence against the Dentists Act 1984, for an unregistered person to engage in the practice of dentistry and it is the responsibility of all dentists who intend to practise to renew their registration annually. Failure to do so may lead to disciplinary proceedings.

Professional conduct

4. One of the principal functions of the General Dental Council under the Dentists Act 1984 is to promote high standards of professional conduct among dentist. Dentists have a duty to ensure that, at all times, their conduct is compatible with the high standard which the public and their profession have a right to expect from them and that their responsibility to their patients is their first priority. Section 27 of the Act provides that a dentist shall be liable to have his name erased from the Dentists Register or his registration suspended if, either before or after he is registered, he has been convicted of a criminal offence or has been guilty of serious professional misconduct. References in the booklet to 'misconduct', 'professional misconduct', 'unprofessional conduct' or 'unethical behaviour' may all be considered to indicate 'serious professional misconduct'.

5. This booklet refers to the Council's procedures for dealing with misconduct and indicates for the information and guidance of dentists the kinds of offences which have in the past led to action being taken by the Council; the pamphlet is not a complete list of offences which may lead to erasure nor should it be regarded as a comprehensive guide to professional ethics.

6. The Council's jurisdiction in cases of professional misconduct and criminal offences extends to all registered dentists.

7. The Council receives information concerning convictions (except for minor offences) from the police and notifies the dentist concerned that the information has been received. The Council also receives from the appropriate public authorities information concerning inquiries under the National Health Service by a Dental Service Committee or Tribunal which reveal any indication of serious professional misconduct by a dentist. A complaint alleging that a dentist has been guilty of serious

professional misconduct may be made by any member of the public. However, unless it is made by a person acting in a public capacity*, it must be supported by one or more statutory declarations/affidavits. The dentist concerned is informed about any such complaint or information, including its source, and is given a copy of any statutory declaration/affidavit; the dentist is invited to submit any explanation or observations he or she may have to offer.

8. The Council attaches great importance to membership of a defence society for every dentist involved in the treatment of patients, both in the interests of patients, for whom compensation may be provided in appropriate circumstances, and in the interests of dentists who then have access to assistance and representation in connection with professional, legal and disciplinary matters. Dentists who require advice in connection with such matters would be well advised to contact their defence society or professional association without delay.

Preliminary Proceedings Committee

9. Reports of convictions and complaints or information relating to conduct are considered in the first instance by the Preliminary Proceedings Committee, which sits in private. The Committee normally meets twice a year, in March and September, but may meet at any other time as circumstances require, to consider whether or not a case should be referred to the Professional Conduct Committee for a public inquiry. It may decide that no prima facie case has been made against the dentist and that no action should be taken. It may decide that no inquiry shall be held but that the dentist should be warned that it may reconsider its decision if any further information about him or her comes to its notice. If it decides to refer the matter to the Professional Conduct Committee a formal 'notice of inquiry' is sent to the dentist by the Council's Solicitors at least four weeks before the date of the Professional Conduct Committee meeting.

Interim suspension

10. If, having decided to refer a case to the Professional Conduct Committee, the Preliminary Proceedings Committee is satisfied that it is necessary for the protection of members of the public, it may order that the dentist's registration be suspended immediately pending a determination by the Professional Conduct Committee. The Preliminary Proceedings Committee may not make such an order unless it has afforded the dentist an opportunity to make representations, in person or through advisers, concerning whether the order should be made. The dentist has the right to apply to the High Court for the termination of any such order.

Professional Conduct Committee

11. The Professional Conduct Committee also normally meets twice a year, in May and November, but may meet at any time. The Committee sits in public. A legal assessor who is a barrister or solicitor of not less than ten years standing attends the proceedings of the Committee to advise it on matters of law. Evidence is taken on oath and any party to the proceedings may subpoena witnesses. The procedure is set out in a statutory instrument (General Dental Council Professional Conduct Committee (Procedure) Rules 1984). The rules of evidence are almost the same as those in a court

---

*A person acting in a public capacity means an officer of a Health Authority, Health Board, or of a Government department or of a local or public authority or of any of the dental authorities (i.e. university or other body granting dental diplomas) acting as such, or the Solicitors to the Council, or any person holding judicial office, or any officer attached to a court.

of law and the standard of proof is the same as in criminal proceedings, namely beyond reasonable doubt. The parties may be legally represented.

12. If at the inquiry the Professional Conduct Committee finds that the dentist has been convicted or has been guilty of serious professional misconduct it then has to decide whether the gravity of the offence which the dentist has committed, or the cumulative gravity of the offences committed on more than one occasion, makes it necessary in the public interest to erase the dentist's name from the Dentists Register or to suspend his or her registration. It may reach a decision immediately or may postpone its decision until a future meeting of the Committee at which it will have an opportunity of considering the dentist's conduct during the intervening period. If it decides that the name should be erased or the registration be suspended, the determination takes effect after 28 days unless during that period the dentist appeals to the Judicial Committee of the Privy Council. If, however, it appears that it is necessary for the protection of members of the public or that it would be in the interests of the dentist, the Committee may order that the determination should take immediate effect, notwithstanding any appeal that may be made against the determination.

13. A dentist whose name has been erased from the Dentists Register following a conviction or for misconduct may apply for restoration not less than ten months after erasure. In considering such applications, the Professional Conduct Committee will take account of the circumstances which led to the dentist's erasure, together with any evidence of professional rehabilitation submitted by the applicant.

Convictions

14. Dentists should be aware that, when considering convictions, the Professional Conduct Committee accepts the findings of the court on matters of fact as sufficient proof of those facts; it is therefore unwise for dentists to plead guilty in a court of law to charges of which they believe they are innocent, since such pleas will be regarded by the court, and subsequently by the Committee, as admissions that the charges were well founded. Dentists are not, therefore, permitted to go behind the conviction at an inquiry before the Committee in an effort to claim that they are innocent of the charge. The Committee is not precluded from considering convictions for offences which are not directly connected with the dentist's profession or practice, or which occurred while the dentist was not registered.

15. Some of the offences which have in the past led to proceedings before the Committee include criminal deception (formerly known as false pretences), forgery, theft and comparable offences; offences involving drunkenness or misuse of drugs; and offences involving indecency.

Serious professional misconduct

16. The kind of conduct which may be regarded by the Professional Conduct Committee as serious professional misconduct is not defined or limited and is likely to vary with the circumstances of the time. The Council will in general hold dentists responsible for the actions of their employees. Dentists should, therefore, ensure that their staff are sufficiently well trained to enable them to carry out competently the tasks which are allotted to them. In the case of enrolled dental hygienists or dental therapists, these tasks must be within the limitations set by the Dental Auxiliaries Regulations, 1986. Examples are given below of types of conduct which have in the past given rise to complaint leading to action being taken by the Council. The list is not, and cannot be, exhaustive and dentists who are in doubt or who need advice

about professional ethics should consult their professional association or defence society.

General anaesthesia and sedation
17. Where a general anaesthetic is administered, the Council considers that it should be by a person, other than the dentist treating the patient, who should remain with the patient throughout the anaesthetic procedure and until the patient's protective reflexes have returned.

18. This second person should be a dental or medical practitioner appropriately trained and experienced in the use of anaesthetic drugs for dental purposes. As part of a programme of training in anaesthesia the general anaesthetic may be administered by a dental or medical practitioner under the direct supervision of the said second person.

19. Where intravenous or inhalational sedation techniques are employed a suitably experienced practitioner may assume the responsibility of sedating the patient, as well as operating, provided that as a minimum requirement a second appropriate person is present throughout. Such an appropriate person might be a suitably trained dental surgery assistant or dental auxiliary, whose experience and training enables that person to be an efficient member of the dental team and who is capable of monitoring the clinical condition of the patient. Should the occasion arise, he or she must also be capable of assisting the dentist in case of emergency.

20. For these purposes, the following definition of simple sedation should be understood to apply: 'A technique in which the use of a drug, or drugs, produces a state of depression of the central nervous system enabling treatment to be carried out, but during which communication is maintained such that the patient will respond to command throughout the period of sedation. The drugs and techniques used should carry a margin of safety wide enough to render unintended loss of consciousness unlikely.'

21. Neither general anaesthesia nor sedation should be employed unless proper equipment for their administration is used and adequate facilities for the resuscitation of the patient are readily available with both dentist and staff trained in their use. Resuscitation is very much a matter of skill and timing and dentists must ensure that all those assisting them know precisely what is required of them, should an emergency arise, and that they regularly practise their routine in a simulated emergency against the clock. The Council considers it essential that the equipment necessary for basic life support, including suction apparatus to clear the airway, oral airways to maintain it and positive pressure equipment with appropriate attachments to inflate the lungs with oxygen, must be immediately to hand and ready for use in the operating room.

22. A dentist who carried out treatment under general anaesthesia or sedation without fulfilling these conditions would almost certainly be considered to have acted in a manner which constitutes serious professional misconduct.

Cross infection
23. By the very nature of the work of a dentist, there has always existed the risk of cross infection in the dental surgery. Dentists have a duty to take appropriate precautions to protect their patients and their staff from that risk. The publicity surrounding the spread of HIV infection has served to highlight the precautions which dentists should already have been taking and which are now more important than ever. By following appropriate precautions to avoid cross infection, dentists may continue to treat uninfected members of the public with total security for all concerned

as well as patients who might be HIV positive. Detailed guidance on the matter has been issued by the Health Departments and the British Dental Association. Failure to provide and use adequate sterilization facilities may render a dentist liable to proceedings for misconduct.

24. It is the ethical responsibility of dentists who believe that they themselves may have been infected with HIV to obtain medical advice and, if found to be infected, to submit to regular medical supervision. Their medical supervision will include counselling, in particular, in respect of any changes in their practice which might be considered appropriate in the best interests of protecting their patients. It is the duty of such dentists to act upon the medical advice they have been given, which may include the necessity to cease the practice of dentistry altogether or to modify their practice in some way. By failing to obtain appropriate medical advice or to act upon the advice that has been given to them, dentists who know that they are, or believe that they may be, HIV positive and might jeopardize the wellbeing of their patients are behaving unethically and contrary to their obligations to patients. Behaviour of this kind may raise a question of serious professional misconduct.

Dental radiography and radiation protection
25. In accordance with the Ionizing Radiation (Protection of Persons Undergoing Medical Examination or Treatment) Regulations 1988, dentists have a number of statutory duties in relation to dental radiography and radiation protection, over and above their clinical and ethical responsibilities with regard to the exposure of patients to ionizing radiation. Dentists who delegate the task of effecting medical exposures (i.e. taking dental radiographs) must be satisfied that the person to whom the task is delegated has received adequate training in conformity with the Regulations. It is the duty of every dentist who clinically or physically directs medical exposures to ensure full compliance with the Regulations and safe radiological practice for the protection of the patient.

Abuse of professional relationship
26. The professional relationship between dentist and patient relies on trust and the assumption that dentists will act in the best interests of their patients. Acts of indecency or dishonesty or other acts involving abuse of the professional relationship in which the dentist stands to a patient may render the dentist liable to proceedings for misconduct.

27. In this context, particular note should be taken of the following:

(i)   Confidentiality: dentists who disclose to a third party, without the patient's permission, information about a patient acquired in a professional capacity, may be considered to have been guilty of an improper breach of confidence. There may, however, be circumstances in which the public interest outweighs the dentist's duty with regard to confidentiality and in which disclosure would be justified. Dentists requiring advice about a question of confidentiality should consult their defence society. Dentists should also be aware that the duty of confidentiality extends to their staff.

(ii) Chaperonage: when treating a patient, a dentist would be well advised to have another member of staff or other person present in the operating room at all times and, as appropriate, in the recovery room.

(iii) Consent: dentists must obtain valid consent prior to treatment and have a duty to explain what treatment they propose to provide and, if an anaesthetic or sedation is to be given, what form it will take.

(iv) Treatment of children: there can be no justification for intimidation or, other than in the most exceptional circumstances, for the use of physical restraint, to pacify a difficult patient. When faced with an uncontrollable child, it may be better to cease treatment, make an appropriate explanation to the parent and arrange necessary future treatment for the child.

(v) Referral for further advice/treatment: when accepting a patient for treatment, a dentist assumes a duty of care which necessitates a willingness to refer the patient for further professional advice or treatment if it transpires that the task in hand is beyond the dentist's own skills.

(vi) Emergency treatment: whilst recognizing that it is extremely difficult to define what constitutes a dental emergency, nevertheless, the Council considers that a patient experiencing dental pain will properly expect to be seen by a dentist and would regard it as the duty of dentists, as members of a caring profession, to make themselves available. It follows, therefore, that dentists should make appropriate arrangements to ensure that their patients have access to emergency treatment outside normal surgery hours and should make those arrangements known to their patients.

Improper statements or certificates; misleading announcements
28. Making a statement or declaration, or signing a certificate or other document, or inducing or permitting any other person, such as an employee of the practice or a patient, to sign a certificate or document which the dentist knows, or ought to know, to be untrue, misleading, or otherwise improper, may render the dentist liable to proceedings for misconduct. Included under this heading are false certification and improperly demanding or receiving fees under the National Health Service Regulations, and inducing a patient to accept private treatment by falsely suggesting that similar treatment could not be carried out under the National Health Service.

29. The Council considers that it is the responsibility of the dentist to explain the nature of the contract clearly to the patient, that is, whether the patient has been accepted to receive treatment under the National Health Service Regulations or privately, with an indication of the probable cost. Where a fee is to be charged for an initial consultation, this should be made clear to the patient at the outset. Where treatment is being offered privately, the dentist should inform the patient that treatment may be available elsewhere under the National Health Service. Misunderstandings can be avoided if the dentist gives the patient a written treatment plan and estimate and obtains the patient's agreement to these terms in writing. A dentist who has done so is better placed to refute an allegation that a patient has been misled with regard to the nature of the contract or the type or cost of treatment provided. In general, the Council considers that any act or omission by dentists in connection with their practices which is calculated to mislead the public may be held to constitute serious professional misconduct.

Use of debt collecting agencies
30. The use of debt collecting agencies as a means of obtaining settlement of outstanding accounts should only be considered as a last resort when all reasonable steps to obtain payment have first been taken in writing.

Covering
31. Under section 38 of the Dentists Act 1984, it is unlawful for anyone to give, or even to suggest that he or she is prepared to give, any treatment or advice (including any treatment or advice in connection with the fitting, insertion or fixing of dentures, artificial teeth or other dental appliances) such as is normally given by a dentist, unless the person is registered in the Dentists Register or the Medical Register, or is an

enrolled dental hygienist or dental therapist practising dentistry to the limited extent permitted by the Dental Auxiliaries Regulations 1986. Dentists who employ any person to practise dentistry have a duty to satisfy themselves that that person is permitted by law to practise, by inspecting his or her practising certificate. A dentist who knowingly or through neglect of this duty enables a person to do dental work which that person is not permitted by law to do is liable to proceedings for misconduct. Dentists would, therefore, be well advised to check the practising certificates of those they employ annually.

32. Dentists should be aware that where they practise in premises which are not self-contained but which are shared with a dental laboratory, they could be held responsible for covering the illegal practice of dentistry if dental technicians in the laboratory were found to be practising illegally.

33. A dentist should not delegate responsibility for instructing patients in the principles and practice of oral hygiene unless:

(i)   the practitioner is satisfied that the person to whom the responsibility is delegated is fully competent to discharge it; and
(ii) the practitioner understands that he or she is personally responsible for whatever instruction is given in his or her name.

Drink and drugs

34. Complaints of drunkenness or the misuse of drugs, particularly if this involves an abuse of the privileges conferred upon registered dentists by legislation in relation to the prescription of controlled drugs, may render the dentist liable to proceedings for misconduct, even if the offence has not been the subject of criminal proceedings. (See also paragraphs 52–58.) The Council takes the view that dentists should exercise the right to prescribe only in connection with the provision of bona fide dental treatment.

Reputation of the profession
35. Any behaviour or activity which is liable to bring the profession into disrepute and/or to undermine public confidence in the profession may constitute serious professional misconduct.

Canvassing
36. The Council considers that the use of unsolicited telephone calls to promote a practice would be likely to diminish public confidence in the profession and bring the profession into disrepute.

Advertising and publicity
37. Dentists may only use, in relation to their practices, publicity or advertising material which is legal, decent and truthful and has regard for professional propriety. The following notes may serve as a guide to dentists seeking further information.

38. Publicity or advertising material shall not:

(i)   be of a character that could reasonably be regarded as likely to bring the profession into disrepute;
(ii) contain any reference to the efficiency, skills or knowledge of any other dentist or practice;
(iii) make a claim which is not capable of substantiation;
(iv) make a claim which suggests superiority over any other dentist or practice.

39. Publicity about dentists or their practices which arises through or from interviews

with representatives of the media and which may be regarded as likely to bring the profession into disrepute should be avoided. The Council takes the view that those whose comments are invited by the media have a particular responsibility to ensure that their statements are factually accurate. They have a duty to distinguish between personal opinion or political belief and established facts and should whenever possible request sight of a proof of any article or statement before publication. In general the Council considers that any public statement which is calculated to mislead the public or damage public confidence in the profession may be held to constitute serious professional misconduct.

40. Flamboyant, grandiose or misleading descriptions of any services offered at a practice should not be included in any advertisement, display or other information provided to the public.

41. The name of every dentist regularly attending patients should be shown at the premises where the dentist practises by means of a professional plate. The display of a sign indicating that a dentist is in regular attendance at a practice when this is not the case may be considered to be misleading. Dentists should not carry on a practice in a name other than that in which they are registered in the Dentists Register.

42. In accordance with section 26 of the Dentists Act 1984, dentists may use in connection with their practices only those qualifications which are entered against their names in the Dentists Register and the title 'dentist', 'dental practitioner' or 'dental surgeon'. The letters 'Hons' with reference to an honours degree are not registrable and may not, therefore, be used in connection with a dentist's practice. It also follows from this that dentists may not use the title 'Dr' in connection with their practices unless they are registered medical practitioners or possess doctorates which are entered against their names in the Dentists Register. However, all qualifications which dentists possess, whether registered or not, may appear in connection with their names in books on scientific or professional subjects or articles or correspondence in professional journals.

43. The names of persons other than dentists employed in the practice, such as dental hygienists, may not appear in advertisements or on signs outside the premises.

44. No publicity or advertising material should indicate that a dentist has specialist expertise but it may indicate that a practice is wholly or mainly devoted to particular types of treatment.

45. If a statement of fees relating to a professional service is advertised then it should indicate:

(i)   what is covered by any quoted fee and in what circumstances a fee may be varied;
(ii) whether the fees relate to private or National Health Service treatment;
(iii) except in the case of the fee for an examination, including any necessary radiographs, that any fee may vary until it has been confirmed by a full examination, or alternatively that the fee is fixed and will not be changed at any time during the course of treatment.

Screening of windows
46. A dentist should take care that the windows of the waiting room and surgery areas are adequately screened.

Practice agreements
47. In the interests of their patients, dentists should give careful consideration to the practice arrangements they adopt. Experience has shown that it is essential that

dentists should sign a formal written agreement about practice arrangements before entering into partnership or other association in dental practice. Any breach of the agreement may then be resolved through legal channels. Dentists seeking advice on the provisions of such agreements should consult their professional association or defence society.

48. Dentists employed as assistants or working as associates in a practice should not be required to achieve a fixed target earning. Such a requirement places an unacceptable pressure on the dentist and it is not in the interests of patients for dentists to be practising under such a constraint.

Leaving a practice
49. It is the duty of dentists who leave a practice to ensure that arrangements have been made both for the completion of any treament which they have started and for the continuing care of their patients. In the case of treatment under the National Health Service Regulations, the National Health Service authorities should be informed of the arrangements which have been made.

Carrying on the business of dentistry by laymen: responsibility of dentists
50. By sections 40 to 44 of the Dentists Act 1984, it is in general illegal for an unregistered individual or for a body corporate to carry on the business of dentistry unless the business was being carried on by that individual or body corporate on 21 July 1955*. For the purpose of the Act, a person is treated as carrying on the business of dentistry if he or she or a partnership of which he or she is a member receives payment for services rendered in the course of the practice of dentistry by that person, or by a partner or by an employee of that person or of that person's partners. Accordingly, a dentist who enters into partnership with or is employed by an individual who is illegally carrying on the business of dentistry, or a dentist who becomes a director or an employee of a body corporate which is illegally carrying on the business of dentistry, is liable to proceedings for misconduct.

51. A dentist who enters into a partnership or becomes a director of a body corporate legally carrying on the business of dentistry accepts responsibility for the maintenance of a high standard of professional conduct in that business and may be required to answer to the Council for any act or omission in the conduct of that business which appears to the Council to constitute serious professional misconduct.

Fitness to practise: Health Committee

52. The Dentists Act 1984 gives the Council jurisdiction in cases where the fitness to practise of a dentist is seriously impaired by reason of a physical or mental condition. The procedure which governs the consideration of such cases is set out in a statutory instrument, the General Dental Council Health Committee (Procedure) Rules 1984, which also sets out the terms for the operation of the Health Committee.

53. Where the Council receives information suggesting that the fitness to practise of a dentist may be seriously impaired, the information is first considered by the President or other member of the Council appointed for the purpose. If the President is satisfied from the evidence that a question does arise that the dentist's fitness to practise is

---

*Exceptions to this provision include a person or company providing dental treatment for employees without a view to profit. Special provision is also made for a widow or widower to carry on the practice of a deceased spouse and for a trustee in bankruptcy to carry on the practice of a dentist who has been made bankrupt.

seriously impaired, the dentist is then informed of this and invited to agree within 14 days to submit to examination by at least two medical examiners. These medical examiners are chosen by the President from panels of examiners nominated by professional bodies. Examiners are nominated in all parts of the United Kingdom so that examinations may be arranged locally if this is considered appropriate. It is also open to dentists at this stage both to nominate other medical practitioners to examine them and report to the President on their fitness to practise and to submit observations or other evidence in regard to this.

54. Where a dentist agrees to submit to examination the medical examiners are asked to report on the dentist's fitness to engage in practice either generally or on a limited basis and on the management of the case which they recommend.

55. Where the dentist refuses to be medically examined, or the medical examiners report unanimously that the dentist is not fit to practise or is not fit to practise except on a limited basis, or if, in the case of a difference of opinion among the medical examiners, it appears to the President that the dentist may not be fit to practise except on a limited basis, the President may invite the dentist to attend a meeting of the Health Committee. Cases may occasionally be referred to the Health Committee by the Preliminary Proceedings Committee or Professional Conduct Committee where a dentist has been convicted or is alleged to have been guilty of serious professional misconduct, but it appears to either Committee that the dentist's fitness to practise may be seriously impaired by reason of a physical or mental condition.

56. The Health Committee meets in private and in most cases the principal evidence before it consists of the reports of the medical examiners. Its proceedings are regulated by rules and are of a judicial nature. The Health Committee is assisted by a legal assessor and by medical assessors. The medical assessors are chosen by the President, with regard to the nature of the physical or mental condition which is alleged to impair the dentist's fitness to practise, from panels nominated by professional bodies.

57. The Health Committee may, if it thinks fit, either adjourn consideration of a case or proceed to determine whether the dentist's fitness to practise is seriously impaired. If the Committee finds that the dentist's fitness to practise is seriously impaired, it may impose conditions upon the dentist's registration for a period not exceeding three years or suspend the dentist's registration for a period not exceeding 12 months. Cases where conditions have been imposed or a dentist's registration has been suspended are reviewed by the Health Committee from time to time.

58. There is a right of appeal to the Judicial Committee of the Privy Council against a direction of the Health Committee but only on a question of law.

It should be obvious to the reader that it is inadvisable, to say the least, to go it alone in any disciplinary involvement with the Council. Practitioners should contact their protection organization and be guided accordingly.

Suspension by the Health Committee

Where the Health Committee directs that a dentist's registration be suspended, it will be for a period not exceeding 12 months, at the end of which the Committee will review the case. The Health Committee may also impose conditions upon a dentist's registration for a period not exceeding three years.

Auxiliary dental workers

The practice of dentistry by auxiliaries in the United Kingdom is controlled by the Dentists Act 1984 and the Dental Auxiliaries Regulations 1986. The Regulations require the General Dental Council to keep a separate Roll for each class of auxiliary, to determine the fees related to enrolment, to approve courses of instruction and examinations and to exercise disciplinary control.

Auxiliaries at present recognized are dental therapists and dental hygienists. Each class is restricted in operative procedures and these are detailed, together with advice to supervising practioners, in Chapter 10.

British Dental Association

Every practitioner is recommended to join his national dental association. The British Dental Association, 64 Wimpole Street, London W1M 8AL, represents the profession in the United Kingdom and publishes, fortnightly, the *British Dental Journal*. It is only by membership of such an association, and preferably by attendance at meetings, that the practitioner can participate fully in his profession, keep up to date with current affairs and opinions, and voice his grievances.

At present, the structure of the BDA comprises 21 Branches with about 120 Sections. The main governing body of the Association is the Representative Board. Comprising 115 members, the Board is largely directly elected by the membership based on constituencies of Branches. There is also provision for representation of minority groups such as the hospital and community services and university teachers and research workers. It meets three times a year to discuss the activities of its various committees (listed below) and to take decisions on new policy. General BDA affairs are handled by the Council (22 members) which acts as an executive committee of the Board.

AUTONOMOUS COMMITTEES
General Dental Services Committee
Central Committee for Community Dental Services
Central Committee for Hospital Dental Services
Central Committee for University Dental Teachers and Research Workers

NATIONAL COUNCILS
Scottish Council
Northern Ireland Council
Welsh Council

OTHER COMMITTEES
Dental Health and Science Committee
Ethics Committee
Auxiliary Personnel Committee
Students Committee
Armed Forces Committee
Disciplinary Committee

General Dental Practitioner's Association

The GDPA, as the name implies, is an organization which accepts only general dental practitioners into membership. All of the officers of the Association are in general practice. The GDPA offers its members a wide range of advice and assistance associated with problems faced by general dental practitioners, which include practical, administrative, and political issues. An arbitration/conciliation service is offered to members who find themselves in dispute with each other. All members receive monthly the Association's journal *The General Dental Practitioner*. The contact address for the GDPA is: GDPA House, Thorpe-le-Soken, Clacton-on-Sea, Essex CO16 ODY.

The International Dental Federation

Membership of this excellent organization, whose actual title is the Fédération Dentaire Internationale, generally referred to as the FDI, should be of interest to all practitioners who wish their horizons to extend beyond immediate local and national boundaries. Certainly dentists in the United Kingdom should have a keen interest in the affairs of all the other participating countries of the European Community.

Membership of the FDI creates opportunities to attend congresses in various parts of the world with the obvious advantages which can thus be gained from a broadening of both professional and other interests and of knowledge of the problems and ways of life of colleagues living and working in different environments.

The FDI publishes the *International Dental Journal*, which keeps readers informed of dental matters from the four quarters of the globe and includes articles of scientific, practical and general interest by eminent colleagues from numerous countries and specialities.

Practitioners requiring further information should communicate with the International Dental Federation, 64 Wimpole Street, London W1M 8AL. A *Handbook of Regulations of Dental Practice* is published by the FDI. This provides a guide to registrations for dentists who wish to practise in a country other than their own.

The protection/defence organizations

Three such organizations exist in the United Kingdom: the Medical Protection Society (MPS), the Medical Defence Union (MDU), and the Medical and Dental Union of Scotland (MDDUS). Of these the Medical Protection Society, having accepted dentists into membership since 1892, has the greatest number of dental members, some 30 000 at the present time. The society accepts into membership duly registered medical and dental practitioners as well as certain classes of auxiliary workers, including dental hygienists and dental therapists.

The objectives of these three organizations are similar and include, *inter alia*:

1. Complete indemnity in all non-Health Authority cases undertaken by the Society within the provisions of the Articles of Association against legal costs incurred on behalf of a member and costs and damages which may be awarded, including settlements out of court falling within the jurisdiction of home and overseas courts, excluding cases arising from practice in the United States of America and Canada.
2. Advice and assistance with regard to any question or matter affecting a member's professional character or interests, including, when appropriate, the initiation or defence of proceedings.
3. Advice and assistance in connection with matters arising from the practice of the member's profession, including matters of law and ethics and, when necessary, the opinion and assistance of the Society's solicitors.
4. Initiation or defence of proceedings involving questions of professional principle affecting the general membership.
5. Defence of a member in proceedings brought in respect of an act or omission by a partner, assistant or locum tenens who is a member of the Society or any other protection organization with which there is a reciprocal arrangement; a subordinate medical or dental officer whether or not a member of any protection organization; or an assistant or subordinate who is not a registered medical or dental practitioner, such as a nurse or dental auxiliary employed within the normal range of medical or dental practice.
6. Defence of proceedings taken against a deceased member's estate in respect of a professional act or omission during the member's lifetime.
7. Advice and assistance, with legal representation when necessary, at Courts Martial, Boards of Enquiry, Tribunals, Disciplinary Hearings, Coroner's Inquests, etc.

As there are some small differences in acceptability for membership of the protection organizations, and the Council of each has the right to determine the course its own society will take, the authors can only give the views of the Medical Protection Society. Basically every practitioner who has a qualification registerable with the General Medical Council or General Dental Council may be eligible for membership of the Society. In addition, many overseas colleagues are taken into membership whose qualifications are not registerable in the United Kingdom but which are acceptable to the national dental or medical association of the country of practice. Thus the society has members world-wide including Australia, New Zealand, Hong Kong, Singapore, Malaysia, the West Indies and Africa, and direct members in other countries where there may not be a scheme of cooperation. Members are not accepted, however, who practise in areas coming under the jurisdiction of the Courts of the United States of America or Canada.

With modern communications, distances create no problems and the Society has experienced legal agents in most areas where members practise.

The services of the medically and dentally qualified secretariat, as well as the Society's legal advisers, are available to all members requiring advice and assistance with problems arising directly from the practise of their profession.

The majority of 'principal' general practitioners require partners, associates, assistants or locums to be members of a protection organization. Every practitioner is strongly advised to join such an organization immediately on registration and certainly before attending a single patient. An accident could occur with the first patient, and lack of professional indemnity prove ruinous.

In recognition of the special needs of dentists, on 1 May 1989 the Medical Protection Society formed Dental Protection Ltd, a company wholly owned by the Medical Protection Society to administer the benefits of membership to its dental members. The professional dental secretariat is responsible to the Board of Dental Protection which, in turn, is directly responsible to the Council of the Society. Dental members remain members of the Society.

NHS/HCHS ('Crown') Indemnity

From 1 January 1990, Health Authorities and Health Boards in the UK have been responsible for the financial consequences of medical negligence in the hospital and community sectors of the National Health Service. These new arrangements, known variously as Crown Indemnity, NHS Indemnity or the Hospital and Community Medicine Health Services Scheme, apply to medical and dental staff employed in the National Health Service. The NHS Indemnity Scheme is not comprehensive, however, and the protection organizations have altered their subscription arrangements to ensure a continuing comprehensive range of benefits for members.

Hospital and community doctors and dentists continue to need the benefits of membership of the protection organizations in respect of the many areas of professional work not covered by NHS/HCHS Indemnity. These include: private work outside the contractual arrangements of the NHS, category 2 work which includes the writing of reports, General Dental Council proceedings, Health Authority disciplinary proceedings, general practice locum sessions, criminal matters, complaints procedures, public enquires, Coroner's Inquests, Tribunals, Courts Martial, 'Good Samaritan Acts' and matters affecting the member's professional reputation.

Chapter 2

The choice of field

Having qualified, registered and become a member of a protection organization the dental surgeon must consider in which type of practice he wishes to engage. The choice is wide and includes general practice (single-handed, assistant, associate, partner, group practice, locum tenens or employing principal), hospital appointments, research, community service appointments, the armed forces and industrial clinics.

The dental trading firms and professional journals are recognized sources from which to obtain information of practices available and of posts vacant.

General practice

Obviously on graduation experience in operative, administration and business procedures is lacking. Single-handed practice is therefore inadvisable until experience has been gained in all aspects of both practice management and clinical dentistry. The new graduate deciding to enter general practice is recommended to seek initially an assistantship or associateship where the principal and his staff are willing and able to advise and to give practical help in practice manangement, clinical and ethical problems and Health Service, or equivalent, regulations and procedures where appropriate. Experience in more than one such assistantship or associateship is advisable as this enables the graduate to compare different types of practice as well as management techniques. New graduates wishing to commence their first job in general practice are strongly advised to obtain from the BDA a leaflet entitled 'If you're thinking about going into general practice'.

Vocational Training Scheme

The Vocational Training Scheme is intended for recently qualified dentists who wish to pursue a career in general practice or Community Dentistry. Schemes are at present being set up throughout the United Kingdom. Trainees in general dental practice are appointed to approved trainers for a period of 12 months. Trainees work in practice and are required to attend one day per week on a day release course during university terms. The overall administration of the scheme is the responsibility of the Postgraduate Dental Dean through the Regional Advisors in General Dental Practice who carry out the day-to-day administration.

There are two elements of the scheme: experience gained in practice, working with and under the guidance of a trainer, and the educational input from the day release course. The scheme lasts for one year. The trainer receives a grant of 15% of TANI (Target Annual Net Income) and the value of the work done by the trainee accrues to the practice.

Trainees are taken on by trainers as assistants in accordance with a standard contract for a period of 12 months. They receive a salary of 50% of TANI from the trainer, who is reimbursed in full through the Family Health Services Authority Trainees are required, by contract, to regularly attend the release days.

All applicants for the post of trainer have to satisfy certain criteria with regard both to themselves and to their practice standards and environment. All practices are visited and applicants are required to attend a selection committee for interview. On completion of the course, there is no further obligation on either the trainer or trainee to enter into a new contract, although many do. The trainer's responsibilities on appointment are:

1. To accept the trainee into their practice in accordance with the agreed contract, and to provide satisfactory facilities in order to afford the trainee the experience of a wide range of NHS practice. Every effort should be made to ensure, as far as is practicable, that the trainee is fully occupied.
2. To act as tutor to the trainee in the practice and to offer guidance in both clinical and administrative matters.
3. To be involved in the educational element of the scheme and to be available for training courses.

Further information can be obtained from:

- Committee on Vocational Training (England and Wales), BPMF Central Office, 33 Millman Street, London WC1N 3EJ.
- Northern Ireland Council for Postgraduate Medical Education, 5 Annadale Avenue, Belfast BT7 3JH.
- Scottish Dental Vocational Training Committee, Scottish Council for Postgraduate Medical Education, 8 Queen Street, Edinburgh EH2 1JE.

Single-handed practice

A dental surgeon wishing to practise single handed may either lease or purchase an existing practice or start a new practice, sometimes referred to as 'squatting' or 'putting up a plate'.

Leasing a practice

Generally speaking the leasing of an existing practice is not to be considered a permanent arrangement. The opportunity may occur when the owner is likely to be away for some considerable time or possibly the practice is a 'branch' and no longer worked by the owner, or where a widow or other relative of a deceased practitioner does not wish to sell the practice immediately but prefers to obtain income from it. By leasing such a practice the dentist is of course a principal in his own right and his only commitments to the owner are to comply with the conditions of the lease, e.g. payment of the rent and possible maintenance of the premises and equipment etc.

It will be appreciated that the rent payable for leasing an existing practice will generally be in excess of that demanded for equivalent premises only. Rent for the former is normally based on (1) a figure for the rent of the premises, (2) an amount for the rent of the equipment, and (3) an amount for 'goodwill' usually related to the average of the gross takings over the previous three years. In some instances an agreement is reached whereby the rent varies as the turnover varies. If a practice has not been worked for some months then many patients may have found it necessary to attend elsewhere. Numerous names may appear in the records therefore but some may no longer represent potential patients. Needless to say the degree of security of tenure is important and would affect the amount of rent a practitioner would be prepared to pay. The possibility of future purchase should also be borne in mind.

In the United Kingdom the Dentists Act 1984 permits a dentist's widow, his children, trustees, or his personal representatives, to carry on his practice for three years from the date of his death. When death occurred prior to 4 July 1956, the widow, or the trustees on her behalf, may carry on the practice during the widow's lifetime.

Purchase of a practice

Where a practice is for sale it does not follow that the premises are included. They may, however, be available as a separate purchase or for lease and the terms of any available lease must then be given serious consideration. It is obviously an advantage for a practice to continue on existing premises, provided satisfactory arrangements for the future can be made. Security of tenure is of major importance and legal advice on an existing or proposed lease should therefore be taken.

Precautions when leasing and purchasing

When interested in a practice a would-be lessee or purchaser should tour the locality, call on local dental and medical colleagues and pharmacists, inspect the premises, equipment, appointment books, day books (if available), *numerous* treatment record cards and the *audited* accounts for at least the past three years. A fair idea of the area, type of practice, forms of treatment previously provided and the financial position and future potential can thus be ascertained. A dental qualification does not imply experience in, or even basic knowledge of, accountancy and law; failure to employ experienced professional help initially may well prove disastrous and therefore the services of an accountant, solicitor and surveyor should be utilized as soon as serious interest is taken in a specific practice.

Valuation of a practice takes into account the location, goodwill, fittings and furnishings, equipment and stock together with the freehold or leasehold value of the premises. An extensive examination of the treatment record cards is most important. In some areas many patients of a practice may be elderly and thus the majority of treatments involve prostheses and give little opportunity for the provision of the more sophisticated forms of treament.

Equipment and stock

These should be valued by an independent assessor, and the dental trading firms are both competent and experienced to undertake this task. The vendor normally arranges for this to be done and if a dental firm has been employed it can normally be accepted that the valuation quoted is a fair assessment.

Valuation of goodwill

Placing a value on the goodwill of a practice has always been difficult. However, goodwill continues to retain a considerable value as many practitioners having 'put up a plate' have subsequently realized when, after many months, the appointment book has shown little sign of mass influx of patients. The mere availablity of the original telephone number is of considerable value.

Certainly in family type practices the patients tend to form a close attachment to their practitioner. However, when he leaves the practice, either retiring or to practise some distance away, these patients are faced with accepting future treatment from a stranger. The majority of such patients tend to continue at the same practice, partly from habit and convenience, and partly because of the familiar surroundings and the presence of receptionists and chairside assistants already known to them.

Numerous factors affect the value of goodwill and an intending purchaser should note such items as future potential, type of district, number of other practitioners in the locality, whether the vendor is retiring or intending to practice elsewhere and if so, how far away, and the efficiency and personalities of lay staff already employed and the likelihood of their remaining. Obviously the practice expenses and the average gross and net incomes over the past few years, the approximate number and type of patients seen per day and the form of treatment provided will all give some indication of the value of the goodwill. The ultimate figure agreed must, in any event be such as the vendor is willing to accept and the buyer willing to pay.

Advice from the local branch and/or headquarters of the national dental association or from individual local practitioners could also prove helpful in assessing a value.

Putting up a plate

It is considered of sufficient importance to repeat that new graduates are not advised to commence practice by putting up a plate on their own. The administration of a dental practice is complex, and the prudent new graduate will benefit greatly from 'learning the ropes' either as an assistant on the Vocational Training Scheme (page 21) or as an assistant or associate in the practice of an experienced dentist.

Practitioners do of course from time to time put up a plate in an area where they consider a practice would flourish, but a dentist wishing to initiate a new practice must appreciate that at least some months, if not years, will elapse before any worthwhile income is obtained. Unless he has a private income he will need to be assured of a loan, since decorating, plumbing and equipping a surgery, waiting room and office is expensive, and whilst paying for these items, as well as rent or mortgage, ancillary staff will have to be paid, dental materials purchased, and the practitioner subsist. Such a venture, therefore, is not to be undertaken lightly. Undoubtedly the most economical way of practising is to live on the premises as this enables certain proportions of outgoings to be assessed for tax relief, e.g. rent, rates, heating, lighting, cleaning, and it also avoids the additional expenses involved when both a home and professional premises have to be maintained. The fact that such a practitioner is readily contacted 'out of hours' must be appreciated, however, and accepted. A point which should be borne in mind is that in the United Kingdom a private dwelling used also for business purposes is liable to Capital Gains Tax if the house is sold, and both this aspect and all others relating to taxation should be discussed fully with an experienced accountant.

Local authorities have differing regulations concerning the use of premises and a practitioner wishing to begin practice in a particular area in particular premises should obtain clearance from the authority. Local authority officials are usually helpful in such matters, and it is better to be sure than sorry! Frequently it is found that only one surgery will be allowed in a house in a certain district. This may suit the practitioner initially, but if the practice flourishes and a second surgery is required later then difficulties could arise. Consideration has to be given to car parking for patients and the availability of public transport. Rates on domestic premises used also for professional purposes are invariably increased, sometimes quite considerably. Clearly it is wise to procure full information from the local authority and obtain approvals where necessary, before getting deeply involved with agreements in regard to purchasing or leasing a property.

Assistantship

A principal is vicariously liable for an assistant's act and omissions. This includes legal liability for any acts of professional negligence by an assistant and, where appropriate for any breaches by the latter of the Terms of Service of the National Health Service, or the regulations of similar schemes. Every individual is, however, liable in law for his own acts and omissions and if, therefore, a dissatisfied patient brings a successful action and is awarded 'damages' against a principal in respect of the assistant's actions, then the principal could sue the assistant for 'contribution or indemnity' (see Chapter 4, pages 56–57).

When a practitioner is contemplating employment as an assistant it is advisable that a meeting be held with the prospective employer at the practice premises and preferably during working hours so that various aspects of the practice can be noted and/or enquired into. It is usual for a discussion to take place on methods of remuneration, hours of work, starting date, holidays, responsibilities, ancillary help, laboratory arrangements etc., and then, if both parties are happy, for an agreement to be drawn up. There are certain advantages in a fairly simple agreement at this stage and neither a principal nor an assistant can be advised to include in this any long period of notice for terminating employment as subsequent dissatisfaction by either party may create a situation unbearable to one or the other, but not necessarily to both. A comprehensive written agreement drafted by solicitors experienced in such matters is certainly advisable as soon as both parties are confident that the arrangements are suitable. In the United Kingdom, and some other countries, certain information of the terms of employment is required by statute and must be given to an employee within a set period of starting employment (see Chapter 9, page 121).

Principals are advised never to employ an assistant without first ensuring that the applicant is duly registered and is a member of a protection organization, or has an adequate professional risks indemnity cover from an insurance company. Failure to check the former could result in an allegation of 'covering', and the latter in financial disaster.

Associateship

This is a status which arose initially as a result of the incomes of many dentists in the United Kingdom participating in the General Dental Services of the National Health Service appearing much higher than the figure intended by the Government. When determining the average income of a practitioner within the NHS, only those persons having a 'list' number in the Service are counted, the number of assistants employed being disregarded. The total of the fees paid to the listed practitioners is divided by the number of those practitioners and the resulting amount taken as the 'average remuneration'. Originally these mathematics led to high average incomes appearing, whereas many assistants were employed who thus, in fact, shared these incomes with their principals. The apparent high average income led the authorities to consider reducing fees to bring the 'average remuneration' to a more reasonable amount and the status of associate was devised to produce more realistic figures of participating practitioners. This it did by increasing the number of 'principal practitioners' on the NHS lists, for the basis of an associate is that so far as the Service is concerned he is a principal in his own right. He has his own NHS list number and is entirely responsible for all his acts and omissions within the Service.

Another reason which has influenced the involvement of associates is that principal practitioners within the NHS are normally only permitted to employ two assistants for the provision of general dental services whereas any number of associates can work in a practice as each one is considered a principal.

There are certain other advantages to be gained by the practice owner having associates, the main one being that the latter, as already stated, are entirely liable for all their acts and omissions within the National Health Service and thus they and not the practice owner carry the responsibility for all treatment provided and for any breaches of the Regulations and Terms of Service of the National Health Service (see Chapter 13).

The advantages to the associate are that there is no capital outlay and that being self-employed he deals with his own income tax arrangements. Thus for the first year he pays no tax at all and his second year in practice is assessed for tax purposes on his income during the first year. He has immediate entry to a practice which, if wisely chosen, will provide ample patients for his full-time employment. He has, or should have, full clinical freedom. He should have few problems involving practice management as the administration side of the practice is normally undertaken by the owner and his staff. It is the author's view, however, that the new graduate should initially obtain employment as an assistant, even if only short term, as in such a situation he will be guided and otherwise assisted by his principal in the Regulations and Terms of Service of the National Health Service and in many aspects of clinical dentistry wherein he, personally, has little experience (see Vocational Training Scheme, page 21).

As the basis of an associateship is the renting of facilities and services from a practice owner, a method of calculating the rent must be established. There are two methods in general use: (1) a fixed sum paid at agreed regular intervals; (2) a percentage of the gross earnings of the associate in respect of treatments provided at the premises. Of these two the latter is more commonly in use.

The 'continuing care' provision of the new NHS contract (see Chapter 13) has raised the question of practice goodwill and the contractual status of 'associates/ assistants'; at the time of writing this has yet to be resolved.

Form of agreement for an associateship

The British Dental Association has produced a booklet containing model forms of agreement* and both parties concerned are advised to study this and use it, at least as a basis for a comprehensive written agreement, which should be entered into as soon as the parties are content that such an arrangement would be in their best interests.

Associateship problems

The majority of problems which arise from associateships occur because of a failure by the parties concerned to deal adequately with those numerous items which need to be covered in an agreement. All too frequently it is found that the actual agreement has been but a simple verbal one wherein the associate has agreed to pay $x\%$ of his gross earnings to the practice owner! Disputes can thus readily arise if the associate does not put in the daily hours expected, if he takes long holidays, does not collect patient's statutory payments, gives or is given summary notice to leave the premises, is not provided with adequate or suitable lay assistance, fails to agree whether the percentage of his earnings deductable for 'rent' is a set figure regardless of the type of treatment provided or to be varied when prostheses are involved, or if such an agreement has been reached then what exactly comes under the heading of prostheses, e.g. crowns, inlays, bridges, orthodontic appliances etc. (N.B. It is not uncommon for the percentage attributable to such items to be calculated *after* deduction of laboratory fees.)

Particularly when no comprehensive and written agreement has been entered into some owners look upon an associate as an assistant, and thus when treatment by the latter has failed, and has to be re-done by the owner for no further fee, wish to deduct the original fee from the associate's remuneration. Unless there is a clause in the agreement relating to this the practice owner has no right in law to adopt such a procedure. The associate is a self-employed principal and it is entirely his liability therefore to provide satisfactory treament. If he fails to do this then a patient can look to him for reparative treatment or compensation, the practice owner having no legal liability.

A clause is normally included in an associateship agreement which states that an associate on terminating shall not, for a given period of years, attend any patient previously treated or advised by him whilst at the premises, and thus all patients remain in effect those of the practice owner. Certainly, the majority of, if not all, practice owners consider an associate's patients to be patients of the practice and thus whilst there is no legal obligation there is at least a moral one for the owner to ensure all treatments are satisfactorily provided. It should be made clear to patients

Practising together. A guide to ethical, legal and financial aspects of non-partnership associations between dentists.

given appointments with an associate that he is a principal practitioner and not an assistant and in this respect the associate's name and qualifications should be displayed on a plate on the outside of the premises. It is important also that consideration be given to the attitude adopted by a practice owner and his reception staff to all patients to be seen by an associate so that these patients will appreciate the status of the dentist attending them.

The payment or non-payment of retrospective awards and increases in fees to an associate following implementation of recommendations of the Review Body Report on Doctors and Dentists Remuneration is a common source of dispute between practice owners and associates when the latter pay rental based on a percentage of fees earned. In many instances the associate has left the practice before the award is announced, but being retrospective, usually to 1 April, it relates to a period when he was working at the practice. When no clause relating to this is included in an agreement the legal position would be in doubt as no court has yet considered the issue and thus no precedent has been established. The general opinion, certainly, is that a practice owner has a moral and ethical obligation to remit the appropriate amount to an associate, but if the percentage is calculated from a day book then there may be no legal obligation. If the calculation is made from monthly schedules, however, then it is considered there could be a legal requirement to compensate accordingly. The BDA draft Associateship Agreement has a clause which states, in effect, that retrospective awards should be included in the gross earnings from which the percentage rental is calculated. This means, therefore, the associate would be entitled to his appropriate percentage of a retrospective award if that clause was not amended in the final form of agreement.

The law recognizes principal practitioners, partners, assistants and locum tenentes, and thus the status of an associate must fall within one of these categories and which category in a specific instance can only be determined in the light of any contract, written or verbal, between the parties and by an examination of the conduct of the parties. It may not be sufficient therefore merely to examine the form of agreement between the parties as much could depend on how an associate was represented to the general public. If the actions of a practice owner and his ancillary staff indicated that an associate was not a principal but merely an assistant then in the event of a mishap or the provision of unsatisfactory treatment a practice owner could find himself vicariously liable (Chapter 4, page 55) for an associate's act.

It is to be hoped that practice owners and would-be associates will now appreciate some, at least, of the complexities and potential problems of this form of arrangement and thus also the absolute necessity for a comprehensive written agreement to be entered into at the earliest possible moment.

Group practice

This may be defined as two or more practitioners sharing certain basic practice overheads but each entirely responsible for his own practice. Those items for which expenses and responsibilities are to be shared should be detailed in an agreement drawn up by solicitors experienced in such arrangements. A practitioner contemplating buying into such a practice must consider the advice given in preceding paragraphs under the headings: Purchase of a Practice, Leasing and

Purchasing, Equipment and Stock and Valuation of Goodwill, all of which may be relevant according to the circumstances.

It is the authors' experience that this form of arrangement is the most successful when two or more colleagues wish to practise on the same premises. Each practice is an independent entity and is run as such. The only professional involvement is with emergencies which might occur during the temporary absence of a practitioner. If a second opinion is required it is generally available on the spot, and apparently the only bone of contention is when a jointly employed lay person is working to the satisfaction of one but not all of the practitioners. Disputes coming to the notice of the Medical Protection Society from this type of arrangement are very rare indeed, due undoubtedly to the virtually complete independence of each practitioner and the recognition of the absolute necessity for a written agreement in the first instance.

The shared expenses are normally rent, rates, salaries of joint receptionists, cleaners, gardeners etc., heating, lighting, repairs and decorations to the outside of the building and to those internal areas which are common to all, and the waiting room and office furnishings.

The practitioner's individual commitments are normally his own practice equipment and its maintenance, decorations and repairs to his own surgery unless otherwise specified in the Agreement, purchase of dental materials, employment of lay surgery assistants and such other staff as he might require (e.g. hygienist and/or assistant practitioner), laboratory expenses, locum if employed during holidays and sickness periods, and the administrative side of his practice. Each practice within the group is thus run as a separate entity and each practitioner is free to organize this as he pleases. Clearly the normal causes of friction between colleagues working in practice as partners or as employer and employee are reduced to the minimum.

It is important, whenever two or more practitioners have surgeries on the same premises but are not in partnership, that separate professional plates be displayed externally and individual note paper, account forms etc. be used. All staff should avoid intimating to patients that such practitioners are 'partners' – in fact the reverse implication should be stressed. In other words care should be exercised to prevent the outside world from supposing that the practitioners are anything other than individual principals with their own separate practices. Situations could arise where it would matter not what the actual relationship between practitioners was, but when their respective liabilities to the public would depend on how their image had been projected.

Partnerships

It has been said that one should choose a partner in practice even more carefully than a spouse. Agreements should, of course, be most carefully drafted, each party employing his own solicitor. Preferably would-be partners should have worked together previously for some time so that both can be confident such an arrangement would be to their mutual advantage. In a partnership where one partner is much older than the other, consideration must be given to the future, otherwise serious disagreements may occur especially if the younger and probably junior partner subsequently finds himself producing the greater part of the practice income, working longer hours but receiving a minor share of the profits. Appropriate clauses in the agreement therefore should deal with this aspect.

Partnership problems

The majority of problems which arise are related to difficulties of dissolution, the position of the remaining practitioner on retirement or death of his partner, easing-up of one partner due to increasing age or long-term illness, interference by spouse, employment of staff, disagreements on expansion and associated capital expenditure and breaking of the contract by one partner. It is in the interests of all parties to an agreement that appropriate clauses are included to obviate as far as possible all potential problems which can be envisaged in these spheres.

Written agreements

Binding out or barring out

Basic forms of agreement for assistantships, associateships and partnerships are available from the British Dental Association and in other countries the national dental association can advise. All parties are strongly advised to study the proposals carefully, with their own solicitors, as deletions, additions or other alterations may be found advisable to suit particular circumstances.

Partnership/assistantship/associateship agreements usually include a 'binding out clause' which stipulates that on termination of the agreement a departing practitioner shall not practise within a specified distance for a set period of time. Distances vary enormously, usually being greater in country districts than in heavily populated areas. Many binding out clauses are unreasonable and thus likely to be unenforceable at law and therefore an expert opinion on the possible legality of any such clause is advisable before it is embodied in an agreement.

If no binding out clause is agreed, then there is nothing legally to prevent an assistant, associate or previous partner from opening a practice nearby or working with another local practitioner. Professional ethics would, of course, demand that patients from the previous practice were not canvassed in any way but it will be readily appreciated that such a situation is fraught with difficulties and is therefore to be avoided. It must be remembered that unethical behaviour may be reported to the registration authority and/or the national dental association, and the former can impose the penalty of suspension or erasure from the Register, the effect of which may prove far more severe than that emanating from the courts.

AN UNENFORCEABLE BINDING OUT CLAUSE

A female dental member practised as an associate of a practice owner, who was not a member of the Society, whose premises were on the edge of a large provincial city. The associate was alleged to have signed the standard British Dental Association form of associateship agreement and in this agreement there was a binding out clause which prohibited the associate, in the event of her terminating the contract, from carrying on practice anywhere within a five mile radius of the principal's surgery for a period of five years. The five mile radius included the whole of the city. She was further prevented, in this eventuality, from treating any patients who had been patients of her principal or, indeed, of the practice. The principal and associate fell out and the associate decided she wished to leave, obtaining an alternative situation at another practice approximately two miles away in a straight direction and 3.1 miles by road. The principal invoked the clauses of the agreement in order to exclude her from so doing and commenced proceedings for damages for breach of the agreement. He obtained an injunction in the High Court to prevent the associate from starting work and this caused her severe personal and financial hardship, especially as she had the responsibility for her two children. The original form of agreement was never produced, only a photocopy showing the member's signature but not those of any witnesses. The associate could not recall ever having signed the agreement.

At this stage the associate contacted the Society and requested assistance. An immediate appeal was lodged by the Society's solicitors and, as this was the summer vacation and the courts were adjourned, a special application had to be made to expedite the hearing. This was granted and within a very short space of time the Court of Appeal in London considered the case and concluded that the injunction granted by a Judge of the High Court was unreasonable and causing great hardship. The associate had previously offered to give undertakings to comply fully with the profession's ethical code. These undertakings were again offered and the court ordered that the injunction be immediately lifted.

The Society's solicitors then carried out lengthy negotiation with the principal's advisers and eventually the action started by the principal for damages was withdrawn. The principal acknowledged that he could not enforce the restrictive covenants on the associate as they were quite unreasonable and void, being in restraint of trade. The principal was forced to pay a substantial contribution towards the member's and the Society's legal costs.

Members of the Society should perhaps note that clauses of this type are always judged on their merits. Only the particular facts of each case can decide whether the restraint of trade clause is reasonable or not. In this case in a large provincial city, five miles and five years were clearly unreasonable, and the courts strongly disapprove of restraint of trade clauses unless they can be clearly justified. Members are strongly advised to take legal advice before seeking to impose restrictive covenants in any agreements. If such advice had been sought in this case expensive, painful and protracted litigation would have been avoided. Similarly, members who are asked to sign an agreement containing a restrictive covenant are strongly advised to seek legal advice before so doing.

N.B. The Society is always prepared to arbitrate in matters of dispute between colleagues, provided, of course, all parties agree to this and that the findings and recommendations be binding.

Medical Protection Society case history

Verbal agreements

The reader should by now appreciate that verbal agreements are far from ideal for even if they do cover all essential matters, differences of opinion may well occur subsequently as to exactly what was agreed. If despite this advice, however, a practitioner does accept an appointment with only a verbal agreement then this should cover those items already referred to in this chapter as well as those on which information has, by law, to be given in certain circumstances (see Chapter 9, page 121).

In the opinion of the authors, the so-called 'gentleman's agreement' can be described at best as a loose verbal agreement. When disputes arise between the parties, it is therefore usually of little value.

Sharing of premises

In the past the sharing of premises by a dentist with a member of the medical or an allied profession has been frowned upon as being conducive to canvassing patients and infringing, to some extent, the principle of free choice by patients of the dentist they wish to consult.

The present closer relationship existing between all branches of medicine has, however, brought about changes in attitudes and of course the implementation of

Health Centres has in some areas necessitated a complete revision of thought on this issue. There are also certain recognized professional districts in some cities where the sharing of premises is long established and totally accepted; the W1 area of London is an obvious example.

A dentist contemplating sharing premises with a doctor, pharmacist, optician or similar person should try to arrange for separate surgery, waiting room and reception facilities and ensure that no patients are accepted from, or referred to the other practitioner unless such patients have specifically requested a recommendation and are not currently under the care of some other equivalent practitioner. No one should interfere with the free choice of a patient to select a practitioner and therefore no persuasion should on any account be used. Needless to say any agreement between practitioners to refer patients to one another is highly unethical.

Before deciding to share premises with members of allied professions, it is advisable to ascertain the views of local colleagues to avoid, if possible, any disharmony.

In no circumstances should a dentist share premises with a dental technician who offers his services directly to the public, nor should he enter into any form of arrangement to cooperate with such a technician.

Locum tenens

Such a position is generally offered when a practitioner is going on holiday or is absent from his practice due to illness, and therefore the appointment is of short duration. Remuneration is usually based on a percentage of fees earned, or a set salary, or a small basic salary coupled with a percentage of gross earnings above an agreed figure. As patients in these circumstances realize their dentist will be returning in the near future many prefer to await that return rather than be seen by a stranger, and in many instances therefore it is preferable for a locum to accept a fixed salary, or basic salary plus commission rather than risk the complete unknown.

Occupational and industrial practice

A number of large companies have for many years provided dental treatment facilities for staff at work and a significant proportion of the adult working population is currently served in this way. Although occupational dental services are better known amongst the larger organizations, there have been instances where groups of smaller companies have joined together locally to share the advantages of a common dental practice. Providing dental facilities at work has the effect of drastically reducing the time staff spend away from work for dental treatment.

The majority of such arrangements are based on the provision of the surgery premises and equipment by the company, who also pay all the running costs. The company will also be responsible for the salaried employment of the dental practitioner(s) and the ancillary staff.

Treatment is generally provided under the National Health Service with staff paying the statutory contribution and the fees being assigned by the practitioner to the company.

Non-NHS treatment may be provided under a separate scale of charges, with these fees being paid to the company to offset the costs involved.

In a few instances the equipped surgery is let, at a nominal charge, to the dentist, who then pays all the running costs and employs his own staff, retaining the fees obtained. There can, however, be a number of problems with the contractor-based kind of service: the practitioner may encounter difficulties in running the practice effectively and the company may not get the service it envisages.

The company should neither pay nor contribute to the patient's statutory payments, neither should the company direct staff to the company dentist without giving them the opportunity to consult a dentist of their choice.

Career opportunities within occupational dentistry are obviously limited due to the relatively small number of posts available, although it is hoped that the number will increase as the benefits to both company and employee become more widely appreciated. It is appropriate to stress the importance of the occupational dentist working in close co-operation with the other disciplines in the field of occupational health and not to view the dental service in isolation.

Posts in occupational and industrial dentistry are advertised in the professional journals and generally a company would expect a successful applicant to have had appropriate experience in general practice, although a broader experience may be an advantage.

Hospital appointments

These may be part or full-time and the latter resident or non-resident. Vacant posts are advertised in the dental journals. The terms of service in hospitals within the National Health Service are laid down in Statutory Regulations *Terms and Conditions of Service for Hospital Medical and Dental Staff*. Graduates are strongly recommended to try to obtain the post of house surgeon on qualifying if likely to be interested in future hospital appointments.

To advance materially within the hospital service it is necessary to obtain higher degrees or diplomas, and a medical as well as a dental qualification is a distinct advantage, certainly if a practitioner is interested eventually in specializing in oral surgery.

University teaching appointments

These also are advertised in the professional journals and the teaching aspect of the profession undoubtedly can prove most attractive to the academically minded practitioner. Some give opportunities for research work and for obtaining higher qualifications. Full- and part-time appointments become available, the latter being of particular interest to practitioners wishing to participate in both general practice and in the academic field. The advantages of having held house surgeon and registrar posts initially will be obvious to persons considering such appointments.

Research

As already stated certain teaching appointments offer facilities to undertake original research. The Medical Research Council and other bodies offer financial assistance in this field and details of scholarships available for research work both in the United Kingdom and overseas are published in the dental journals.

The Community Dental Service in the United Kingdom

The Community Dental Service is the public health arm of dentistry. As such it works in close collaboration with general dental practitioners and other primary health care services.

The role of the service is to monitor and promote the dental health of the community in conjunction with the general dental service. This is done by identifying individuals in priority groups who have dental needs and by facilitating their receiving care from the general dental service. In the event of such care not being available from either the hospital or general dental services, the community service will provide treatment, acting as a safety net.

Entry into the service for new graduates is through a vocational training scheme (see Chapter 2, page 21) which provides training and support over a two-year period. Initial appointment is to a trainee post, with the opportunity for a permanent appointment at the end of the training. Terms and Conditions of Service are agreed nationally and appointments may be full- or part-time.

The service offers good opportunities for postgraduate training and senior posts are available for dentists with specialist clinical and managerial responsibilities. Dentists appointed as Specialists in Community Dental Health are developing a wider role. Using epidemiological and planning skills they are monitoring the dental health of populations so that treatment needs can be identified and appropriate services established in conjunction with Family Health Service Authorities.

Community dentists provide care for individual patients in clinics, health centres and mobile surgeries and may also be used to take services directly to schools. The dental team may contain auxiliary workers such as dental therapists and hygienists, but also trained staff for dental health promotion and prevention programmes.

The armed forces in the United Kingdom

All dental surgeons in the armed forces are commissioned officers and rates of pay are common to all three Services except for the most senior appointments. Entry is by one of two methods:

1. Direct entry following qualification as a dental surgeon and registration with the General Dental Council.
2. By obtaining a cadetship whilst a dental student. These are awarded for the last seven or less terms of study remaining before the expected date of qualification. Cadets hold commissioned rank with appropriate pay and allowances and with college and tuition fees paid. On qualifying a cadet is promoted in rank and must undertake a short service commission as a dental officer. On completion of a short service commission, the cadet is required to repay the education grant element included within the salary of cadets, together with college and tuition fees paid by the Ministry of Defence from public sources. During the period of

the short service commission, cadets can apply for a permanent commission and if granted no deduction is made from the terminal gratuity if taken at a pensionable retirement point.

As with Community Service appointments, Service officers have a graded career structure, the opportunity to attend postgraduate courses and to take higher dental degrees and diplomas and to specialize. Detailed information can be obtained from:

- Office of Director, Royal Naval Dental Service, Room 828, First Avenue House, High Holborn, London WC1V 6HE.

- Deputy Commandant, HQ & Central Group RADC, Evelyn Woods Road, Aldershot, Hants GU11 2LS.

- Office of Director, RAF Dental Service, Room 827, First Avenue House, High Holborn, London WC1V 6HE.

For advice on Service appointments outside the United Kingdom the graduate is advised to contact the appropriate national dental association or registration authority.

Chapter 3

Legal processes

The practice of dentistry is likely to involve the practitioner in various legal processes and obvious examples are: suing for payment of fees, supplying reports on patients when litigation is envisaged, appearance in court as a witness of fact, or as an expert witness, and even possibly as defendant when negligence or assault has been alleged. A few very unfortunate colleagues do also find themselves called to provide a report to, and then appear at, a coroner's court when a patient has died following administration of a general anaesthetic.

The protection organizations receive numerous requests annually from members for advice and assistance on various aspects of legal processes and civil and criminal law and therefore this and subsequent chapters have been designed to give general advice and information which it has become apparent is required in many instances.

Suing for fees

The practitioner contemplating suing a patient for non-payment of fees should bear in mind that such an action is likely to have one of two immediate effects on the debtor: payment of the debt or filing of a 'defence' (denial of the claim), possibly coupled with a 'counter-claim' (i.e. the patient makes a claim against the dentist). Although payment is the object of the exercise the filing of a defence and/or counter-claim invariably comes as a most disagreeable shock and may provide the first intimation to a practitioner that his patient either is merely dissatisfied or that problems developed necessitating further treatment which was provided elsewhere. Even a rapid withdrawal of the summons in such an instance is unlikely to prove the end of the matter as the patient, having been goaded into action, may wish to pursue the counter-claim and cannot be prevented from doing so. Wheels have therefore been set in motion and there may be no brakes! Thus before deciding to issue a summons a practitioner should realize that the action may well be defended, at least, and his presence in court would then be necessary to prove his claim. The time so spent is usually uneconomic unless the debt is for a substantial sum. Whilst the issuing of a summons is a simple procedure the dental practitioner, not well experienced in law, is ill advised to initiate legal proceedings on his own account but should be advised by a solicitor. The legal processes which can arise from the serving of a summons are manifold, and the following case history will indicate some of these processes and their complexities.

Bill Bloggs, dental surgeon, provides bridgework for Mrs Gappy at an agreed fee. Numerous accounts are rendered with no effect, so he sends a letter stating 'unless this account is settled within the next 14 days the matter will be placed in other hands'. No reply is received. Bill Bloggs decides that in order to save solicitor's fees he will issue the summons and goes to the county court office where he provides two copies of his 'Statement of Claim' (the account), his name and address, the patient's name and address, and the dates and nature of treatment provided. He pays the 'issuing fee', and the court subsequently serves the summons on Mrs Gappy. (Bill Bloggs can, if he wishes, serve the summons personally.) When the summons is served Bill Bloggs is informed by being sent a Notice of Service.

Mrs Gappy receives the county court summons and has 14 days in which to pay the debt or file a 'defence' to which may be added a 'counter-claim'. Failure by Mrs Gappy to take either of these actions will entitle Bill Bloggs to enter Judgement for Default, which is achieved by attending the court offices and completing a form for entry of judgment. This can be negated by the patient by legal processes which involve an adequate explanation for the reason no action was taken at the time! To enforce judgment obtained 'in default' there are a number of alternative procedures of which the following two are those most commonly employed.

1. A warrant of execution which enables a baliff to demand the payment which if refused entitles him to seize goods to the value of the debt.
2. An order for attachment of earnings. Bill Bloggs will have to attend before the court registrar and apply for this, the effect of which would be to order the debtor's employer to deduct, by instalments possibly, the sum involved, from the employee's wages.

In this instance Mrs Gappy enters a defence and a counter-claim. Her defence is that after the fitting of the bridgework she had pains in her jaws and gums, was unable to eat properly and the porcelain front of a tooth broke off. She returned to Bill Bloggs on a number of occasions complaining of her pain and other dificulties but, apart from 'bits of grindings' of her own teeth and the 'refixing of the broken porcelain piece' on her first visit, she was told, 'everything is all right. It's only a matter of getting used to it'. After some 3 months of pain and no help from Bill Bloggs she saw another dentist who informed her that the bridgework was bad and should be removed. In the circumstances she is not willing to settle Mr Blogg's account, and counter-claimed £x for the removal of the bridgework and provision of a new bridge, and £y for the pain, suffering and inconvenience caused.

Bill Bloggs is now wondering just what he has started, and what to do next. He cannot accept there is anything wrong with the bridge and is incensed at the other practitioner for saying the work was bad. He now needs more information. To obtain this he has to request from the patient or her solicitors 'Further and Better Particulars' of the defence and to stipulate exactly which these are. When received these may not be sufficient to give a clear clinical picture and yet more 'Further and Better Particulars' might be required together with a report from the other dentist. The latter might be refused, as might a sight of any radiographs and/or models taken by the other practitioner. Lack of such information is prejudicial to Mr Bloggs. A 'Pre-trial Review', however, will be held before the registrar of the county court when all directions necessary for the future conduct of the action will be given. At this stage Mr Bloggs can request that an order be made for 'Discovery of Documents' and by this means therefore obtain information previously denied to him.

Once Bill Bloggs has obtained all documentary evidence available, he may consider it would be advisable to have a second opinion on the bridgework, if in the meantime this has not been removed and replaced. The patient's solicitors may or may not agree to an examination of their client. If they do agree then Mr Bloggs is currently responsible for the expenses incurred. The patient having been examined and Mr Bloggs being in possession of the report, he may find it not in his favour. If this is so then he may consider an out of court settlement which is likely to include the expense of reparative treatment, 'damages' for pain and suffering, 'special damages' for other expenses incurred, e.g. fares, fees of examining practitioner, cost of baby-sitter etc., and legal costs. However, if the opinion is that the bridgework is satisfactory, then the patient's solicitors can be so informed. This may cause them to make overtures to terminate the action or decide to obtain an independent report of their own. In the event of a subsequent court hearing it is obvious that Mr Bloggs should be able to call an expert witness who could give evidence to the effect that his treatment was satisfactory. The other side would be able to call as a witness of fact the practitioner who was mentioned in the 'defence', he having seen their client after Mr Bloggs and, if their client was examined elsewhere for a second opinion, that examining dentist also could be called in the capacity of an expert witness. Mr Bloggs would, therefore, need to have equivalent, if not more powerful, ammunition at his disposal.

The authors have no intention, or the specialized knowledge, to delve deeper into the intricacies of legal proceedings, but they are confident that the reader will have begun to appreciate the problem which can be initiated by the simple issuing of a summons for non-payment of a fee, and that due consideration therefore should be given to the 'nuisance value' of pursuing fees through the courts, before initiating any such action.

Small claims – county court arbitration (England and Wales)

The administration of Justice Act 1973 provides for the registrar of a county court to refer cases involving a sum of £500 or less to arbitration. Arbitration can take the place of trial regardless of the sum at issue provided both parties agree. The maximum limit, however, on county court jurisdiction is £5000. Arbitration provides a speedy, fairly informal and cheap method of dealing with small claims and the parties involved generally handle their own cases without legal representation. As a general rule, no award of legal costs is made in favour of the successful party.

A practitioner wishing to pursue a small claim against a patient and to utilize the arbitration machinery should initially provide the court with written particulars of the claim setting out facts in its support. These need only be given very briefly, e.g. to provision of dentures fitted on 30/4/90, £300 as per estimate agreed 18/4/90. Such particulars must be headed by the name of the county court, include the practitioner's name and address as plaintiff and that of the patient as defendant. Three copies should be made, one for the court, one for the defendant and one to be retained by the practitioner. The fact that it is desired the case should go to arbitration, if a defence is filed, should be included in the 'particulars'.

The court staff will advise on the procedure and arrange for a summons to be issued and served on the patient. For this purpose a fee for the issue of the summons must be paid in cash to the court, the amount varying with the amount of the claim being pursued, and a further small fee, for its service.

On receipt of the summons the patient will have to decide whether to agree to pay the amount of the claim or to enter a defence. Failure to take either action entitles the plaintiff to have judgment entered in his favour. As well as a defence the plaintiff may also enter a counter-claim.

When there is any likelihood of a defence being entered and particularly if this will involve technical dental matters then a practitioner is not advised to begin an action without the advice and assistance of a solicitor and in such circumstances it is doubtful whether arbitration is a suitable procedure.

Useful reading

The reader is referred to *Small Claims in the County Court* issued by the Lord Chancellor's Office and obtainable from county courts.

Use of agents

From the foregoing the reader will understand that when the rendering of accounts and subsequent sending of appropriate letters requesting payment have proved unsuccessful, he is advised not to go it alone, but either to write the debt off, place it in the hands of a reputable debt collection agency, or instruct his solicitor. Debt collecting agencies enjoy a reasonable degree of success, and are able to advise their client when, following failure to recover the fee, legal action remains the only method likely to achieve success. Their charges are generally based on the degree of success, and thus 'no success–no charge'.

It is not, however, usually prudent to instruct a debt collection agency against a patient who is genuinely dissatisfied with the treatment provided. This often acts as a 'red rag to a bull' which goads such a patient into initiating a claim and/or complaint (e.g. to the FHSA or GDC), thereby negating the chances of an amicable settlement (see page 12, paragraph 30).

Dissatisfied patients occasionally use the NHS disciplinary procedure as a testing ground pending possible future litigation. A finding of breach of the NHS Terms of Service (see Chapter 13, page 173) by a Dental Service Committee will often encourage a patient to pursue a claim for compensation.

In the event of an allegation of negligent or unsatisfactory treatment being raised as reason for non-payment of a fee, then the practitioner should consult his protection organization which could undertake the case on his behalf.

Avoidance of bad debts

Having mentioned the problems of the pursuit of fees by the legal processes it seems opportune now to suggest that prevention is better than cure. The nuisance value of trying to collect numerous small unpaid accounts has led more and more practitioners, especially those working within the National Health Service, to create a system intended to avoid the situation arising. A foolproof system probably is non-existent, but the demand for a deposit initially and subsequent payment of the balance prior to completion obviates many potential bad debts. Difficulties can and do arise even with this system, for example where a patient has insufficient money at the time and needs no further appointments, or where he has further appointments and promises to pay at the next visit – giving the same excuse on that occasion, and possibly the next! A practitioner having booked an appointment for such a patient is naturally loath to waste that time, trusting that, as the majority of people are honest, this patient will duly pay up. There is nothing unethical or illegal in claiming fees prior to completion provided the patient is made aware of this condition initially (see Chapter 5, page 84).

Attendance at court as a witness

Earlier in this chapter reference has been made to the court attendance of a dental practitioner as a witness for the plaintiff or the defendant in a civil action, and then either as a witness of fact or in the capacity of an expert witness. Confusion frequently exists in the minds of the uninitiated regarding these two categories, and recently qualified practitioners in particular view the word 'expert' inevitably as implying someone of consultant or similar status, and of vast experience in a specific field. This is not necessarily the situation, however.

Witness of fact

A practitioner who has attended a patient and thereby ascertained the clinical condition prevailing at the time may be called as a witness of fact to disclose those clinical matters of which he thus became aware. Under examination, and cross-examination, his opinion may be requested as to the extent of damage occasioned, and possibly of methods of repairing the damage, and the cost; for example from alleged earlier unsatisfactory treatment or from trauma occurring as the result of an accident. A practitioner called to give evidence of this kind can take with him and then, with the permission of the court, refer to notes and records made at, or immediately following, his attendance on the patient. A witness of fact can be subpoenaed, if necessary, to attend and provide evidence. The fees applicable vary with the status of the court.

The expert witness

Such a person may be called by either the defendant or the plaintiff, to guide the court in its deliberations. The witness may or may not have seen the patient involved prior to the hearing, but would at least previously have been supplied with detailed information relating to the matter at issue. In some instances a general dental practitioner would have the necessary qualifications and/or experience to appear as an expert witness whilst in others a specialist opinion might be required. An expert witness gives an opinion on a condition, on treatment provided or the necessity for treatment, or even the possible outcome of a recommended treatment plan. He can be compelled to attend court by either of the parties. It is highly desirable that the solicitor instructing the expert witness agrees, in writing, to be personally responsible for that witness's fee. As well as a fee for actual attendance an expert witness is entitled to remuneration for his report, for 'qualifying' (studying the case in advance), for being available to attend court (when attendance has been requested but the case not then heard at that time), and for travelling expenses. For the most part it is the value the witness places on his time which enables him to assess his fees.

Giving evidence

A dental practitioner called to give evidence in any court, whether as a witness of fact or as an expert witness, must appreciate he is there to assist the court to reach a just decision. He should not exhibit bias towards one side or the other but confine his evidence to matters of fact and to his own unprejudiced clinical opinion.

Evidence is given on oath or after solemn affirmation. A practitioner should not allow himself to be drawn by either side to answer any question or give an opinion on an aspect he considers beyond his capability either through lack of training or experience. In such instances he should inform the court that he is not competent to reply to the question. Where disclosure of 'confidential' matters arises the practitioner can appeal to the judge for his directions. Refusal to provide available evidence when directed to do so can result in the witness being committed for contempt of court.

Requests for reports

When legal actions are envisaged which will involve dental evidence it is usual for the patient, or someone acting on his behalf, usually a solicitor, to request a report from the dentist who attended that patient at the appropriate time, or who subsequently was invited to examine the patient for the purpose of giving an opinion. Many practitioners faced with such a request seek advice from their protection organization, frequently hoping that they will be able to avoid becoming involved. In such circumstances, however, they are generally advised to accede to the request for three specific reasons:

1. The provision of a report may result in the evidence then available persuading either the patient's solicitors not to pursue a claim, or the 'other side' that no satisfactory defence is feasible and that settlement should be explored. Either way, therefore, a report may avoid a court hearing and thereby the attendance of the practitioner, thus reducing the legal costs of the action.
2. Refusal to submit a report could result in the practitioner being subpoenaed to attend court as a witness of fact when he would then have to disclose the information which he had obtained from his attendance on the patient.
3. Professional people have a moral obligation, as indeed has every good citizen, to assist in the administration of justice, and certainly no practitioner should act, or refuse to act, to prevent justice being done.

Writing reports

Essentially a report should consist of chronological factual statements giving the history, present symptoms, the result of examination and investigations, immediate treatment necessary and prognosis. In some instances it will be necessary to add an opinion on possible future treatment and costs involved.

Normally the reason why a report is requested will be known to the practitioner and this would guide him accordingly. It is wise to appreciate that in certain circumstances attendance at court might follow and the practitioner would then have to support his opinion against that of another, and possibly more experienced, colleague. When a practitioner does not consider he has the necessary knowledge and/or experience to give an opinion on any particular aspect, either in a written report or in verbal evidence, then he should not hesitate to make this clear and in such circumstances should not let himself be persuaded to give an opinion.

Example

Practitioner's address
Date
Reference

Messrs (*solicitors*)

Dear Sirs,

Report on:
Patient's full name ....
Patient's address .... Age ......
....

I attended this patient on (*date*) when she informed me she had been involved in a car accident on (*date*), and received injuries to her face and mouth.
Examination revealed bruising of the forehead, nose and upper lip. Teeth present were
$$\frac{876\text{--}432\text{--}}{7654321} \Big| \frac{123456}{12345\text{--}7}$$

At $1\rfloor$ a very recent socket was noted and was consistent with the patient's statement that this tooth has been knocked out at the time of the accident. $2|12$ exhibited some degree of looseness but pulp testing indicated they were still vital. Caries was noted in $\frac{4\mid6}{76\mid7}$, the general periodontal condition was good and the mouth had been well cared for. Full mouth radiographs were taken from which a retained root tip at $1\rfloor$ was noted.

Treatment provided
The root at $1\rfloor$ was surgically removed and a temporary splint provided to support $2|12$. A partial denture was subsequently fitted (*date*) to replace $1\rfloor$. Fillings have now been provided at $\frac{4\mid6}{76\mid7}$. On the last occasion I saw the patient $2|12$ had regained normal tightness and were still vital.

Prognosis
In my opinion the partial denture provided will need to be replaced by a further denture within a few weeks due to shrinkage of tissues following loss of $1\rfloor$, and bridgework to replace that denture would be advisable in about 6 months' time. $2|12$ appear to have recovered fully and no problems should be expected to arise from these teeth as a result of the trauma they received.

Opinion
This patient suffered much pain and discomfort for some weeks as a result of this accident, and was unable to eat comfortably for a period of about 2 weeks. She lost an upper right central incisor tooth which she stated was sound before the accident. As a result she now has to wear a partial denture. The caries noted at $\frac{4\mid6}{76\mid7}$ were small lesions only and had no

connection with the accident. Had the accident not occurred there is every reason to suppose this patient would not have required any artificial replacement of teeth for many years. A bridge to be provided in the near future will involve fees of £x, and may have to be replaced on one or more occasions during the lifetime of the remaining natural teeth.

I enclose, at the patient's request, an itemized account from which you will note my fees to date, for the treatment necessary as a direct result of the accident, amount to £y. This account has been settled by your client.

> Yours faithfully,
> (*Signature*)
> (*Name of practitioner*)

Such a report should be enclosed with an appropriate covering letter and an account for the fee involved.

Careful reading of the foregoing report will show that all the information is given which solicitors, preparing a claim for their client, are likely to require.

1. The damage which could be attributed to the accident.
2. The degree and duration of suffering occasioned to the patient.
3. The cost and type of reparative treatment already provided and to be provided in the immediate future.
4. Indication of future treatment to maintain the *status quo*.
5. Opinion on the oral condition generally and its future had the trauma not been occasioned.

Wisely the practitioner did not attempt to estimate the cost of replacing bridgework in the long term, for it would be unpredictable as to when this might prove necessary as also would the degree of inflation of costs in the interim. Having quoted a fee for the initial bridge the dentist did at least give the solicitors a basis from which to consider that aspect.

Reports to the police

A dental practitioner may be approached by the police for information relating to a patient. Before any statement is given the reason for the request should be ascertained and then the aspects of confidentiality considered (see page 44).

The most usual situations which give rise to such approaches are:

1. A check on the whereabouts of a suspected person on a certain day and time.
2. To obtain evidence of an assault (not by the practitioner).
3. To obtain dental identification of a deceased or unconscious person, or one suffering from loss of memory (see also Chapter 12).
4. Through the science of forensic odontology to establish the guilt or otherwise of persons suspected of murder or assault, coupled with the infliction of bites (Chapter 12).
5. A complaint received by the police that the practitioner had been guilty of assault on a patient (bodily, or indecent).

Situation 5 is in a category of its own and is dealt with in Chapter 7. In the other instances the reason for the requested information must determine the practitioner's decision to assist without the permission of the patient (parent or guardian in the case of a minor). Where the identification of a deceased person is involved a practitioner should have no hesitation in assisting the authorities, as many processes of law which are helpful to relatives cannot be put into operation until death has been legally established.

The authors have been asked for advice from practitioners following requests by the authorities for the dental records of persons suspected killed in air crashes and other major disasters, and victims of death by accident or suicide. The advice given is always the same: 'in such circumstances cooperate'.

The police have a job to do and, not unnaturally, when requiring information wish to obtain this in the simplest and thereby most direct method possible. Like many dental practitioners the police are overworked but unlike the dentist they do not have to consider the ethics of a situation, only the legal aspect. Because of this they may, on occasions, adopt a somewhat demanding attitude when requesting information, and the dentist or his staff can thus be led to believe that a statement *must* be made, or answers provided, and instantly.

This is rarely the correct interpretation as no person except in very special circumstances (Road Traffic Act 1988) *has* to make a statement to, or reply to questions from, the police. When it is accepted by a practitioner that his duty is to cooperate with the police he might be well advised to inform the latter that he will provide a written statement in due course. Verbal statements made on the spot can contain unfortunate words or phrases and the statement thereby misconstrued; a written statement made in the practitioner's own time can be checked and double checked before submission. This is particularly important when clinical details relating to injuries received by a patient need to be incorporated.

Road Traffic Act 1988

Section 172 of this Act provides that where the driver of a vehicle is alleged to be guilty of certain traffic offences the person keeping the vehicle (the owner) or any other person 'shall if required give any information which it is in his power to give and may lead to the identification of the driver'. (References to the 'driver' include references to a person riding a cycle, not being a motor vehicle.)

An appeal by a doctor in 1974 against a conviction in the magistrates court for refusing to give information required under the corresponding earlier statute was dismissed. The doctor considered he would be in breach of the ethical code of his profession if he gave the information requested by the police. He had, however, advised two patients he had treated for injuries received in a car accident that they should report to the police. The appeal court judges accepted that the wording of the section was clear and unambiguous and that a doctor therefore was compelled by the law to break a professional confidence in this situation. Any dentist, therefore, who treats a patient and thereby gains information that could lead to the identification of the driver of a vehicle, who is alleged to be guilty of an offence under this Act, has by law to give that information, if so required by the police.

Confidentiality

From time immemorial it has been an accepted rule that information gained by a practitioner in the course of his professional relationship with a patient is confidential, and should not in any normal circumstances be conveyed to a third party. Situations do arise, however, when the public interest might be considered as of greater importance than the maintenance of this rule. A practitioner approached by the police for information relating to a patient must therefore first satisfy his own conscience in the matter. Whilst observing the rule of professional confidentiality a practitioner must bear in mind that in grave matters the interests of the community may properly override such a rule (see also Road Traffic Act, 1988, above).

When serious crimes have been commited, e.g. murder, sexual assaults on young children and acts of extreme physical violence on innocent persons, then any information a practitioner may possess that is likely to be helpful to the authorities in apprehending and/or convicting the perpetrator should be supplied. Many such situations pose no problems of conscience searching. The practitioner is not having to determine the guilt or otherwise of the person or persons involved, but merely to act as a responsible citizen for the benefit of the community.

The protection societies are always ready to assist a member faced with a problem arising from approaches by the police. Indeed, the authors have received many such requests for assistance, some of which, made by telephone, have occurred whilst the police have been on the practitioner's premises.

No member of a dentist's staff should supply information relating to a patient to any third party without the express permission of the dentist.

The courts (England and Wales)

Basically the courts are divided into two groups, those which consider civil cases and those concerned with criminal prosecutions; overlaps do, however, occur. One other type of court is in a category of its own, the coroner's court.

Coroner's court

A coroner has to be a barrister, solicitor or a registered medial practitioner of at least five years' standing. He is appointed by the local authority and the appointment is for life unless he is removed by the Lord Chancellor for neglect of duty or misconduct in the course of duty. His main function is to inquire into violent or unnatural death or cases where the death is unexpected and/or the cause unknown.

In the majority of cases the coroner will order a post-mortem examination and certify the death to the registrar on the basis of the pathologist's report. Where the cause of death is unnatural, however, the coroner is bound to hold an inquest which must be in public. It is rare for a dentist to be involved in an inquest but it can occur, and one important example would be when a patient dies following the administration of an anaesthetic given for dental purposes. In the event of this occurrence both the anaesthetist and the operator will certainly be required to complete and submit a report to the coroner. Reports may also be requested for any other person present at the time of the incident. A copy of any report given should be retained by the person providing it.

An inquest is an inquiry and not a trial. From this inquiry the coroner determines the identity of the deceased and the place, time and cause of death.

By far the majority of inquests are held by the coroner sitting alone. The coroner has the power to call a jury and in certain cases, for example, industrial accidents, he is obliged to do so.

The coroner's verdict should be limited to the determination of 'who, where, when and how'. The coroner should express no views on negligence. If evidence points to a crime having been committed the coroner may (and in some cases must) adjourn his inquest and refer the matter to the Director of Public Prosecutions. Riders should be limited to statements designed to prevent the recurrence of the circumstances which led to the death which is the subject of the inquiry.

The coroner's verdict can only be challenged with the consent of the Attorney-General by application to the High Court, which may, in circumstances where the coroner has erred substantially in law or in the interpretation of the evidence, quash the inquest and order it to be held afresh.

Procedure at an inquest

The coroner has the power to compel witnesses to attend and failure to do so can result in a fine or imprisonment.

Any person attending can be legally represented but witnesses may not be examined or cross-examined except with the permission of the coroner. Proceedings are conducted in a somewhat informal manner compared with other courts but all witnesses are examined on oath and the evidence may be taken down in writing.

Any dental practitioner who is required to submit a report and/or attend at an inquest should contact his protection organization for advice and, if deemed advisable, legal representation will be provided.

Civil courts

The county court

The Judge is addressed as 'Your Honour'. Claims up to £500.00 in value are adjudicated by the court's Registrar, who is addressed as 'Sir'.

There is no jury.

The limit of jurisdiction is claims up to £5000.00. The High Court can transfer claims of greater value to a county court for trial.

The High Court of Justice

There is no limit to the value of claims. Its work is divided among: (1) Queen's Bench Division, (2) Chancery Division, and (3) Family Division.

The Queen's Bench Division, which deals with contract and negligence cases, is most likely to involve dentists. Each court in these divisions is presided over by a judge, addressed as 'My Lord'. Except in actions for defamation (slander and libel), there is no jury. The Queen's Bench Division hears appeals from the GDC Preliminary Proceedings Committee against orders for interim suspension.

The Court of Appeal (Civil Division)

Presided over by two or three senior judges known as Lords Justices of Appeal.

Hears appeals in civil cases from the High Court and county courts. The court rarely hears evidence and normally adjudicates on transcripts of the original hearing amplified by legal argument only.

The House of Lords

The Judicial Committee of the House of Lords is the final court of appeal in the United Kingdom and consists of the Lord Chancellor and the Lords of Appeal in Ordinary.

Both civil and criminal appeals can be heard. No fresh evidence is heard and adjudication is on transcripts only.

The Privy Council

The Judicial Committee of the Privy Council is of concern to the dentist as it is to this body that appeals from final decisions of the Professional Conduct Committee of the General Dental Council can be made (see page 9, paragraph 12). The findings of the Judicial Committee are strictly recommendations, not judgments, but they always receive the confirmation required by Her Majesty in Council.

The other function of the Judicial Committee is to hear civil and criminal appeals arising from decisions made in a dwindling number of Commonwealth countries which allow a right of final appeal to it.

Criminal courts

The magistrates' court

This is the first-level criminal court which deals completely with the majority of cases and in which every case starts.

Presided over by at least two lay Justices of the Peace or in major cities by a single stipendiary (professional) magistrate, addressed as 'Sir' or 'Your Worship'. There is no jury.

Many minor offences can be tried only in the magistrates' court. In intermediate cases the defendant can elect for trial at the magistrates' court or to be committed for trial in the Crown Court by a judge and jury. The most serious cases must be committed to the Crown court. Dentists accused of offences such as drunkenness, road traffic offences and lesser forms of assault may be convicted at the magistrates' court, which like all criminal courts has a duty to report convictions of practitioners to the General Dental Council (see page 7, paragraph 7). Practitioners accused of offences arising from the practice of their profession should inform their protection organization and be guided accordingly. The court is limited in the penalties it can impose. The current (1988) maximum fine is £10 000.00 and the maximum sentence of imprisonment is six months.

Appeals against both conviction and sentence of a magistrates' court go to the Crown Court. In the case appeals there is no jury at the Crown court.

The Crown Court

Presided over by a High Court judge, a circuit judge or a recorder according to the seriousness of the case being heard.

Tries, by jury, indictable offences which are basically more serious types of offence.

Hears appeals from the magistrates' courts.

The Central Criminal Court, generally known as the 'Old Bailey', is a Crown Court for the City of London. It also hears very serious cases and those where for any reason a fair trial in a local Crown Court may not be possible.

The Court of Appeal (Criminal Division)

Presided over by two or three judges.

Hears appeals against conviction and sentence from the Crown Courts.

Generally no evidence is heard and adjudication is on transcripts of the original hearing. It has power to increase as well as to reduce sentences.

Scottish legal procedures

These vary quite considerably from the English system. There is no coroner's court, the duties of that court being undertaken by the Procurator Fiscal, who is a solicitor employed whole-time and appointed by the Lord Advocate, the latter being head of the criminal administration in Scotland.

The Procurator Fiscal also has the duty of acting as a public prosecutor and as Crown Inquiry Agent to investigate fires and explosions occurring within his area of jurisdiction, and in suspicious cirumstances to report to the Crown Counsel. He also investigates certain complaints referred to him by the Lord Advocate.

In cases of suspicious or sudden death or of death occurring in the course of employment a Fatal Accident Inquiry may, and in the latter case will, be ordered by the Lord Advocate's Department. The inquiry will be held before a sheriff who sits without a jury. The Procurator Fiscal has the duty of citing relevant witnesses, although any interested party can also adduce evidence. The sheriff is obligated to make a 'Determination' setting out from the evidence (1) where and when the death and any accident took place, (2) the cause of such death and related accident, (3) the reasonable precautions by which the death or accident might have been avoided, (4) the defects in any system of working which contributed to the death or accident, and (5) any other relevant facts. The sheriff's Determination is not admissable in any subsequent judicial proceedings.

The District Court

The judge is either a Justice of the Peace or a stipendary magistrate, addressed as 'Your Honour'.

Hears minor criminal cases. There is no jury.

The Sheriff-court

Presided over by the Sheriff-Principal or the Sheriff, addressed as 'Your Lordship'.

Hears both civil and criminal cases; the latter may be tried either summarily (without jury) or on indictment. There are limits in the amounts involved in small debt cases but no limit to awards in civil actions. The Sheriff-court's power of sentence is limited to two years' imprisonment. Appeals on civil issues may be taken to the Sheriff-Principal or directly to the Inner House of the Court of Session (see below). Appeals in criminal cases are remitted to the High Court of Justiciary.

The High Court of Justiciary

The highest criminal court in Scotland.

Presided over by the Lord President, then termed the 'Lord Justice General', the Lord Justice Clerk and other judges of the Court of Session. Can hear all criminal cases other than those minor offences excluded by statute and is the appeal court for convictions from inferior criminal courts.

The High Court sits in Edinburgh but also goes on circuit in other cities, except in appeal cases.

The Court of Appeal

This sits in Edinburgh and is presided over by three judges of the High Court of Justiciary and hears appeals from that Court, and inferior criminal courts.

A decision from the Court of Appeal is final. There is no right of appeal from its decisions to the House of Lords.

The Court of Session

The Supreme Civil Court in Scotland, having two 'Houses'.

The Outer House is a court of first instance, having exclusive jurisdiction in certain cases excluded by statute from the Sheriff-court.

The Inner House has two divisions; the first division is presided over by the Lord President and three Lords Ordinary, the Second Division by the Lord Justice Clerk with three Lords Ordinary. This House deals mainly with appeals from the inferior civil courts and from the Outer House.

Appeals from the Inner House can be taken to the House of Lords (see page 00).

Verdicts in criminal cases

In England and Wales and in Northern Ireland a majority verdict of either 'Guilty' or 'Not Guilty' must be found. In Scotland a further alternative is permissible, 'Not Proven'.

Northern Ireland legal procedures

The court structure is very similar to that in England and Wales.

Coroner's Court

The coroner must be a barrister or solicitor. No questions of civil or criminal liability can be raised.

Civil and criminal courts

Civil

The magistrate's court
A limited civil jurisdiction up to £100, but unlimited jurisdiction in matrimonial, separation, and maintenance cases. Sits with a single resident magistrate.

County Court Recorder's Courts
1. *Small Claims Court:* The county court circuit Registrar sits to hear small claims of which the current upper limit is £300. There is almost no legal representation as no costs are awarded. Limited witness expenses may be awarded.
2. The ordinary jurisdiction presided over by a judge or recorder. There is no jury and claims up to a current limit of £5000 are heard. Hears appeals from magistrates' courts in civil cases by way of re-hearing. These appeals are final.

High Court
Divided into three divisions: Queen's Bench, Chancery and Family. Has original jurisdiction in all cases with no upper limit. Hears appeals by way of re-hearing from the county court. The Queens' Bench, which hears personal injury cases, sits with judge alone, who decides questions of both liability and quantum of damages.

Court of Appeal: Civil Division
Hears appeals on points of law from the High Court and by way of case stated from various tribunals and magistrate's courts.

Criminal

The magistrate's court
This has original jurisdiction in all minor matters, and takes depositions for the Crown court in more serious cases: sits with a single resident magistrate except in juvenile cases where lay magistrates are added.

County Court Recorder's Court
Judge sitting without a jury to hear appeals by way of re-hearing of the case from the magistrate's court. There is no further appeal from this re-hearing.

Crown Court
Sits with a jury and a judge of the High Court or county court according to the seriousness of the case, it has original jurisdiction in all indictable criminal cases, except scheduled terrorist crimes which are heard by 'Diplock' courts which sit with a judge alone. The Crown Court also sits with a jury to hear appeals from the magistrate's court.

Court of Appeal Criminal Division
Hears appeals on points of law only from the Crown Court and also by way of case stated on points of law from the magistrate's court.

House of Lords

Hears appeals from both the civil and criminal courts of appeal, but only on points of law of public importance.

For the most part the law in Northern Ireland is the same as that in England. The Dentists Act applies as, therefore, do the Dental Auxiliary Regulations. The Limitations Act is equivalent to that in England and the ages of majority and consent are the same, i.e. 18 and 16 years, respectively. The Misuse of Drugs Act applies and there is legislation similar to that in England relating to National Insurances, Factories, Health and Safety at Work, Offices, Industrial Relations, Contracts of Employment and Redundancy. The Road Traffic (NI) Order 1981 incorporates the same provisions for supplying information as does that for England.

Chapter 4

Civil law 1

Negligence

Negligence may be defined as a 'failure to exercise reasonable skill and care' or the 'omission to do something which a reasonable man, guided by those considerations which ordinarily regulate the conduct of human affairs, would do, or something which a prudent and reasonable man would not do'.

'Reasonable skill and care' means exactly what it says, if indeed one can define 'reasonable'. Every qualified dental practitioner is expected by virtue of his qualification to possess a degree of skill and to appreciate that care must be exercised to the same standard as by the majority of his colleagues. He is not expected to possess the skill of the specialist, unless he is in that category, but equally he is not expected, in normal circumstances, to attempt treatment which should be provided by a specialist–indeed any decision to do so could be construed as a failure to exercise reasonable care.

When a patient is accepted for treatment by a practitioner it is an implicit, though unstated, condition of the contract thus established that reasonable skill and care will be exercised. This applies whether the patient be private, Health Service or even being treated gratuitously.

Any patient can initiate an action to recover damages by way of compensation against his dental practitioner on the grounds of negligence but for this to succeed it has to be proved that: (1) the dentist owed a 'duty of care' to that patient in the prevailing circumstances; (2) there was a breach of that duty; and (3) damage was sustained as a result. As one of the authors' former colleagues, Dr J. L. Taylor, has stated: 'Gross carelessness which does not lead to any harm will not ground a case in Civil Law, or, to put it another way, would give the patient a very good claim for nothing.'* In other words: no injury, no liability.

Proof of negligence

A dentist is not an insurer that all treatment he provides will prove uneventful. Indeed many accidents which occur are recognized hazards, and thus their happenings may not in any way involve a lack of skill and care. For an allegation in

*Taylor J. L. (1970) *The Doctor and the Law*. London, Pitman Medical.

negligence to succeed it is for the plaintiff to prove that harm has been occasioned and this as a result of a lack of reasonable skill and/or care on the part of the operator which the latter had a duty to apply. If the evidence the plaintiff produces fails to satisfy the court in all these respects then his claim will fail.

Res ipsa loquitur

This is a legal maxim which translated means 'the thing speaks for itself' and may be pleaded by the plaintiff in certain circumstances where the very nature of the incident is sufficient to suggest a lack of care, e.g. an obvious mistake by extracting an incorrect tooth. If the plea is accepted then the onus is on the defendant to prove that he is not guilty of negligence but that some agency outside his control was responsible for the damage occasioned to the patient. The following case history from the records of the Medical Protection Society illustrates the use of the maxim by solicitors acting for a patient.

Tooth inhaled during general anaesthesia–judgement for practitioner

A patient attended a practice in which both principals and an assistant were members of the Society. The assistant arranged to extract three lower teeth under nitrous oxide anaesthesia administered by one of the principals. After induction an appropriate gauze throat pack was placed in position and a lower molar extracted. Forceps were then applied to a premolar which shot out of the socket and disappeared. Administration of the anaesthetic was stopped and the mouth searched for the missing tooth. The pack was removed carefully and the premolar observed to be on the back of the tongue. When an attempt was made to recover the tooth it slipped further back and vanished. As soon as the patient recovered consciousness she was encouraged to cough and was conveyed to the local hospital for radiographic examination of her throat, chest and stomach. The radiographs did not reveal the presence of the tooth and it was assumed that the patient must have ejected it by coughing. She was not in discomfort and was allowed to return home and told to contact the member immediately if she experienced any trouble. The same afternoon a message was received by the assistant that the patient was feeling unwell so he immediately contacted her doctor who arranged to admit her to another hospital where further radiographs confirmed the presence of the tooth in the right bronchus. Attempts at removal by bronchoscopy were unsuccessful and the patient was transferred to a third hospital where the tooth was recovered by thoracotomy 4 days after it had been inhaled. Healing was uneventful and the patient suffered no residual disability.

Four weeks later the assistant received a letter from solicitors alleging negligence and claiming damages and subsequently a similar claim was made against the principals. The case was undertaken by the Society on behalf of the members, liability was denied and in due course a writ and statement of claim were issued in which it was alleged that the defendants were negligent in.

1. Failing to grip the tooth securely by forceps.
2. Failing to use the proper instruments for removing the tooth.
3. Failing to fit any, or any suitable, throat pack in the throat.
4. Failing to ensure that the throat pack was properly fitted in the said throat.
5. Failing to observe the whereabouts of the said tooth after it had been lost.
6. Failing to remove the throat pack with sufficient care.
7. *Res ipsa loquitur.*

Subsequently items (2) and (3) were deleted from the particulars of negligence but an additional allegation was made that the defendants were negligent in failing to bend the patient forward once it was known that the tooth had escaped from the forceps. Prior to the case coming to trial solicitors for the plaintiffs were invited to agree reports from a dental consultant in which the opinion was expressed that the fact that a tooth was lost was not in itself negligent since teeth do sometimes shoot out of the forceps and also that whatever pack is used in association with a short general anaesthetic in the dental chair it is doubtful if it is possible to pack with the certainty that no tooth or foreign body could pass the pack.

During the hearing of the case it was argued for the plaintiff that immediately the tooth was lost the head should have been brought forward and that once the tooth had been observed to pass beyond the back of the tongue the patient should have been suspended upside-down by her feet. The defence contended that the practitioners had taken every reasonable care and that when a tooth escapes from forceps the first duty of the operator, if his patient is unconscious, is to ascertain if the tooth is still in the mouth and, if so, to remove it. He could not perform this search properly if his vision was impeded by the head having been brought forward. A different condition would pertain if the patient were conscious and able to assist in the search with the tongue.

Judgement was given for the defendants, the judge stating that there had been no failure to pack the throat properly. When a tooth escaped the operator had to find it and that was what the defendant had set out to do. If there are alternative acceptable methods of dealing with an emergency an operator would not be negligent merely because the method he adopted proved unsuccessful.

Medical Protection Society, *Case Report*, 1965.

It will be appreciated that here the patient's solicitor made six actual allegations of negligence concluding with item 7, *Res ipsa loquitur*. This gave them a stand-by in the event of the practitioner being able satisfactorily to refute items 1 to 6, but in this event the court did not accept the plea and the plaintiff failed in her action.

Contributory negligence

An accident may occur or its effect worsen because of some action or failure by the patient. In such instances 'contributory negligence' can be pleaded by the defendant, and may prove either a complete defence against an allegation of negligence or enable the blame to be apportioned between defendant and plaintiff and thus reduce the amount of 'damages' awarded to the plaintiff. 'Contributory negligence' on the part of a patient can arise, for example, by a failure to heed pre- or postoperative instructions, by grabbing the dentist's hand while an operation is in progress or an injection being given, by failing to attend a particular appointment or by refusing, during a course of treatment, to accept certain advice given. An illustration is given by the following case history, taken from the records of the Medical Protection Society.

A young lady, aged 17 years, required the emergency extraction of a lower right molar tooth. An inferior dental block injection was administered and the patient was left in the care of the dental surgery assistant. When the dentist returned to the surgery he noticed that the patient's lip was swollen, but that the mucous membrane was intact. He suggested that she must have bitten her lip and warned her against doing this again. Following the extraction of the tooth, the nurse repeated the same warning before the patient was dismissed.

Two hours later a telephone message from the casualty department of the local hospital reported that the patient had presented with a badly damaged lip in which a segment of the tissue was missing (Figure 4.1). At a later date, the injury was repaired by a plastic surgeon with the result that after six months only a small scar remained.

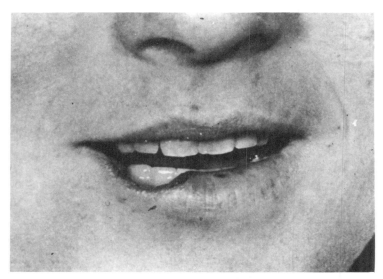

Figure 4.1 Bitten lip

Compensation was sought from the dentist and the Society's assistance was requested. It was considered that liability should be denied as the patient was old enough to be responsible for her own actions and that despite the warnings given she had obviously continued to bite her lip. At the County court hearing the plaintiff's claim was dismissed and all allegations of negligence against the practitioner were rejected.

Vicarious liability

At law a master (employer) can be responsible for any negligence on the part of a servant (employee) committed whilst performing a duty of his employment. This responsibility is termed 'vicarious liability'.

A dentist can thus be held responsible for all acts and omissions both of his lay and professional staff whether or not the member of staff involved was acting according to instructions given. However, although a master has this liability for the acts of his servants, every individual remains liable for his own acts, and thus a claim in negligence could be brought against the servant or his master or both.

Whose liability?

In view of the responsibility of a master for the acts of his servants in the discharge of the duties of their employment, and of the liability of the individual for his own acts, confusion might arise in the mind of the reader regarding his own liability in various circumstances. Some of these, therefore, are now detailed.

Partners

The Partnership Act 1890 provides that every partner is both individually and jointly liable with his co-partners for all matters involving the firm. Thus if one partner commits a negligent act the patient may sue him individually or the partnership.

Partnership agreements normally contain a clause which provides for the indemnification of the firm by any partner causing financial damage to his colleagues.

The membership of a protection society by all partners in a dental or medical partnership is also normally a requirement of partnership and this does, of course, avoid indemnification of colleagues by a partner when a successful action for negligence has been brought against him as costs and damages awarded would be the responsibility of the Society.

The employing principal

The employing principal has a liability for the actions of his lay staff, qualified assistants and auxiliaries and may therefore be sued for damages by patients in respect of a breach of care committed by one of these persons or be joined in an action with that person. In some instances the principal may never have seen the patient but nevertheless as the master is liable. In the event of a successful action against a principal for a negligent act by an employee the principal can seek 'indemnity or contribution' for the sums involved from that servant, the decision being a matter for the court.

Where the servant is a registered practitioner he is almost invariably a member of a protection organization or 'covered' by some other arrangement and the foregoing situation is therefore most unlikely to develop as the organization concerned would be involved early in the proceedings. In those circumstances where the servant is a lay member of staff or has no applicable 'cover' then rarely is it worth while for an employer to seek 'indemnity or contribution' for the chances are that such a servant would not have sufficient material assets to meet any liability determined. To put it simply 'you cannot get blood out of a stone'. In any event the employer's professional risks cover, membership of his protection organization or, in particular instances, his comprehensive practice policy should cover his vicarious liability for the acts and omissions of lay staff.

The assistant

The assistant is liable for his own acts and therefore may be sued by a patient following an act of negligence or joined with his employer in an action for damages. As explained under the previous heading an assistant may, following a successful action against his employer, be involved in proceedings initiated by the employer seeking 'indemnity or contribution' when the assistant was directly responsible for the negligence concerned.

The auxiliary dental worker

In most instances auxiliary workers, i.e. therapists or hygienists, are employees, and thus the employer has a vicarious liability at law for their acts and omissions.

An auxiliary, however, is still responsible for his/her own actions and should a successful action be brought against the employer in respect of a failure by an employed auxiliary then the employer could seek 'indemnity and contribution' from the employee. Where an auxiliary is self-employed there is still nothing to prevent an aggrieved patient suing the practice owner, and it could be difficult for the latter to show he had no vicarious liability, especially as, in most instances, the auxiliary can only provide treatment as prescribed by a practitioner.

Auxiliaries, being permitted by law to practise a limited form of dentistry provided they are enrolled or registered with an appropriate statutory body, do, of course, have to comply with certain laws, rules, regulations and an ethical code and any breach of these could result in the removal of the right to practise. This, together with the responsibility the auxiliary has to 'exercise reasonable skill and care' and the possibility, therefore, of being named as a defendant in an action for negligence or joined in such an action, makes it advisable that a form of professional risks indemnity be held (see page 19).

EMPLOYED OR SELF-EMPLOYED?

A dental hygienist who worked in general practice regarded herself, and was also regarded by the practice owner, as self-employed. There was no written agreement. She paid her own tax under schedule D and paid Class 4 (self-employed) National Insurance contributions. As is usual, she treated patients booked in for her by the dentist and practised only on fixed days each week when a surgery was free. She was paid a fixed amount each week subject to annual review, but was not paid for holidays or sick leave.

After the hygienist had worked in the practice for some five years, the dentist gave her one month's notice of dismissal in respect of her allegedly disruptive behaviour in the practice and inadequate (as he saw it) clinical performance. Despite considering herself as self-employed, she decided to challenge the dismissal before the Industrial Tribunal. At the hearing of the preliminary issue which only considered her employment status, the Industrial Tribunal considered she had but a limited role in the practice. Although the hygienist provided some of her own hand instruments, the dentist supplied the chair and other fixed equipment. She could only provide treatment prescribed by the dentist, and could only work when a dentist was on the premises. She was paid a fixed sum without regard to the amount of work she did. The Tribunal considered that the hygienist was subject to such a degree of direction and control in the practice that it found in fact and law that she was an employee, and so came within the protection of the rules against unfair dismissal.

The dismissal procedure followed by the dentist was deficient in that he gave the hygienist no warning or counselling but had simply given her notice. The main hearing to determine whether the dismissal was unfair did not take place as compensation to be paid to the hygienist was negotiated out of court.

Medical Protection Society, *Case Report,* 1983.

Lay staff

It is indeed rare, in fact unknown to the authors, for a lay employee of a practice to be sued by a patient as the latter instinctively turns to the employer on the assumption that he is the more financially viable and because of his vicarious liability. The following case history is relevant.

FAILURE OF COMMUNICATION

A patient, accompanied by his wife, attended a dental surgeon early one evening requiring the extraction of three teeth. His only previous visit to the practice had been some two years earlier when one tooth was extracted without incident. In the interim he had suffered myocardial infarction and was receiving continuous anticoagulant therapy. On arrival at the surgery premises his wife asked the receptionist to inform the dental surgeon that her husband was currently taking anticoagulant drugs but unfortunately the receptionist omitted to convey this message. Moreover the patient did not mention it to the practitioner when he entered the surgery and his wife remained in the waiting room. The practitioner extracted three teeth under local anaesthesia and when the sockets appeared to be clotting satisfactorily dismissed the patient with the usual instructions. Subsequently haemorrhage recommenced and the patient's doctor was called just after midnight when he found the patient to be shocked and having lost a considerable amount of blood. He immediately arranged for the patient to be admitted to hospital where the sockets were sutured and blood transfused. The patient remained in hospital for two weeks and was unfit to resume work for a further two months.

Subsequently the member received a letter of complaint from the patient's wife and sought the advice of the Society regarding a suitable reply. The wife remained dissatisfied and a further letter was received from solicitors alleging negligence and claiming damages for pain and suffering and loss of income while the patient was unable to work. It was indeed regrettable that the patient himself neither informed the dental surgeon that he was taking anticoagulant drugs nor produced the warning card which is usually issued to patients receiving this therapy. However, the receptionist had failed in her duty to convey the information to her employer and for this lapse he was vicariously liable. The Society was advised that a degree of negligence could not be denied. Fortunately it was possible to settle this claim for a small sum.

Medical Protection Society, *Case Report*, 1965.

Locum tenens

The exact position of a locum tenens must depend on the contract he has with the practice owner. In some instances he would be considered as the servant, and in others as the agent of the owner. It is clear, however, that in any instance a locum could be sued for his own negligent action because of an individual's liability for his own acts.

Health authorities

Health authorities have at law a liability for the acts and omissions of their servants, including doctors and dentists (see Chapter 1, page 20).

The anaesthetist

In some countries, including the United Kingdom, it is permissible in law for any person to administer an anaesthetic, no qualification, medical or dental, being necessary. In the event, therefore, of a mishap occurring, attributable to the anaesthetic and not to the operation being performed, the status of the administrator is all-important when considering liability.

THE UNQUALIFIED ANAESTHETIST
In the past it was not unknown for practitioners to operate on patients to whom a general anaesthetic was being administered by an unqualified person such as a

dental technician, chairside assistant or receptionist. In such instances liability for any negligence by the administrator would be the responsibility of the qualified practitioner present, and the latter could also be held personally negligent for permitting or indeed deputing an untrained and unskilled person to perform a duty which is accepted as requiring training, experience and skill. Such practice is now unacceptable (see page 10, paragraph 18).

ASSUMPTION OF DUAL ROLE OF OPERATOR/ANAESTHETIST
This is dealt with in detail in Chapter 6 (see page 91) and is mentioned here only to be deprecated. The Department of Health, General Dental Council and the Protection Organizations have consistently held for a considerable number of years that the assumption of the dual role of operator/anaesthetist is unacceptable practice other than possibly in wholly exceptional circumstances. Many will contend that, in the United Kingdom at least, such exceptional circumstances would be hard, if not impossible, to envisage (see page 10, paragraph 17).

THE QUALIFIED MEDICAL PRACTITIONER AS ANAESTHETIST
Dental anaesthesia has particular problems for the administrator and in general practice it is the responsibility of the dentist to his patient to employ an anaesthetist of known capability. Accidents can and do occur which create situations where there is difficulty in determining where liability rests and an example of this is the positioning and maintenance of gags, props and throat packs. A patient suffering harm during an operation under general anaesthesia, in a dental practice, might sue either the dentist or the anaesthetist, or both, and only the actual circumstances of the case should show where liability might in law exist. Responsibility to ensure the patient's fitness for the anaesthetic, however, would seem to rest on the medical practitioner (see page 10, paragraphs 17–22).

THE QUALIFIED DENTAL PRACTITIONER AS ANAESTHETIST
The position of a second dentist administering a general anaesthetic is similar to that of a registered medical practitioner, with the exception possibly of responsibility for ensuring the fitness of the patient. This might well depend upon the experience and status of the two dentists concerned and whose patient is involved. Certainly no dentist should administer an anaesthetic unless assured that an adequate medical history had been taken which confirmed that no contraindications existed (see page 10, paragraphs 17–22).

Time limits

Time limits for actions involving personal injury

In the United Kingdom these are fixed by the Limitations Acts of 1939, 1963, 1975 and 1980, the Law Reform (Limitation of Actions) Act 1954 and the Law Reform (Miscellaneous Provisions) Act 1971 which stipulate that in cases involving personal injury arising from negligence or breach of contract an action must be started within three years of the incident from which the cause of action occurred or, with the leave of the court, within three years of when the plaintiff became aware, or ought to have become aware, of a cause of action. The Limitation Act of

1975 gives the court a general power to override these limits if it is deemed equitable to do so.

An example of the necessity for an extension of the basic years is the inhalation by a patient of a foreign body, e.g. a tooth, and being unaware of this for some years, until its presence is revealed by a radiograph or during an operation possibly necessitated by recurrent chest complaints in the interim, or a sudden onset of illness.

Time limits for actions in contract

Where an action is brought for breach of contract not involving personal injury, e.g. unsatisfactory prosthesis, the time limit is six years from the date of performance of the contract.

Time limits relating to minors

When no action has been initiated by parents, or others having appropriate authority, on behalf of a minor, then that person can, on reaching majority, commence an action on his own behalf. The time limits then apply as from the date of attaining majority, i.e. three years for personal injury and six years in contract.

As a writ can be issued but then not served for up to 12 months it is apparent that, in the United Kingdom, where the age of majority is 18 years, an allegation of unsatisfactory treatment may not become known to the practitioner prior to the patient reaching the age of 25 years. Records of minors, not subsequently treated should, therefore, be retained until they have attained that age. If treated after reaching their majority then the records should of course ideally be retained for a further seven years from the last date of treatment.

The effect of consent to a risk

A practitioner who is aware that a certain operation carries a particular risk of damage to his patient should inform that patient accordingly and obtain consent to the operation. The potential damage may occur and the patient, despite the informed consent he gave, sue the practitioner for negligence. To succeed in such a claim the patient would need to prove that although aware of the risk the practitioner still failed to exercise reasonable skill and care, either in the manner of his operating, or even by attempting the operation himself instead of arranging for a more experienced colleague to undertake it. Obviously, however, the practitioner attempting such an operation without informing his patient of the known hazard places himself at a much greater risk of subsequent legal action than when informed consent is obtained.

Cases involving allegations of negligence

The duty to exercise 'reasonable skill and care' begins from the moment a patient is accepted as such by the practitioner. The initial examination must be adequate for its purpose and may necessitate the taking of radiographs to enable an accurate diagnosis to be made; study models also may be required before a satisfactory treatment plan can be devised.

A failure to examine adequately, and the consequences, are apparent from an account of the following case reported to the Medical Protection Society.

A child was taken to the parents' dentist in an emergency situation having fallen down in the school playground, and then complaining of pain in his front teeth. The child was fitted in between other patients and was rather uncooperative, but when asked what was hurting pointed to $\overline{1}$. The dentist felt the tooth, then explained to the parent that it had been lossened up in a few days and the pain would go. A few days later the practitioner received an irate telephone call from the parent stating that following failure to obtain a reply from his telephone on the following Saturday morning he had taken the child, in much pain, to another practitioner who diagnosed a fracture of the crown of $\overline{1}$, just below gum level, and had extracted that tooth. This dentist had at the same time allegedly informed the parents that had the fracture been noted earlier the root might have been saved by appropriate treatment. A solicitor's letter alleging negligence and claiming compensation was later received by the original dentist. It is apparent that the practitioner who first saw the child failed to examine adequately and that as a consequence the patient at least suffered pain for a further few days. Whether an earlier diagnosis of the actual trouble would have enabled the root to be saved is a moot point, as also of course is whether root canal therapy should not have been attempted by the second practitioner instead of an immediate extraction. These, however, are questions to which no positive reply can be given.

The positioning and maintenance of equipment

Negligence in positioning and maintenance of equipment can give rise to accidents causing damage to a patient and the following case histories indicate the responsibilities of practitioners and staff in these respects:

Trapped finger

A girl aged 6 years who attended for dental treatment required the extraction of a deciduous tooth. While the practitioner was reassuring her the chair was raised and her finger trapped between the arm rest and the spittoon. The chair was immediately lowered, but the finger had been severely damaged.

The child was taken to a nearby hospital where radiographic examination showed a comminuted crush fracture of the terminal phalanx of the right little finger. The wound was bleeding, the nail split with a laceration over the palmar aspect of the finger as far as the distal interphalangeal joint. The remnant of nail was removed, the cut sutured and a dressing applied.

Despite antibiotic therapy and regular dressings the wound failed to heal and two months later the split on the palmar aspect was wide open. Granulation tissue and a small fragment of loose bone were removed and the wound resutured. Some 10 days later the wound was seen to have broken down again and to be infected. A radiograph showed slight necrosis. Healing eventually occurred but obvious deformity of the finger tip persisted. The dental practitioner received a letter from solicitors acting for the parent alleging negligence and claiming compensation.

The Society arranged for a consultant orthopaedic surgeon to examine the patient and provide a report. The child was extremely cooperative as were the parents. It appeared that use was without handicap and no pain was experienced. The finger was ³⁄₁₆th of an inch short due to loss of part of the terminal phalanx and thus there was no support for the terminal part of the nail which tended to curl over the shortened finger tip.

The specialist opined that the little finger would remain short and the nail tend to curl over the tip necessitating it being kept cut short to prevent growth to a normal length. The deformity therefore was cosmetic only and not functional, although it would prevent the proper playing of a stringed instrument. The patient, however, according to the parents, had shown no inclination in that direction.

The Society's solicitors were instructed to explore a settlement and this was eventually negotiated at £300 to include special damages.

Medical Protection Society, *Case Report,* 1970.

This is not a unique case. Similar ones have been handled by the protection organizations, generally involving power-actuated chairs with the button being pushed by chairside assistants or anaesthetists, neither of whom are as familiar with the ranges of movement involved as the dentist who is altering the positions numerous times daily.

A further example of unfortunate positioning of equipment is apparent from the following summary of a case handled by the Medical Protection Society.

A patient attended her dentist on a Friday evening when an examination and scaling were provided. On the following Monday the practitioner noticed a bur, left in the air rotor head, was fractured and assumed this had occurred whilst the equipment was being cleaned that morning. Later the same day, however, a doctor telephoned to say the patient had attended his surgery complaining of a sore arm and examination had showed an abscess present. The patient had stated she had scratched her arm on entering the dental chair. A radiograph taken at a hospital showed the presence of a fragment of a dental bur.

Two days later the patient's husband telephoned the dental surgery to cancel his own appointment for that day stating he had to take his wife to hospital for the removal of the foreign body in her arm. Subsequently the dentist received a solicitor's letter alleging negligent positioning of dental equipment and claiming damages on behalf of their client. They stated that on entry into the surgery their client was asked by the receptionist to 'occupy the treatment chair' and to do this 'she had to squeeze past the instrument tray or other projections from the console . . . and in doing so her left upper arm came into contact with the dental drill, the bit of which entered her arm although this was not known at the time.' Their client had to endure hospital treatment on a number of occasions before the bit was removed, was still suffering the effects of the operations and her arm was badly scarred.

On receipt of the subject matter the Society undertook the case on the member's behalf and made further inquiries. It transpired that an attempt had been made initially in the casualty department of the hospital to open up the puncture wound and later a radiograph had disclosed the foreign body. The wound was reopened again but it proved impossible to remove the object. Additional radiographs were taken and further unsuccessful attempts made at removal. The patient was then referred to another hospital where yet another incision was made, the bur end located and removed and then the wound sutured. The arm was still (one month later) very inflamed and tender to pressure.

The Society considered the case could not satisfactorily be defended and therefore a settlement should be explored. Its solicitors were instructed accordingly and eventually settlement was effected for just under one half of the original amount claimed, plus costs.

Burns

Burns to the face, lips and oral tissues occur from overheating hand-pieces and when instruments are insufficiently cooled after sterilization (see *Figs.* 4.2 and 4.3). Every care must be taken to ensure that hand-pieces are regularly and properly maintained and all instruments thoroughly cooled before use. Any instrument which appears warm to the operator's hands is likely to be retaining sufficient heat

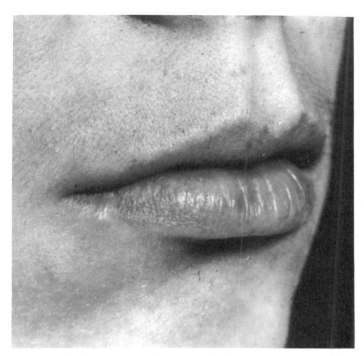

Figure 4.2 Small scar on lower lip, near angle of mouth, from burn caused by overheating handpiece

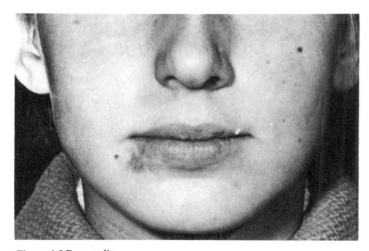

Figure 4.3 Burn to lip

to cause a burn when maintained in contact with the lips and oral tissues. Claims made by patients for compensation following such incidents are usually impossible to defend and settlements therefore have to be explored.

The following case history is taken from the records of the Medical Protection Society.

During the removal of two mandibular third molars under general anaesthesia in a hospital operating theatre, a surgical mallet was used. This unfortunately had been insufficiently cooled after sterilization and was rested on the patient's chin whilst the operator awaited a bone chisel. Burns resulted with subsequent scarring (see *Fig.* 4.4). Immediately the operator appreciated the instrument was hot he removed it from contact with the chin. The teeth were removed and the patient referred to a consultant plastic surgeon who at a later date excised a prominent scar.

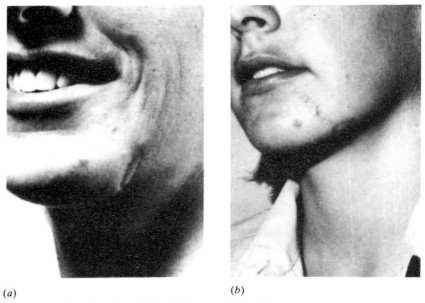

(a)   (b)

Figure 4.4a,b Scar from burn inflicted by hot surgical mallet

In due course a claim for compensation was made. A psychiatrist reported that the patient, a young female, was suffering from depressive feelings and social anxiety and these would continue for some time–this depending largely upon her future relationships with the opposite sex. The basic claim as formulated was for the equivalent of over £5000.

The Society considered the hospital should accept a proportion of the liability as it was deemed to be a theatre sister's responsibility to ensure instruments were adequately cooled before being handed to the operator. The hospital, however, denied liability but was named as Second Defendant in the case. A settlement was subsequently effected, with the hospital making a contribution.

Burns also arise from the use of chemicals and generally occur in one of three ways:

1. Use of an excessive quantity in the mouth whereby spreading occurs to areas other than that requiring the application (see *Fig.* 4.5).

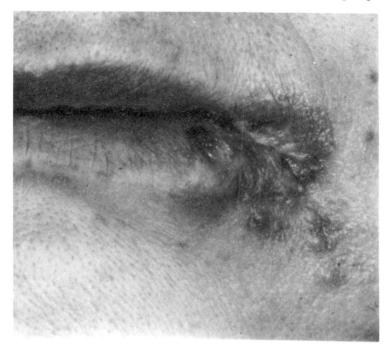

Figure 4.5 Burn from tannic acid used on swab to control postoperative haemorrhage. (Reproduced with kind permission from H. C. Killey and L. W. Kay, *Prevention of Complications in Dental Surgey*, Edinburgh, Churchill Livingstone)

2. Inadvertent use of an incorrect solution.
3. The dripping or spilling of a caustic solution onto exposed areas of skin.

Extreme care must be taken by both the dentist and his chairside assistant to avoid conveying caustic solutions across a patient's face. This is especially important when the supine or semi-supine operating position is in use.

Dangerous chemicals

A patient attended her dental practitioner complaining of pain in her lower left quadrant. The practitioner diagnosed acute pericoronitis around the lower left third molar. The immediate treatment plan was to cauterize the operculum chemically. After clearing the area of pus, two drops of trichloracetic acid were applied to the gingival margin distal to the adjacent lower second molar. The practitioner then applied what she thought was glycerine to the area from a 5 ml syringe which she had asked her dental surgery assistant to fill. The patient reacted immediately, complaining of a burning sensation in the mouth and throat. She felt no better after an application of glycerine taken by the practitioner from a labelled bottle. The practitioner was mystified as she was under the impression that only two drops of trichloracetic acid had been placed around the wisdom tooth. As the patient was still distressed, however, immediate arrangements were made for her to see her general medical practitioner.

It was not until the patient had left the surgery that the dental practitioner had a chance to question her assistant when, much to her horror, learned that she had filled the 5 ml syringe with trichloracetic acid instead of the glycerine as requested. The practitioner immediately telephoned this information to the patient's doctor who arranged admission to hospital. By this time the patient was extremely distressed, unable to swallow and had severe blanching of the mucous membranes of both mouth and pharynx. Later she developed difficulty with breathing. Treatment included steroids, analgesics and intravenous fluids. After two weeks in hospital the patient was discharged, still only able to swallow sloppy food. Subsequently, the patient was readmitted to hospital on many occasions for treatment of her oesophageal stricture.

A claim for damages was made which could not be resisted, and settlement was effected on behalf of the practitioner for £12 000 damages plus costs.

Medical Protection Society, *Case Report*, 1984.

Hazards of local anaesthesia

Problems allied with the injection of local anaesthetics and which give rise to allegations of negligence are:

1. The fracture of a needle *in situ*.
2. The production of a haematoma.
3. Neuropraxia.
4. Fainting of the patient.
5. Trismus.
6. Injection of an incorrect fluid.
7. Anaphylactic shock.

Fractures of needles still occur, albeit rarely with the current use of disposable needles. Those which usually give rise to claims for compensation are when the fractured portion has to be surgically removed, or an unsuccessful attempt is made to do so. Generally it is found that the needle used was of insufficient length for the purpose, coupled sometimes with excessive thinness. Such needles, when used in particular for inferior dental injections, necessitate insertion to the hub and it is at this point that fracture usually occurs, and the thinner the needle the greater the possibility.

Very thin and sharp needles are also more likely to puncture a vessel or strike a nerve than a thicker variety which tends to push such tissues aside. Whilst the occurrence of a haematoma, neuropraxia or trismus are all natural hazards of an injection, the use of a needle of suitable thickness coupled with 'very' slow penetration of the tissues can reduce the possibility of such complications.

Good communication between practitioner and patient, following such occurrences, can do much to prevent allegations of negligence being preferred in these instances by enabling the patient to understand and appreciate the situation.

Alleged negligent injection into a vein

A married woman had attended a dental practice for seven years during which time she had received extensive conservative treatment, many cavities having been prepared under local anaesthesia.

At a recent visit an inferior dental regional injection of 2 ml of 2 per cent lignocaine and 1 in 80 000 noradrenaline was administered. After the injection the patient complained that her heart beat forcefully and she felt faint. The chair was therefore tilted until the patient was supine and when after resting she felt better a filling was completed in a lower premolar.

The practitioner could not subsequently remember precisely what discussion he had with the patient regarding her faintness but thought it probable that he had suggested it might have been caused by some of the anaesthetic solution entering a vein.

About two or three hours later, as the practitioner was leaving his surgery, the patient telephoned to report that she still did not feel normal and that if she exerted herself her heart beat forcefully. She asked if this could be due to the local anaesthetic and inquired if she should return to the surgery or call her doctor. She was assured that the anaesthetic solution would by then have been detoxicated and that nothing abnormal had happened. She was advised to retire early and rest but to inform the practice if she felt unwell the following morning. Some time during the week the patient telephoned and stated that she had had to call her doctor who informed her that she must be allergic to local anaesthetics and should not have a dental injection again.

Six weeks later the practitioner received a letter from the patient's solicitors alleging that as a result of a negligent injection into a vein their client had for three weeks suffered palpitations as soon as she attempted to make any physical effort, that she had been unable to perform her normal household work, and that her relations with her husband had been disturbed. A claim for damages was intimated.

At this stage the practitioner consulted the Society who undertook the case on his behalf and instructed their solicitors to deny liability. In the course of repudiating liability the Society's solicitors point out that even had some of the anaesthetic solution entered a vein, which was not admitted, this would not have constituted negligence nor would it have given rise to the symptoms of which the patient complained. The patient's solicitors replied renewing their allegations and suggested measures which should have been taken to ensure that a needle did not enter a vein.

The Society's solicitors continued to deny liability and offered to accept service of any proceedings the patient might issue, but nothing more ensued.

Medical Protection Society, *Case Report,* 1968.

There are, fortunately, very few serious results of accidental intravascular injections. Nevertheless, their avoidance is an essential part of local anaesthetic technique. An aspirating syringe should be used if available, but until an ideal system is devised the risk can only be reduced.

Both dentist and surgery assistant must appreciate that any patient is likely to faint during or after dental procedures, and particularly following the administration of a local anaesthetic. Patients should therefore be kept continuously under observation in the surgery and should on no account be left unattended. Patients have come to harm in such instances, having knocked against equipment when collapsing, and have even fallen downstairs on leaving the surgery. Allegations of negligence cannot normally be defended when such accidents occur to unattended patients, as it is difficult to show that 'reasonable care' has been exercised in such circumstances. The injection of an incorrect solution causing harm is clearly an indefensible action as illustrated by the following case history.

Carelessness with local anaesthetic cartridge

A dental member's nurse filled a used local anaesthetic cartridge with Milton and loaded it into a hypodermic syringe for a patient who was to attend that day for endodontic treatment. The patient, however, failed to keep his appointment and the nurse unthinkingly placed the cartridge with those which still contained local anaesthetic.

Later the same day the dentist used this cartridge on a patient prior to filling the $\overline{3|}$, unaware that it contained Milton and not local anaesthetic. After injection of 1 ml the patient complained of intense pain and the needle was withdrawn at once. The patient was referred to hospital, he developed numbness of the right cheek and partial anaesthesia of the mental region. Apart from some paraesthesia the symptoms settled quickly.

A claim for damages which was received one month after the accident was considered indefensible and settlement was effected on payment to the patient of a small sum of money.

Medical Protection Society, *Case Report,* 1972.

Incorrect treatment

This may give rise to allegations of negligence and these usually arise from the treatment of the wrong patient or the wrong side, generally through failure to examine the patient and relevant record card immediately prior to treatment.

A bit of a mix up

During a 'gas session' a patient was called and a young lady aged 26 years entered the surgery. She was examined, anaesthetized and had four teeth extracted. Soon after, the practitioner's partner received a letter from the girl's father stating he was amazed to find that without any notification his daughter had been 'administered gas' and had teeth extracted. He further stated that legal action would be taken.

In due time a solicitor's letter was received which alleged their client had an appointment with Mr 'A' for fillings but instead she was directed into the surgery of Mr 'B' where teeth were extracted under a general anaesthetic. They understood the teeth were removed under the erroneous impression that their client was another person altogether and therefore the circumstances amounted to negligence and a breach of contract.

Correspondence between the Society and Mr 'B' elicited that he was not aware the wrong patient had been seen until the end of the session when the correct patient was found still awaiting treatment. Her name was identical in sound to that of the patient involved but spelt with a 'C' as opposed to a 'K'.

In this instance the teeth extracted for Miss 'K' were not in fact those charted for Miss 'C', as in the more usual type of mistake which does occur from time to time, but were determined after examination and because pain was being experienced.

There was no doubt that the patient had an appointment with Mr 'A' for conservative treatment and his clinical opinion was that the teeth removed could have been successfully filled and have a reasonable life expectancy. Furthermore, he had hoped to avoid the need for a denture in this case because of bite complications and the patient's mental condition.

The practitioner who extracted the teeth had gained the impression that this patient was somewhat mentally subnormal and she had therefore not realized, when examined, that her teeth were to be extracted. This view was strengthened when in a further letter from the solicitors, written to the Society, it was stated that the girl had become generally more irritable and less communicative. Whilst intensely shy beforehand she had at least been prepared to communicate with her parents and those she knew well at the training centre she attended. Following the 'incident' she had become withdrawn and it was now their intention to have her examined by a neurologist.

The Society through their solicitors made it quite clear that they could see no justification for an examination by a neurologist and eventually no such examination took place; nevertheless the plaintiff's solicitors intimated that the claim was considered to be worth some £2000 plus costs. The Society considered this to be extravagant and therefore the opinion of counsel was taken who suggested that £450 be offered plus cost of any remedial treatment. In the meantime the patient returned to Mr 'A' who provided a partial denture through the National Health Service.

This offer was duly put to the patient's solicitors who then took counsel's opinion after which they quoted £790. The Society's solicitors countered this with an offer of £500 plus costs. This was accepted and the case concluded for a total of £574.

Medical Protection Society, *Case Report,* 1971.

Extraction of wrong teeth

A girl aged 10 years requiring orthodontic treatment was seen by the principal of the practice who extracted both upper second premolars and provided further treatment achieving excellent alignment of the maxillary teeth. Two years later it became apparent that further treatment was necessary to reduce overcrowding in the mandible and the principal advised the extraction of both lower first premolars. He made a note to this effect and arranged for his assistant to perform the extractions. Unfortunately despite the written instructions and clinical appearance of the jaws the assistant extracted in error both upper premolars. As soon as the patient arrived home the mother observed that upper teeth had been extracted instead of the lower teeth advised and she telephoned the assistant and wrote to the principal. The latter immediately consulted the Society and replied to those and other letters as advised. He arranged for the girl to see a consultant orthodontist for advice regarding future treatment to reduce the maxillary gaps. Throughout the matter the Society had been in close cooperation with the Medical and Dental Defence Union of Scotland of which the assistant was a member. Subsequently a letter was received from the parents' solicitors demanding compensation for the incorrect extractions. At this stage the Scottish Society agreed that any liability rested wholly upon their member and settled the claim.

Medical Protection Society, *Case Report,* 1975.

During the course of every year the Society hears of the extraction of incorrect teeth but in relation to the total number of extractions the number of these errors is remarkably small. It is noticeable, however, that of these errors a high proportion occur in orthodontic cases where extraction is not performed by the dental surgeon who decided which teeth should be removed. In such cases a small risk of failure of communication is amplified when the need for removal is not so clearly apparent to the operator as would be the case if the teeth to be extracted were grossly carious or mobile. Extra care is necessary to identify teeth of which the extraction has been advised by another practitioner. The importance of clear and accurate records in such circumstances cannot be overemphasized.

The extraction of teeth

Difficulties can arise with the extraction of teeth both operatively and postoperatively. The duties of a dentist to his patient, however, are:

1. To obtain consent for the extractions and the use of any agreed form of anaesthesia (see Chapter 5, page 80).
2. To give such preoperative instructions as required.
3. To ensure that the correct teeth only are extracted.
4. To check extracted teeth to determine whether each extraction is complete or otherwise. If incomplete then the patient should be informed and a decision taken on whether or not to operate further.
5. To check that the number extracted, and then to hand, corresponds with the treatment plan. If this number does not correspond then a check on the mouth

should be made to see if a tooth is still present which was to be extracted, and if it is not then a search should be instituted. Should a search not reveal the missing tooth then abdominal and thoracic radiographs must be considered.

6. To advise the patient adequately on postoperative care and where to contact the operator, out of hours, in the event of an emergency arising.
7. To take adequate pre- and post-extraction radiographs when necessary (see page 74, Use of radiographs).
8. To provide such postoperative attention as the exercise of 'care' dictates.

Numerous foreign bodies as well as teeth and portions of teeth are swallowed or inhaled during dental treatment. Unless the object is very minute and thought to have been ingested, a radiographic investigation should be done. Objects reported as ingested and inhaled include: root canal instruments, calculus, fillings, crowns, bridges, inlays, dentine screws—and screw drivers, head of an air turbine, surface anaesthetic spray nozzle, portion of plaster impression, root posts and a fractured suture needle (see *Figs* 4.6, 4.7 and 4.8). It is an essential part of a practitioner's duty of care to take reasonable precautions to prevent such incidents occurring, and the use of a rubber dam will usually achieve this objective. (One cannot, however, always win despite taking every care; the authors recall a case where a young patient moved his head during the placement of a rubber dam clamp and promptly swallowed it.) *Figure* 4.9 shows the use of a dental napkin as another method of achieving this objective, the patient in this instance being in the supine position. Although not ideal, the use of a paper tissue or dental napkin as illustrated would probably prevent the entry of the majority of dropped objects into the pharynx or larynx.

Possible consequences of the ingestion and inhalation of foreign bodies are, of course, abdominal and thoracic surgery (*Figs* 4.10 and 4.11) coupled almost invariably with an allegation of negligence and claim for compensation against the practitioner whose lack of reasonable skill and care precipitated the incident.

Provisions of unsatisfactory treatment

Differentiating between negligent treatment and unsatisfactory treatment can prove an impossible task and thus when practitioners are accused of providing unsatisfactory treatment the matter is considered to be within the scope of the protection organizations and is then conducted as though negligence had been alleged.

Dentures

Many allegations of unsatisfactory treatment arise from the provision of dentures, both 'immediate' and 'permanent', and whilst most practitioners would consider that this form of treatment is the provision of professional services, unhappily the British courts do not. In the past a learned judge ruled that the supplying of dentures came under the Sale of Goods Act 1893, superseded by the Sale of Goods Act 1979. A practitioner has a duty to produce 'goods' (dentures) suitable for the purpose for which they were intended and complying with the terms of the contract agreed with the patient (*see* Chapter 5, page 84). Failure to achieve these conditions can result in either a failure to obtain the fee quoted or a successful claim by the patient for reimbursement of any fees already paid.

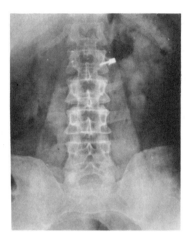

Figure 4.6 Swallowed dentatus screwdriver

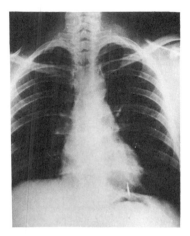

Figure 4.7 Inhaled burr

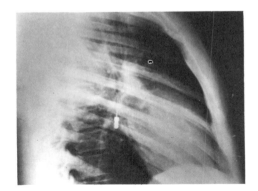

Figure 4.8 Inhaled root canal reamer

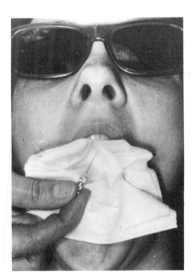

Figure 4.9 Patient in supine position wearing protective glasses and with a paper tissue in position to avoid accidental ingestion or inhalation of root canal instrument. (Photography by courtesy of Dr D. N. Barber)

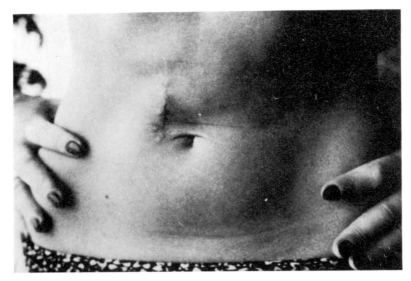

Figure 4.10 Laparotomy scar

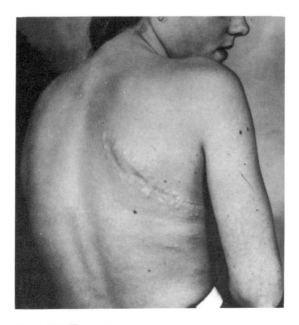

Figure 4.11 Thoracotomy scar

Some allegations of unsatisfactory dentures undoubtedly are made in an attempt to avoid payment and have given rise to the saying, 'the unpaid-for denture never fits'. Most complaints, however, appear genuine, and of those which result in legal processes the majority prove well-founded, as is ascertained by an independent examination of the patient.

Experience shows that many of the complaints, relating to 'immediate dentures' in particular, arise from a lack of communication on the part of the practitioner or to some form of guarantee being given. To tell a patient that a denture 'will look exactly like your own teeth', for example, can be courting disaster, as can a failure on the part of the practitioner to explain the effects of gum shrinkage, the shortcomings of dentures in general and immediates in particular.

The use of a printed slip, on the lines of that given below, for signature by a patient requiring immediate dentures is a useful safeguard to the practitioner. A copy of the slip should be given to the patient and the original retained with the patient's records.

Provision of Immediate Dentures

I agree to Mr.. providing me with denture(s) immediately following the extractions of teeth. I understand that shrinkage of my gums will occur which will render that/those denture(s) loose and ill fitting and it/they may have to be altered by relining and/or replaced with (a) new one(s) and for those treatments further fees will be required.

Signature ....

Date...

Denture problems account for more complaints than any other aspect of dentistry and the comparatively inexperienced practitioner must appreciate this fact. Unfortunately all dentures cannot satisfactorily be made 'according to the textbook' and the more elderly patient, in particular, having worn the same denture for many years, can create a difficult problem even to the most experienced general practitioner. Dental practitioners, unlike their medical colleagues, do not seem readily to consider the obtaining of a second opinion, yet the occasional adoption of this practice, particularly with denture cases, might well be of great value to practitioners and patients alike. Naturally all persons have a tendency to believe that what they have done is right and shy away therefore from any suggestion to the contrary. The dental practitioner, however, who can please all his patients all the time, in a lifetime of practice, must indeed be an exceptional and very fortunate person.

An acceptance of the fact that all cannot be so fortunate coupled with an acceptance of defeat in certain unfortunate circumstances could save many a practitioner further expense, wastage of time and energy and considerable mental stress when dealing with a 'difficult' denture patient. Unfortunately it matters not how much time and money has been expended by a practitioner in the provision of dentures when they are not 'satisfactory for the purpose for which they were intended'. In such circumstances he has no legal entitlement to any fee whatsoever.

Dentures once fitted become the property of a patient and even when not paid for, therefore, should not subsequently be retained or purposely damaged by a practitioner. Retention or threat of retention does sometimes induce a patient to settle his account but if the practitioner receives a demand for their return he would be well advised to comply and preferably by 'recorded delivery'. If fees remain unpaid and the dentures considered satisfactory by the practitioner, then he can but use the normal processes of the law to obtain his fee.

Providing treatment contrary to one's clinical opinion

Persuasive patients do sometimes induce a practitioner to provide treatment against his better judgment and then, when this has failed to come up to their expectations or indeed even culminated in just the sort of situation they have been advised could occur, allege negligence and/or refuse to pay the agreed fees. Frequently the allegations made distort conversations previously held, and unless a third party was present at the time it can be difficult for the practitioner to prove that he had adequately warned the patient and that the treatment was provided against his advice. When such treatment has failed it can be an impossible task to prove that 'reasonable skill and care' were exercised. The obvious advice to any practitioner faced with a patient requesting clinically unsound treatment is, 'Don't do it'.

Use of radiographs

Many dental conditions cannot properly be diagnosed without the assistance of radiographic evidence and failure to obtain this in some instances, coupled with consequential damage to a patient, can be deemed a failure to exercise reasonable skill and care. Equally a film which has been under- or overexposed, incorrectly angled or badly positioned may prove of poor diagnostic value, and operating unsuccessfully with the inadequate information thus obtained can also provide grounds for allegations of negligence.

Situations which normally require the addition of radiographic evidence to a physical examination are:

1. Determination of presence of unerupted teeth (especially in orthodontic cases).
2. Proposed extraction of misaligned or impacted teeth.
3. Monitoring the apical condition of teeth being moved, especially long term, by orthodontic appliances.
4. Before, during and after provision of root canal therapy.
5. To ascertain the suitability or otherwise of teeth to be crowned or used as bridge abutments.
6. Presence of retained roots when such are suspected following a history of difficult extractions.
7. Investigation of a source of infection.

Radiographs being only two dimensional can have their shortcomings and thus it may be necessary to take additional films from various angles and/or an occlusal as well as a lateral view to obtain essential information. Failure to take radiographs as well as insufficient or unsuitable radiographs can lead to allegations of negligence difficult to refute. A member of the society faced an allegation of failure to diagnose an infected retained root after being given a history of difficult extractions and specifically requested to ensure that no roots were present before providing new dentures. Radiographs were taken and the patient assured no roots were present. Dentures were fitted and subsequently numerous adjustments made in $\overline{5|}$ area but to no avail. The patient went elsewhere and a radiograph disclosed the presence of an infected root at $\overline{|5}$. With this evidence an allegation of negligence was made coupled with a claim for damages for pain and suffering and for refund of all fees paid. The practitioner forwarded the treatment record card and radiographs to the Medical Protection Society with the solicitor's letter containing the allegation. The radiograph covering the root area was virtually pitch black, having either been considerably over-exposed, or very incorrectly processed. Examination of the film using a brilliant light source showed 'something' in $\overline{|5}$ area. As an aid to diagnosis, however, the film was useless, and it could not be denied therefore that there had been a failure to exercise reasonable skill and care. A sight of the radiograph taken by the second practitioner was obtained and the presence of a root in the area was perfectly obvious.

A common feature of intra-oral radiographs in the $\overline{8|8}$ regions is failure to cover the full depth of the mandible and thus indicate the relationship of the apices of teeth present to the lower border of the mandible. In some such instances there may be only a small depth of bone between the apices and the lower border rendering the extraction of a tooth in that region liable to be accompanied by a mandibular fracture. If this occurs then any subsequent allegation of negligence could be difficult to rebut successfully.

No dissertation on negligence could ever cover all the incidents liable to occur as the permutations and combinations are manifold. The be-all and end-all, however, is the use or the failure of use of reasonable skill and care and the onus is on every practitioner duly to consider this with every patient and in every circumstance. Accidents will, of course, occur and in many instances through no failure on the part of the practitioner. There are numerous hazards in the practice of dentistry many of which are quite unpredictable and/or unavoidable. When any incident occurs, however, the practitioner's immediate duty is to care for his patient so as to reduce to the minimum the possibility of any more damaging effects which might otherwise occur.

It might appear unnecessary to warn practitioners that as a general rule they should not admit to any liability or offer compensation to a patient when an accident has occurred, but experience has taught the authors that such admissions and offers have been made on some occasions when otherwise a claim could have been defended. Clearly some situations do arise when a patient should be told that a mistake has been made and an obvious example is the incorrect extraction of a tooth. No offer of compensation should be made but the practitioner's protection organization informed immediately. The practitioner's duty to his patient remains, however, and he should take all possible clinical steps to alleviate the condition he has produced. The paramount duty of every practitioner is to his patient regardless of circumstances.

Record keeping

Good record keeping is as important as the provision of good dentistry and is an integral part of the use of reasonable skill and care. Exact knowledge of treatment previously provided may well be necessary for accurate diagnosis of a current complaint.

It cannot be overstressed that one of the most important factors in self-protection is the maintenance of accurate, full and contemporaneous records of all treatment provided, pre- and postoperative advice given, unusual sequelae, drugs prescribed (with dosage) and of any treatment advised but which the patient is unwilling to accept.

There can be no doubt that every visit should receive an entry, as should any appointments made but failed. Regardless of the number of visits for denture easing, every one should be recorded.

All patients are potential litigants and the so-called casual or emergency patient is no exception. Failure to record all visits and treatments etc. can create difficult situations if complaints are made. The production of a comprehensive record may be sufficient to prevent the initiation of a legal action or, failing that, affect the outcome of a court action to the advantage of the practitioner. Incomplete records, or none at all, may render defence impossible. Because of the extreme importance of accurate and complete records the task should never be deputed, all entries being the responsibility of the practitioner. When two or more practitioners provide treatment then entries should be initialled accordingly.

Ownership of records

Dental records are the property of the practitioner concerned, or, in the case of an employee, of his employer. In this connection an associate has to be considered an employee of the practice at which he rents accommodation and services (see page 26), unless the agreement between the parties stipulates otherwise.

It is not unusual for a patient moving to another area, or for some unstated reason, to request his records and radiographs. Practitioners are advised not to accede to such a request but to inform the person concerned that these items will be available to the patient's subsequent practitioner upon the latter's request.

It must be realized that records may come into the possession of another party or need to be produced in court, and personal comments about the patient should not, therefore, be entered but, if necessary at all, made on a separate sheet.

Retention of records

As litigation may be initiated some years after the related incident occurred (see Time limits, page 59) treatment records and all relevant documents and radiographs and, in certain obvious instances, models should be retained for as long as possible and a *minimum* of 7 years from the date of the last entry is recommended. In the case of a minor it is advisable to retain the records until at least 7 years after the child has reached the age of maturity.

Disclosure of records in the course of litigation

The following information, which relates to the United Kingdom and elsewhere, is taken from a Medical Protection Society booklet, *Consent – Confidentiality – Disclosure of Medical Records*, by Dr R. N. Palmer, Barrister, Secretary, Medical Protection Society:

There is an increasing trend towards openness in society generally, and an increasing expectation by patients of access to information such as medical records. Patients now have certain rights of access to information about themselves stored on computer files and there is mounting pressure for a change in the law to permit freedom of access to manually-recorded files. However, in English law there is not – and has not been – any automatic right for patients or their legal advisers to have access to the medical notes of a patient before the commencement of legal proceedings (i.e. before a writ is issued). There is, however, a High Court procedure by which, *in appropriate circumstances*, patients or their legal advisers may *apply* to see *relevant* medical records. Because there is no absolute right, and because the consequences may be far-reaching, members of the Society who are in any doubt whether to comply with an application are urged to seek our advice.

It has long been the rule that case notes may be required to be disclosed in the course of legal proceedings before the actual trial. This happens at the stage (long after the issue of a writ) known as 'discovery', when the parties must produce to each other all documents in their possession which are relevant to an issue in the action. The purpose of the rule is to prevent parties being taken by surprise at the trial by the production of a document of which they had no prior knowledge.

By the Administration of Justice Act 1970, a new provision was introduced into English law whereby, in certain circumstances and *only in actions for personal injuries or in respect of a person's death*, the court could order the production and disclosure of relevant documents *before* the issue of a writ. The object of this provision was to enable the would-be litigant to establish whether or not he or she had *prima facie* grounds on which to bring a claim for damages.

After various decisions in the courts during the 1970s concerning the persons to whom the notes were to be disclosed, the law was codified in the Supreme Court Act 1981.

The Supreme Court Act 1981 deals with two situations so far as disclosure of documents is concerned. The first is where a doctor or health authority is likely to be a party in proceedings (i.e. likely to be sued for alleged negligence and/or breach of contract) – this is dealt with in section 33. The second is where the doctor or health authority is not a party in proceedings but happens to have records relevant to issues in an action already proceeding between the patient and another party – e.g. notes about injuries sustained in a road or industrial accident – this is dealt with in section 34.

Under section 33(2) of the Act a person who is likely to be a party to subsequent legal proceedings for personal injuries or in respect of a person's death may apply to the High Court for disclosure of relevant documents. The High Court then has certain powers to order a person to disclose whether such documents are in his possession, custody or power and to produce them.

Under section 34 of the Act any party to High Court proceedings for personal injury or in respect of a person's death may apply to the High Court for an order which compels a person who is not a party to those proceedings, but who appears to the court likely to have in his possession, custody or power any documents which are relevant to an issue arising from the claim:

(a) to disclose whether those documents are in his possession, custody or power; and
(b) to produce them.

Under both sections 33 and section 34 the High Court has power to order production of documents to the applicant personally or to the following classes of persons:

(i)   to the applicant's legal advisers; or
(ii)   to the applicant's legal advisers and any medical or other professional adviser of the applicant; or
(iii) if the application has no legal adviser, to any medical or other professional adviser of the applicant.

A member who receives a request for disclosure of records and who is in any doubt as to how to proceed is advised to refer the problem to the Society. It is essential to be satisfied about the reasons for, and the reasonableness of, the request before voluntary disclosure of the notes is granted. Those seeking disclosure of the notes (whether patients or third parties or their legal advisers) will usually be requested to submit reasons for the request. If the reasons are satisfactory, the Society usually advises members to comply with the request voluntarily; but if the reasons are unsatisfactory, the Society may advise the member to insist upon a formal application to the High Court. Where indicated, this application may be opposed.

'*Documents*' in the context of the Act will include all relevant case notes, radiographs and laboratory reports etc. They will not include documents which are privileged from production because they have been prepared for the dominent purpose of defending litigation, such as reports prepared at the request of the hospital's legal adviser or reports submitted to the Society because the doctor anticipates litigation and is seeking advice. The decision of the House of Lords in the case of *Waugh v. British Railways Board* renders it doubtful whether accident reports are privileged and care should be taken to make sure that such reports are accurate statements of *fact, without comment*. Where a doctor has the slightest doubt what to include in a report, the Society should be consulted *before* the report is submitted.

Ownership of notes

It has been explained above that if a court order for disclosure is made it lies against the person who has 'possession, custody or power' of the documents. In the case of NHS patients the Secretary of State is the legal owner of the records, and his legal rights are vested in the health authorities. Thus an application for hospital notes should properly be directed to the health authority concerned. The health authority will, in turn, consult with the consultant(s) who have an interest in the case and the Society will be very pleased to assist members and offer advice in connection with a request for disclosure of documents.

In NHS general practice the medical notes are the property of the Secretary of State and, through him, the Family Practitioner Committees although in the actual possession and custody of the general practitioner. Our experience is that FPCs are generally content to leave it to the individual GP concerned, after consultation with his or her protection society, to decide how to respond to an application for access to clinical notes.

In private practice the notes are clearly within the 'possession, custody or power' of the individual practitioner, who is advised to seek the Society's help in connection with an application to see them.

Content of case notes

It will be appreciated from the foregoing paragraphs that a patient's case notes may be liable to disclosure in a variety of circumstances. When disclosed, the notes may be revealed to the patient and to legal advisers. If the litigation reaches court the case notes will also be subjected to judicial scrutiny.

It is therefore the Society's advice to members that clinical records should contain entries which are factual, objective and worthy of independent scrutiny both within and outside the medical profession. Case notes should not be used to record subjective comments of a pejorative nature. Wit, abuse, invective, sarcasm and the like have no place in the medical record. Notes should be made in the knowledge that they may, one day, be read in court.

Exchange of notes for clinical purposes

Finally, the Society wishes to stress that the foregoing advice is concerned only with requests for case notes in the course or consideration of litigation. We do not in any way seek to alter or restrict the long established practice within the profession of making available, as between doctors, any information necessary in the *bona fide* clinical conduct of a case.

N.B. In the foregoing the word 'dentist' can be substituted for 'doctor' as the legal situation is exactly the same.

Data Protection Act 1984

Where records are maintained on a computer, the Data Protection Act 1984 requires the dentist to register as a data user with the Data Protection Registrar. Application forms are available at main post offices in the UK. Failure to register is a criminal offence. The topics of registration, rules as to maintenance of data, and data subject access are complex. The BDA has published a detailed Advice Sheet on the provisions of the Data Protection Act, available free of charge to members on request.

Chapter 5

Civil law 2

Consent to treatment*

Any form of treatment, even an examination or the taking of a radiograph, carried out without the consent of the patient (or some person legally competent to give consent on his or her behalf) is an assault and as such may lead to an action in law. Regardless of this, however, the interest of the patient must always be paramount, and no emergency therefore should wait on consent.

For consent from any person of any age to be valid it is essential that it should be an informed consent. The necessity for treatment as well as the form it will take must thus be understood by the patient. It is therefore incumbent upon the practitioner to give all appropriate information and in such terms that the patient is left in no doubt as to its implications. Where fees are involved an estimate should be included; otherwise, while consent may be obtained there would be no expressed agreement to a financial arrangement.

Consent obtained when the patient has not been fully informed or has failed to understand the information has no legal value. Any likely operative and/or postoperative complications should normally be explained to a patient, but currently there is no requirement in English Law that every possible complication and side-effect should be stated. Both clinical judgement and sound common sense need to be united in determining just how much information it is advisable to give any particular patient; too much can frighten a patient unnecessarily and too little prove a source of subsequent problems.

Where a specialized procedure is to be undertaken by a practitioner of consultant status then he, not someone deputed by him, should give the necessary explanations and obtain the required consent. A deputy may well not be fully aware of the possible hazards and complications of the actual operation to be performed.

Consent may be implied, verbal or written. The fact that a patient has made an appointment with a dentist, enters the surgery and sits in the chair is implied consent to examination, but nothing more. However, a specific verbal request to 'take this tooth out' clearly is consent to the operation but not to any particular form of anaesthesia. A practitioner saying, 'Right, I will give you an injection to numb it' and being met with no form of refusal from the patient has thereby gained

---

*Based on an article 'Consent to Treatment' by J. E. Seear and published in *Dental Update*, Vol. 1, No. 5.

implied consent. The majority of dental treatment is supplied in this manner and it is only when a practitioner does not inform his patient that he is about to give a 'local' or take a radiograph etc. but proceeds with such treatment that he may later successfully be sued for assault. The advantage of the presence of a third party in the surgery is obvious; otherwise in any subsequent dispute as to what was said and agreed it would be merely one person's word against another.

Most difficulties relating to consent arise when very young children, unaccompanied, and young persons living at home or at boarding school and still under protection of parents and guardians attend for treatment. In these days of early maturity, when young persons leave home and become self-supporting before reaching adult age, it is futile to suggest that parental consent in such circumstances must be obtained for essential treatment. Thus practitioners are frequently faced with a situation wherein commonsense alone can provide the answer. It is the view of the Medical Protection Society that unless there is anything in the laws of a country expressly to the contrary, consent to treatment by a mentally normal person of 16 years or over would be judged in court to be valid.

In the United Kingdom the Family Law Reform Act 1969 reduced the age of majority from 21 to 18 and provided that consent to any surgical, medical or dental treatment, including administration of an anaesthetic, by a person who has attained 16 years of age is valid. But it must be appreciated that consent by an adult whose mentality is only that of a minor would not necessarily be valid, because he may not sufficiently understand the necessity for, and the nature of, the treatment to give an informed consent.

Consent in writing has an obvious advantage, for it can more readily be proved. Invariably it is wise to obtain this, either from the patient or from some other person competent to give it, when any procedure involves a special risk, when a general anaesthetic is to be administered, and when comparatively high fees are involved. While consent by a minor might well be valid, failure to obtain the agreement of the parent or guardian to the estimate when luxury forms of treatment are being provided can result in refusal to settle the account, and the practitioner may have no redress in law.

With young children who attend unaccompanied, but are known, there can usually be no objection to providing routine treatment. However, if it is necessary to extract a tooth or give a general anaesthetic, then parental consent should be sought, only palliative treatment being given in the meantime.

If an extraction or some other form of operative treatment is deemed urgent and parents cannot be contacted, emergency relief of pain may be provided but it is wise to retain any extracted tooth in an envelope, duly labelled with name and date, and file it with the treatment record card. It can then be used as evidence and if there is any subsequent suggestion that the extraction was not essential.

Extraction of an incorrect tooth, or of more teeth than the patient understood to be necessary and had agreed to, may lead to a civil claim for damages for assault, for negligence or for both.

A few points are worth stressing:

1. There is an obligation upon the practitioner to secure prior consent to operative treatment. If the patient himself is unable to give consent, that of his appropriate next of kin should be obtained. In the case of a child living with foster parents then the latter have the appropriate authority as too does a legal guardian.

2. The person (patient or another) giving consent must understand to what he is consenting. Appropriate explanations must be given, but in the case of operations or complex medical procedures it is for the practitioner to decide the extent of details to be disclosed.
3. The onus is upon the practitioner to determine whether the patient is capable of giving valid consent or whether consent of another is necessary or desirable.
4. Emergencies must not wait upon consent.

The basic consent form shown on page 84 is recommended, covering as it does the majority of requirements. Where fees are involved an appropriate sentence can be added: e.g. 'I understand that the fees payable for this treatment are £x and I undertake to pay that amount in full before the treatment is completed (or) £y by (date) and the balance of £z on completion/prior to completion'.

Community dental officers, whose duties involve treatment mainly of young persons, are perhaps more liable to allegations involving lack of consent than are their colleagues in general practice. Generally this is well appreciated by local authorities, and consent forms are sent to parents first of all. But it is doubtful if consent simply 'to treatment' is valid as it is virtually consent to an unknown quantity. Many lay persons are not familiar with all the complex forms dental treatment can take and parents are liable to rise in anger when children return home from the dentist with a tooth cut down to the root for crowning, a permanent tooth extracted to 'make room', a general anaesthetic administered, or even radiographs taken, and complaints may later be lodged.

To obtain valid consent to cover all contingencies is almost if not utterly impossible. Provided, therefore, parental or other consent to 'treatment' has been forthcoming for a child, the practitioner certainly must feel free to provide normal and essential treatment. Certainly if a general anaesthetic (GA), intravenous sedation or relative analgesia, is to be administered to a child, written consent should be secured each time except in extreme emergency when the interests of the patient must predominate. Consent forms should include space for the parent to give any relevant medical history, especially if no personal contact is made; if merely consent to 'treatment' has been obtained and it is necessary to extract permanent teeth, then specific consent to this should be gained.

Instances of allegations of treatment without consent including the following:

1. Extraction under GA of more teeth than patient has agreed, e.g. $\overline{7|}$ in addition to $\overline{8|}$ when removal of this proved difficult.
2. Root canal therapy when patient had previously stated this was not acceptable.
3. Radiographic examination of a child, parent not informed.
4. Administration of GA when patient understood a 'local' was to be used.
5. Extraction of $\overline{6|}$ for a child. Parent afterwards suggested tooth could have been saved by root canal therapy.
6. Extractions, by mistake, when patient understood fillings only were necessary.
7. Twelve fillings under i.v. anaesthesia, patient having been informed only eight were necessary.
8. Treatment by a community dental officer of a schoolboy whose parents had refused consent and had notified that treatment was being provided by a private practitioner.
9. Local anaesthetic. Patient convinced this was not mentioned beforehand and did not appreciate injection was to be given until needle was inserted.

Any practitioner faced with a specific problem relating to consent is advised to contact his protection organization.

Medical Protection Society Consent Form

1. I, ...of..
   (name and address of person giving consent)

   *hereby consent to undergo

   OR

   *hereby consent to ....undergoing
   (name of patient)

   the operation/treatment of ....
   the nature and purpose of which have been explained to me
   by Dr/Mr...

   I also consent to such further or alternative operative measures or treatment as may be found necessary during the course of the operation or treatment and to the administration of general or other anaesthetics for any of these purposes.

   No assurance has been given to me that the operation/treatment will be performed or administered by any particular practitioner.

   Date... Signature...
   (patient/parent/guardian*)

2. I confirm that I have explained the nature and purpose of this operation/treatment to the person(s) who signed the above form of consent.

   Date... Signature...
   (physician/surgeon*)

   *Delete whichever inapplicable.

A case of implied consent

A patient was examined by a dental member, who advised the extraction of six upper and three lower teeth and the provision of full upper and partial lower dentures.

The patient attended for the removal of the teeth under general anaesthesia. Prior to beginning induction the anaesthetist inquired how many teeth were to be extracted and the member replied 'nine'. The patient interrupted to say that she thought it was only four and the member explained to her why he considered it necessary to extract all her remaining upper teeth. The anaesthetic was administered and the nine teeth extracted.

Two days later the patient returned very irate that all her upper teeth had been removed, the explanation was repeated and the member proceeded with the construction and fitting of the dentures.

Subsequently a letter was received from the patient's solicitors alleging that the patient had only given permission for the removal of three lower and one upper tooth, that the member had extracted five sound upper teeth, and the patient had thereby suffered injuries due to the member's negligence and claiming damages.

The anaesthetist confirmed that in answer to his inquiry the member had stated that nine teeth were to be extracted, that the patient at first demurred and suggested four but after hearing the reasons advanced by the member for the removal of all the upper teeth appeared satisfied.

The Society undertook the case on behalf of the member and at the conclusion of the hearing in the county court the judge stated that he thought that the plaintiff believed after her mouth was first examined that only four teeth were to be extracted, but that later she was told it was nine and that she knew it was nine. The five additional teeth were extracted with her consent. Judgment was given for the member.

Medical Protection Society, *Case Report*, 1962.

Assault

Although the understanding of most people is that assault is purely a criminal offence, when related to dental treatment provided without consent it can lead to a civil action (see Negligence, Chapter 4, page 52). As a civil action involving a claim for compensation it will have to be shown that damage occurred as a result. As a criminal action for common assault it need only be proved that consent was not given; the authors, however, cannot recall an instance of a charge of common assault brought against a dental practitioner who allegedly provided treatment without consent. The criminal aspects of assault are dealt with in Chapter 7 (see page 98).

The contract between practitioner and patient

Immediately a dentist agrees to attend a patient a contract is established whereby the practitioner has the duty to exercise reasonable skill and care and the patient to cooperate. Once a treatment plan has been agreed then the scope of the contract is enlarged accordingly and the agreement of a fee for the services to be rendered normally completes the terms of that contract. Those terms can then only properly be revised by the agreement of both parties. Disputes do arise because the existence of a legal, and thereby binding, contract is not always fully appreciated by a practitioner, or he has failed to clarify its terms and conditions to the patient.

The majority of contracts between dentist and patient are verbal but these do nevertheless have the same validity as when written, although the existence of a contract in writing obviously has its value when a dispute arises as to the terms involved. Certainly when an expensive course of treatment is to be provided it is in the interests of the practitioner to detail this in writing and quote the agreed fee. A patient receiving such a communication and attending the next appointment without disputing the terms can be considered as having approved the contract.

Occasions do arise when practitioners explain the treatment to be provided but do not quote a fee on the assumption that the patient is aware of the type of charge being incurred. In some instances, however, there is then a refusal to settle the account when received by the patient, usually coupled with a statement to the effect that he had no idea the charge would be so high and such a fee can but be construed as gross overcharging. Such situations can and do lead to many complications and the practitioner invariably is on a 'sticky wicket' in that a most important aspect of the contract was never established. In some such instances patients have alleged that they believed treatment was being provided within the National Health Service and therefore the dentist is only entitled to the statutory payment. It is important, therefore, that every practitioner appreciates that a legal contract is established and that the terms should be clearly defined and complete.

Mention has already been made that it is an implied term of contract that the patient will cooperate in the provision of treatment and thus any failure to do so is a breach of that contract.

The implication of this is apparent from the following case history:

A difficult patient

A patient visited a member and asked to be fitted with a denture. A fee was agreed and an impression taken. Two days later he attended for the 'bite', but an appointment made for the 'try-in' was not kept. Another appointment was made (and this time kept) when some modifications were requested, but these could not be properly checked at the next attendance due to the patient's late arrival. The patient did not return for the dentures to be inserted. No reply was made to a note from the member to say that the denture was ready and the completed denture was eventually sent by post, but the package was returned apparently unopened.

Proceedings were eventually instituted by the practitioner for recovery of his fee and, at the hearing, the registrar adjourned the case *sine die* to enable the patient to return for the denture to be fitted. He was therefore given yet another appointment but on arrival refused to sit in the dental chair and stood in the doorway holding out his hand saying, 'Let me see your product'. Repeated requests for him to sit down were unavailing and he left. To make absolutely sure that he understood the position the dental practitioner then wrote to the patient offering once more to fit the denture but received no reply.

At this stage the conduct of proceedings was undertaken by the Society and counsel was briefed. The defendant contested the claim on the grounds that: (1) the denture in wax form was not suitable, and (2) that he gave no instructions for completion. The adjourned case came to court and judgment was given for our member for the full amount of his fee together with costs.

Medical Protection Society, *Case Report*, 1963.

Defamation

This may be defined as the publication of a false statement which lowers the reputation of a person in the eyes of right-thinking members of society generally. For a statement to be actionable as defamatory in English law it has to be broadcast, have no lawful justification, and be made with the object of discrediting the person concerned or exposing him to hatred, contempt or ridicule.

There are two forms of defamation, libel and slander. *Libel* is when the statement is in a permanent form, e.g. writing, printing, carving, cartoon or film; or when broadcast on radio or television. *Slander* is the spoken word or conveyed by a gesture and thus in a transitory form.

Either type of statement may be actionable at law unless protected by 'privilege' or by defence of fair comment on a matter of public interest.

Absolute privilege

Statements made in the course of judicial proceedings and in Parliament enjoy 'absolute privilege' and are thereby protected.

Qualified privilege

On grounds of public policy the law affords protection on certain occasions to persons who make defamatory statements about another in good faith and without any improper motive. Such occasions are called 'occasions of qualified privilege'. An occasion is privileged where the person who makes the communication has a legal, social or moral interest or duty to make it and the person to whom it is made has a corresponding interest or duty to receive it. An obvious example of this is a character reference given about an employee to a prospective employer. Complaints by patients to the National Health Service authorities, or to the principal of a practice about the conduct of an assistant, and complaints to the General Dental Council would all fall within the category of qualified privilege so that the complainant in each case would have a defence if sued for libel by a dentist concerned.

But this privilege is qualified and not absolute. It extends only to what is relevant and pertinent to the discharge of the duty or the protection of the interest which creates the privilege. Thus if in a letter of complaint to the National Health Service authority a patient went beyond the facts relating to the complaint and added that to his knowledge the practitioner concerned had a bad reputation locally for drunkenness or immorality the latter statement would not be protected by privilege. The privilege is also lost if the plaintiff (i.e. the person defamed) can prove that the person who made the statement was actuated by malice. The burden of proving malice is always a difficult one to discharge. It is not to be derived merely from the fact of the publication of the libel. If a person has a legitimate interest to protect, the law gives him a certain amount of latitude and he does not have to be too mealy-mouthed about the way he expresses his complaint provided that it represents his honest, even though possibly misguided, opinion. In order to defeat the defence of qualified privilege it would have to be proved by positive evidence that the defendant acted from an ulterior or improper motive such as actual spite, ill-will or jealousy, or an unreasoning and blind prejudice, or with knowledge that the statement was untrue, or made recklessly and without caring whether it was true or false. In other words, there would have to be strong evidence that the statement for which privilege is claimed was really made vindictively and with the deliberate object of injuring the other person, and not for the protection of a legitimate interest or the obtaining of redress for an honestly held grievance.

Practitioners unfortunate enough to receive disparaging communications from patients, either directly or by transmission from the NHS authorities, General Dental Council or other source having an interest in patients' welfare, should appreciate the principles upon which privilege is based. Certainly such practitioners should not write back in anger, possibly including a few ill-chosen words or phrases, giving their views of the patients concerned. If a practitioner is in doubt as to an advisable method of dealing with such a communication he should contact his protection organization. When slander is believed to have occurred then a practitioner must realize that unless he can obtain a witness to the occasion able to quote the actual words spoken, and willing to attend court to give such evidence on oath, he would have no admissible proof. Such witnesses invariably are difficult to obtain and in any event the type of publicity resulting from such an action in law would not normally be advantageous to the practitioner whatever the outcome of the hearing. When a dentist is convinced, however, that a certain person has been broadcasting slanderous statements about him, then consideration can be given to instructing solicitors to write an appropriately worded letter of warning to that person. Such courses of action are taken from time to time by the protection organizations on behalf of members and usually have the required effect. No practitioner is advised to act independently, for legal advice and assistance are essential.

Ownership of radiographs

This is a matter on which no precedent has been established in a court of law. The view taken by the protection organizations, however, is that radiographs taken for the purpose of diagnosis, treatment or the furnishing of a report form part of the records and dental history of a patient and as such are the property of the practitioner, even though a fee is paid for this service.

There are occasions when a patient attends a dentist for the express purpose of obtaining radiographs and if this be the form of contact agreed, then in such instances the films obviously become the property of the patient. Other than in the latter situation a practitioner is considered to have no obligation to make radiographs available to a patient. There are instances, however, when the forwarding of films to a dental or medical colleague may be helpful to the treatment of a patient by one of those persons and in such circumstances there can usually be no objection to such a procedure. Such films should, however, be sent direct to the other practitioner and not forwarded via the patient.

Ownership of study models

The situation in respect of study models is exactly the same as for radiographs.

Ownership of dentures

It has been explained in the previous chapter that dentures once fitted become the property of the patient and should not thereafter be forcibly withheld. The only exception to this rule is when the original contract, established between practitioner and patient, includes a definite clause to the effect that full payment is to be made before treatment is completed. Even so if the dentures have been fitted it is an assault on the person of the patient actually to remove a denture from the mouth without that patient's consent.

It is not unknown for a practitioner, driven to desperation by all too frequent complaints from a denture patient, to attack the article in question. Full lowers have been snapped into halves, others stamped on, thrown onto traffic flowing below and even into open fires in waiting rooms. None of these actions can be recommended as even though patients may allege their denture is 'useless', 'impossible to wear', 'no good for eating with' and so on, it is almost certain that at least they look better with it in than out! Damaging property which, theoretically at least, belongs to someone else is an offence and in any event it neither consoles the patient nor resolves the problem.

Ownership of inlays and bridges etc.

Practitioners at times find it necessary to remove permanently from a mouth certain items which have some intrinsic value, e.g. teeth containing gold inlays, bridgework and partial dentures having a precious metal content, gold crowns etc. Such items must be considered the property of the patient and it is unwise to assume that a claim on them will not be made. In most instances patients have no interest and thus no claim is made but it is a sensible precaution to retain the article in question for at least a few months, in a suitable envelope attached to the patient's records. In the event that a patient does subsequently request a return of the article then it would be instantly available. Should the patient suggest a rebate, to the value of the gold, on an account for treatment provided, then such an arrangement should not be agreed but the item returned with advice to take it to a recognized purchaser of precious metal who would properly be able to assess its scrap value. As a known precious metal is involved the majority of patients greatly over-estimate its value by failing to appreciate that the fee paid for the item in the first place was mainly for the practitioner's, and the laboratory's time and skill.

Chapter 6

General anaesthesia and sedation in the dental surgery

The administrator of an anaesthetic whether medically or dentally qualified, general practitioner or specialist, has the duty to exercise 'reasonable skill and care', and any failure to do so, which results in harm is likely to result in a successful action for damages for negligence. It is incumbent upon the plaintiff who alleges negligence to prove it. But sometimes, by the operation of the legal maxim known as *res ipsa loquitur* (the facts speak for themselves), the occurrence of a mishap in itself raises a presumption of negligence unless otherwise explained. The defendant practitioner would then have to rebut the presumption and therefore would find himself, in effect, in the position of having to prove his innocence and satisfy the court that he had exercised skill and care.

The majority of serious accidents which occur during general anaesthesia result in either the death of the patient or the sequelae of cerebral damage from anoxia, the latter, in the opinion of many, being the more disastrous and certainly likely to result in heavier damages being paid in the event of a successful claim against a practitioner.

The advent of numerous new drugs and the vast increase in the number of persons for whom drugs are prescribed have placed yet further and greater responsibilities upon the practitioner. Comprehensive medical histories of patients are a 'must' as well as knowledge of the pharmacology of all drugs involved. Many patients appear either never to have been told of the type of drug prescribed for them or, even if they have, to be vague as to the instructions given. In such cases it is the obvious duty of the practitioner to contact the patient's medical adviser for detailed information and advice before agreeing to the administration of any form of anaesthetic.

When taking medical histories particular attention should be paid to those patients who are known, or appear, to have some psychological disturbance. Such persons may be under treatment with antidepressant drugs (monoamine oxidase inhibitors or tricyclics) and often are reluctant to admit to their problem. It is obviously important that the anaesthetist ensures he is fully aware of the drugs being taken and of their pharmacology.

In view of the number of new drugs which continue to come on the market, and new trade names appearing for existing products, it is advisable for practitioners to have an up-to-date list readily available at the practice. Such a list should indicate dosage, possible interactions with other drugs, side-effects and contraindications.

The importance of taking a medical history has been emphasized with particular regard to drugs being taken by the patient. It is, however, necessary that the dentist elicits information about the patient's present health, past illnesses, operations and allergies; moreover, this information should be brought up to date at each appointment. This 'screening history' not only assists the dentist in determining his treatment, but if conveyed to the anaesthetist before the anaesthetic is arranged may help him to decide upon the appropriate techniques and drugs for that particular case.

The operator/anaesthetist

The practice of anaesthesia has become widely accepted as a specialty and thus the dental operator/anaesthetist with an allegation of negligence levelled against him may well find it difficult to explain why some other suitably qualified person was not present to administer the anaesthetic (see page 10, paragraphs 17, 18, 21 and 22). With numerous antibiotics and sedative drugs being readily available, the absolute necessity for a general anaesthetic for a patient attending a general dental practice must be rare, and the real dental emergency requiring immediate surgery in an acutely infected area almost unknown.

Many consultant anaesthetists appear to share a view that if a serious mishap occurs during the administration of an anaesthetic to a fit and suitable person then the management of the administration must bear critical examination. The commonest fault is failure to appreciate and note the early signs of impending circulatory and/or respiratory inadequacies and thus still be in a position to take the necessary remedial action before hypoxic effects become irreversible. If this view is to be accepted – and indeed it is difficult to dispute – then the position of the operator/anaesthetist, especially if working with but one surgery assistant, is indeed in jeopardy should trouble arise; for it would be difficult to explain that such a team, especially when providing conservative dental treatment, could adequately monitor pulse and respiration, maintain a clear airway, and efficiently carry out such other duties as are involved with the actual dental treatment.

As far back as 1967 the Joint Sub-committee on Dental Anaesthesia considered the problems of general dental anaesthesia as applied to conservative dentistry. Mindful of the mortality and morbidity associated with dental anaesthesia, the Sub-committee published its Report in which it was emphasized that an anaesthetist trained in dental anaesthesia should be the administrator or at least be present during the administration and the subsequent treatment of the patient.

In its Review and Recommendations the Sub-committee also considered that the administration of the so-called 'ultra-light' anaesthetic required the undivided attention of a properly trained anaesthetist as well as the dentist carrying out the treatment.

Although the British Dental Association did not fully accept the Report at the time, it was nevertheless produced by an authoritative body set up for a specific purpose and the conclusions reached are unlikely to be disregarded by the legal profession or the courts.

The protection and defence organizations have constantly advised their members not to accept the dual role of operator/anaesthetist. The advent of sedative type drugs (e.g. diazepam), suitable for intravenous injection and used in conjunction with local anaesthesia, appears to have brought a new dimension into this field. However, as with all new drugs and techniques, problems can and do arise and especially when variations of recommended dosages and/or the technique in question occur.

The need for general anaesthesia

As there undoubtedly are certain hazards associated with general anaesthesia and these obviously are likely to be of a more serious nature than those normally arising from the use of a local anaesthetic, the administration of any form of general anaesthetic must be fully justified. The longer the period of anaesthesia the greater is the danger to the patient, and therefore the risk to a patient undergoing extensive conservative treatment or a difficult surgical extraction under a general anaesthetic is far greater than when simple extractions or very short-term conservation treatment is to be provided. The absolute necessity for a general anaesthetic should be firmly established before any decision is made as to the actual anaesthetic of choice, and must be determined not by the convenience of the operator but by the safety of the patient.

Conservation under general anaesthetic

The Sub-committee on Dental Anaesthesia, already referred to, examined a particular application of dental anaesthetic, namely that in conservative dentistry. It considered that there were four categories or relative indications for such treatment:

1. Spastics or others who because of physical infirmity would be uncontrollable with local anaesthetic.
2. Those who are known to react adversely to or be resistant to local anaesthetics.
3. The mentally sub-normal.
4. Those whose psychological attitude to dentistry is such that they refuse from fear any form of treatment which is not performed under general anaesthetic.

Monitoring under general anaesthesia

Latterly, this topic has been of increasing concern to those who administer general anaesthetics in the dental surgery, be they general medical or dental practitioners. In July 1988, The Association of Anaesthetists of Great Britain and Ireland published 'Recommendations for Standards of Monitoring during Anaesthesia and Recovery', which included recommendations with regard to operations or procedures of brief duration which naturally encompass dental extractions and conservation. Adequate monitoring of patients is recommended and is obviously essential. What could reasonably be considered to be adequate monitoring facilities in out-patient dentistry under general anaesthesia is likely to have far reaching implications in the future.

Case history 1

In 1974 a dental patient collapsed and subsequently died having received i.v. diazepam some 30 minutes after i.v. methohexitone. At the inquest it was suggested the admixture of these two drugs in that particular order may have been the causative factor. A notice in *Society for the Advancement of Anaesthesia in Dentistry Digest* (1974), **2**, No. 6 advised: 'Until more is known diazepam should be used only as first drug, and if two intravenous agents are used the patient should be oxygenated by additional oxygen with a reservoir bag in circuit throughout.'

The fact that various drugs, when used alone, have wide therapeutic safety margins does not of itself indicate in any way that they are safe when used in conjunction with one another.

Case history 2

In 1979 a female patient aged 17 years required a surgical extraction.

The dentist administered, via the i.v. route, 60 mg pentazocine (Fortral) followed by 10 mg diazepam and then local infiltration of 1 ml of a local anaesthetic solution containing 1:80 000 adrenaline. Respiratory failure occurred, attempted resuscitation in the surgery proved ineffective and the patient was taken by ambulance to a nearby hospital where she died some 10 hours later. At the subsequent coroner's inquest a consultant pathologist gave his opinion that the cause of death was severe respiratory depression due to diazepam and pentazocine, pointing out these drugs are both respiratory depressants and that most authorities use them in a ratio of 1:3 and limit the dose of pentazocine to 30 mg (half of that administered in this particular instance).

The need for sedation

It seems there are patients whose disposition is such that they cannot be persuaded to accept dental treatment without sedation, analgesia or general anaesthesia. To attempt to treat some of these patients with only a local anaesthetic, or none at all, could produce stresses and, as has been said, 'stress and sudden death walk hand in hand'.

Sedative or anaesthetic?

To differentiate categorically between an anaesthetic drug and a sedative remains a problem and no clear definition has yet, to the knowledge of the authors, been given. Certainly there can be no rigid distinction as both can be used to produce similar effects. Theoretically the sedated patient should remain conscious throughout and the anaesthetized patient be unconscious for some period of time. Unfortunately, as many are aware, these two situations do not always apply. Sedation, if not provided with skill and experience, can produce anaesthesia, whilst an anaesthetic agent, especially if not properly administered, may not produce anaesthesia! Whilst the distinction between the two should perhaps be sufficiently great as to be obvious, certain incidents have shown this is not always so.

The Working Party on Training in Dental Anaesthesia under the Chairmanship of Dr W. D. Wylie stated in its Report (1978), 'A simple sedation technique is one in which the use of a drug or drugs produces a state of depression of the central nervous system enabling treatment to be carried out during which verbal contact with the patient is maintained throughout the period of sedation. The drugs and techniques used should carry a margin of safety wide enough to render unintended loss of consciousness unlikely'. This obviously was a well-considered definition of the ideal. Situations do arise, however, when practitioners, not initially obtaining the required results, deviate from the 'ideal' and it is then, in particular, that problems can and do arise.

Intravenous sedation, using a single dose of one appropriate drug on a young healthy adult and administered by a skilled practitioner, certainly should be regarded as a safe procedure. This should no more require the attendance of another qualified person than when a local anaesthetic only is administered. When, however, the patient is very young or elderly, or a combination of drugs is used, and particularly when one or more of these is a narcotic, then the picture may well change and that change can be a dramatic one (see page 10, paragraphs 19–22).

Relative analgesia

Inhalation analgesia using combinations of nitrous oxide and oxygen has enjoyed phases of popularity, usually preceded on each occasion by the production of a new piece of apparatus by a manufacturer of anaesthetic equipment. Very short instruction courses on the methods of use then mushroom, with the possible result that some practitioners may well have been influenced to adopt a technique involving an anaesthetic agent while lacking much of the background knowledge essential for patient safety.

With modern relative analgesia machines having automatic safety cut-outs the use of this technique by the well-instructed operator appears without doubt to be an efficient and extremely safe aid to pain relief.

The use of N_2O concentrates as high as 80 per cent is not usually recommended for this technique, better patient cooperation being obtained with 50–50 concentrations or N_2O as low as 30 per cent as recommended by Langa (1968).

All operators using this technique should realize that there are potential dangers and therefore appreciate the absolute necessity to be properly instructed in the essentials of anaesthesia, to have resuscitation equipment immediately available and sufficient adequately trained personnel present both to assist generally and to carry out resuscitation procedures should the necessity arise.

Resuscitation

All equipment, including the anaesthetic apparatus, should be checked in advance. Full resuscitation equipment and drugs must be immediately available in the surgery, and every possible precautions must be taken to avoid the inhalation or swallowing of foreign bodies. At the conclusion of the anaesthetic the patient should never, under any circumstances, be left alone, or moved, even to a recovery room, until declared sufficiently recovered by the anaesthetist. Permission to leave the practice should never be given before full recovery and fitness to travel, accompanied by a suitable responsible person, have been established. The leaving of an anaesthetized patient immediately on completion of treatment in a surgery, either alone or with a surgery assistant is to be deprecated; in the event of any form of collapse a suitably qualified and experienced practitioner should be instantly available.

No one should administer an anaesthetic drug unless familiar with methods of resuscitation and assisted by persons fully trained in emergency procedure. Regular rehearsals should be conducted to ensure each member of the team knows precisely what to do, and when, should an emergency arise. This may never happen – but if it does the wellbeing of a patient then depends on a mere few seconds being very properly used. 'Reasonable skill and care' might well be related therefore to that specific – and extremely short – period of time.

The supine position

Much is still being said and argued about the importance of the supine position during the administration of any form of general anaesthetic or sedation.

Dr J. G. Bourne has been for some years and still is a leading advocate of the use of the supine position for all forms of general anaesthesia and intravenous sedation. He has contributed many articles and letters on the subject and his conclusions, backed by clinical observations, are to the effect that a patient in the upright or semi-upright position is far more likely to faint, causing a fall in blood pressure and therefore an inadequate supply of blood both to the brain and to the heart, than a person in the supine position. With such defective blood supply death may be immediate from cardiac arrest or, delayed in varying degree, from brain damage. He attributes most of the dental anaesthetic accidents reported to the occurrence of a faint and failure on the part of the anaesthetist to recognize instantly this condition and thus immediately take the necessary actions.

Dr Bourne's views are not unanimously accepted, however, and since the supine position does have certain disadvantages, especially for example when a patient is obese or pregnant, many anaesthetists prefer the sitting or semi-reclining position. A most important factor, however, is the need to use a dental chair which can be adjusted rapidly to the horizontal in the event of a faint occurring.

Practitioners must realize that the legal profession, whilst not clinicians, are nevertheless able to call upon the knowledge and experience of all categories of medical and dental practitioners when the necessity arises. In any allegations of negligence against a practitioner, therefore, there is every reason to suppose that counsel for the plaintiff would be fully briefed upon the normal practice and the latest techniques, theories, and pronouncements appertaining to the case at issue. Likewise coroners invariably avail themselves of experts in the appropriate field when inquests are held, and thus questions involving such matters as position of the patient, the necessity for general anaesthesia, experience of the administrator, drugs used, resuscitation measures adopted, medical history, etc. are inevitably asked.

When problems arise

As full-time Dental Secretaries of the Medical Protection Society, the authors' duties have brought them into personal contact with those unfortunate dental colleagues who have administered an anaesthetic to a patient who subsequently died or, perhaps worse still, suffered permanent brain damage. It is indeed difficult fully to appreciate the undoubted torment in the minds of these practitioners. Whilst the Society carries any financial responsibility for these cases, and much time and worry is expended by many at the Society to aid such colleagues, yet this can only lessen and not remove the burden which must be borne for many years to come by those whose patients have suffered at their hands.

When collapse with serious results occurs under general anaesthesia questions invariably need answering:

What went wrong and why?
Had an adequate medical history been taken?
Was a general anaesthetic justifiable and necessary?
Was the agent used a correct one in the circumstances?

Were sufficient properly trained persons present?

Were adequate resuscitation equipment and drugs instantly available?

Were those present properly trained in methods of resuscitation and was each member of the team immediately aware of his duties?

Was the order of procedure during resuscitation correct?

Was there any failing on anyone's part during or after the anaesthetic which contributed to the collapse or to failure to satisfactorily resuscitate the patient?

These questions are basic and every practitioner administering a general anaesthetic or intravenous sedation must place himself in such a position that he could provide satisfactory answers.

There is nothing so dear in life as life itself, and this is in the hands of those administering anaesthetics.

Venepuncture

Whilst only the more serious implications and hazards have been dealt with so far, it will doubtless be appreciated that the operation of venepuncture can and does give rise to incidents which sometimes result in allegations of negligence. In this respect it is imperative that if pre-sterilized disposable equipment is not available, efficient means for sterilization of syringes and needles are employed and the site of the inserted needle is checked to ensure that it is intravenous before any solution is injected. Litigation has resulted from failure to sterilize needles and syringes adequately, the injection of incorrect solutions, extravenous injections, and needle fractures.

The increasing number of cases of serum hepatitis (Australia antigen) which occur apparently worldwide makes, for obvious reasons, the efficient sterilization of syringes, tubing, needles etc. used in intravenous techniques more essential than ever before, and the value of the use of 'disposables' needs no amplification.

The use of multi-dose bottles

Such bottles can obviously become contaminated in normal use and thereby responsible for the transmission of infection from patient to patient. Furthermore, any such bottle can be contaminated with other drugs and instances of such occurrences, and their consequences, have been reported to the protection and defence organizations. An example is when methohexitone and halothane are being used in the same surgery for a particular case or during an anaesthetic session. On completion of the case, or session, some halothane may remain in the vapourizer and this be put, in error, into the methohexitone bottle. The next patient to receive i.v. methohexitone clearly is given, unknowingly, an injection of a mixture of these two agents. The error has resulted in deaths, lung damage and other problems.

Inhaled foreign bodies and throat packing

Irrespective of the type or complexity of a dental operation, the fact that the airway and the operation field are in continuity presents a potential risk of inhalation of foreign bodies or fluid. It is mandatory that a pack of suitable material and of such a size is placed in the correct position to block off the oropharynx from the mouth whilst not obscuring the operation field or obstructing the airway.

Irrespective of whoever places the pack, whether the dentist or the anaesthetist, it is important that an understanding must exist between them regarding the positioning of the pack and maintaining its effectiveness throughout the treatment.

Injuries incurred under general anaesthetic

The injudicious use of a mouth-gag, particularly in the presence of a loose dentition, may lead to displacement of teeth, crowns or bridges. Similarly laryngoscopy performed under poor conditions, for example with inadequate relaxation of muscles or incorrect position of head, may result in similar damage.

A pre-anaesthetic assessment of the mouth may disclose potential difficulties and a pre-operative warning given to the patient of the risks may save much acrimony later. The patient's notes should record the facts and indicate that the patient has been warned.

An anaesthetized patient is particularly susceptible to stimuli to which in consciousness he would respond. The hot instrument from the autoclave may produce a devastating burn to the mucosal or epithelial tissue. Foreign material may settle in the unprotected eyes and lead to a corneal abrasion. The sclerosing effect of decalcifying solutions on the soft tissues of the mouth may lead to scarring and disfigurement.

These examples of mishaps speak for themselves and are particularly difficult to defend. It behoves the operator and anaesthetist to be aware of them and exercise the greatest care in preventing them occurring. Should they result, however, the fullest possible records should be entered in the patient's notes and the patient should be given an honest explanation of what happened.

Current knowledge

The practitioner liable to administer any form of general anaesthetic or intravenous sedation obviously must ensure that he remains fully cognizant of the latest techniques, drugs and literature relating to the subject and act accordingly. Failure to do either of these might precipitate an allegation of negligence or indeed be the cause of such an allegation being proved.

In 1973 suggestions were made, and repudiated in some quarters, that the use of halothane was liable to have adverse effects on the liver, particularly if administered within a few weeks of a previous administration. Whilst there is still controversy regarding this, it is important to assess a patient's previous anaesthetic history and it is advisable not to re-administer the agent within a period of three months. Practitioners should be aware of such pronouncements, of the clinical information available to support or decry them and then come to their own decision, based on authoritative knowledge, as to whether the use of such an agent is in the best interests of their patient in the cirumstances prevailing.

Other countries

In some countries it is illegal for a practitioner having only a dental qualification to administer a general anaesthetic. Practitioners moving to new areas should make appropriate enquiries of the registration authority before assuming their right to administer a general anaesthetic, relative analgesia or i.v. sedation.

The future

By the time this edition is published, the report of an expert working party under the chairmanship of Professor D. E. Poswillo, on 'General Anaesthesia, Sedation and Resuscitation in Dentistry', will be published, and can reasonably be expected to have considerable influence upon the future provision of general anaesthesia and sedation in the dental surgery.

References

Langa, H. (1968) *Relative Analgesia in Dental Practice*. Philadelphia, Saunders

Ministry of Health (1967) *Dental Anaesthesia*. Report of a Joint Sub-committee on the Standing Medical and Dental Advisory Committee. London, HMSO.

Report (1978) Working Party on Training in Dental Anaesthesia. Royal College of Surgeons of England, April 1978.

Report (1988) *Recommendations for Standards of Monitoring during Anaesthesia and Recovery*. The Association of Anaesthetists of Great Britain and Ireland.

Chapter 7

Criminal law

A dental practitioner may as an individual be accused of literally any crime 'in the book'. By the practice of his profession, however, indicated by the records of the protection organizations, he is somewhat vulnerable to allegations of common assault, indecent assault, contraventions of the law relating to controlled or dangerous drugs and fraud (especially in connection with the National Health Service and other similar services where claims are submitted for payment of fees and/or expenses).

Common assault

As the reader will already realize, allegations of assault can arise from the provision of treatment without consent (see Chapter 5, page 81). These, however, usually precipitate civil, not criminal, proceedings as financial restitution is usually the object of the exercise. Strictly speaking, an assault and battery is the correct description of the offence. An assault is any act by which a person causes another immediately to anticipate an unlawful contact with his person. A battery is any act by which one person intentionally inflicts some physical contact on another. However, in everyday language the term 'assault' is used to cover both.

Allegations of common assault can and do arise, however, in particular from the slapping of a difficult child patient, and such occurrences have led to dentists appearing in magistrates courts duly charged with that offence. In such instances there can be but three possible lines of defence for the practitioner:

1. The slapping was for therapeutic purposes. The child was hysterical and the administration of a slap, therefore, an appropriate and well-recognized method of treatment.
2. The dentist, knowing the family well, considered himself as acting *in loco parentis* and felt therefore that the parents would wish him to exercise appropriate control of their child, whose behaviour at the time they would not condone.
3. The child, whilst not hysterical, was out of control and liable to damage itself against the equipment, and a firm hand, literally, had therefore to be taken.

Unfortunately any one of these defences may lack persuasion in court if a parent was present in the surgery at the time of the incident, or if the surgery assistant was not present, and thus unable to give corroborative evidence.

It is the experience of the authors that a practitioner who has slapped a child is more likely to find an irate parent presenting at the practice demanding an explanation and making threatening noises, than to receive a summons for assault. The arrival of such a parent in these circumstances can be a frightening experience, especially when accompanied by a threat to 'knock your b . . . . . . block off for hitting my poor little defenceless child'. Scenes of this nature cause embarrassment to say the least, as they can occur, and apparently usually do, in the waiting room when other patients are present, or are conducted so vociferously that even when behind a closed surgery door the cause of altercation is apparent to all on the premises.

Practitioners are strongly advised never, except in obvious cases of hysteria, to strike a child. Parents, as well as the child, may object to such treatment and repercussions are almost inevitable. If a slap has to be administered then it is advisable to avoid making the face the target as this bruises readily and makes matters appear worse (*Figure 7.1*). If a parent has not accompanied a difficult child patient then cessation of treatment is perhaps the best course to adopt followed by a message to the parents giving the reason. There are methods of treating

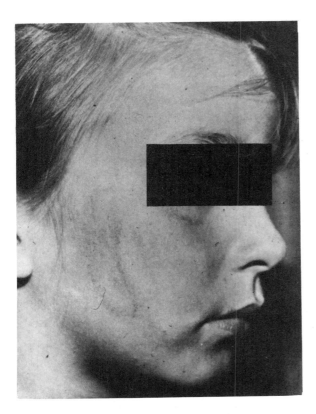

Figure 7.1 Leaving your mark

uncooperative patients other than chastisement and these may have to be considered for any further appointments.

Instances have been known where dentists and anaesthetists have had fingers bitten by a child and gentle persuasion failed to obtain a release. Self-preservation in such instances has usually resulted in slapping the offender and then parents, confronted with the bite marks, or just an explanation of the occurrence, have gone quietly away, possibly even to do a little chastising of the offender themselves.

Indecent assault

Allegations of indecent assault, usually made by a female patient against a male practitioner, but occasionally related to indecent interference with young persons, male and female, by practitioners of either sex, are serious charges indeed. Both inhalation and intravenous anaesthetics are known to produce hallucinatory effects as well as erotic dreams, and either of these, coupled with somewhat disordered clothing occurring from restlessness during an anaesthetic, may provoke such an allegation. The presence of a female surgery assistant can prove invaluable on such occasions.

In an article published in the *Anglo-Continental Dental Society Journal*, September, 1972, John Seear wrote: 'With the patient supine some practitioners apparently rest instruments upon a bib or towel on the patient's chest and the picking up and replacing of such instruments has led to suggestions from some female patients of indecent assault. A suitably placed bracket table is therefore, quite obviously, a better place to put instruments, for not only is it flatter but it is capable neither of being stimulated nor of alleging indecency!'

Some practitioners who administer general anaesthesia examine patients initially with a stethoscope and allegations of indecent assault have been made following such examinations. Here again the presence of a third party in the surgery is a wise safeguard. Particularly damning, when allegations of this nature are raised, are the inclusion of statements to the effect that 'he told his nurse to go and fetch something and then . . .!'

Practitioners accused of assault on patients should contact their protection organization immediately.

Assault on the dentist

Not always is the dentist the person alleged to be behind a blow; there are, rarely, thank goodness, occasions when he is the recipient or the threatened recipient of some form of violence. Unfortunately breakdowns do occur in practitioner/patient relationships and when exceptionally aggressive patients are involved difficult situations can arise. At these times it may become necessary to threaten to call the police or actually to do so, more especially when such patients are refusing to 'go quietly'.

It has been reported that a dental surgery assistant, aggrieved at being told to 'look for another job', struck her employer on the head with an item of dental equipment. The force applied necessitated his being taken by ambulance to hospital for treatment which included suturing.

Fraud

Allegations of fraud against a dentist usually follow the submission of forms to some authority claiming fees for attendances or the provision of treatment, travel expenses or other allowances.

Clerical errors do of course occur from time to time in almost every dental practice and this is appreciated by such bodies as the Dental Practice Boards in England and Scotland, and the Dental Estimates Committee in Northern Ireland, to which claims are submitted.

Investigation of suspicious claims within the NHS usually results either from a complaint by a patient to the authorities, or following the examination of a patient by a Dental Reference Office, either as a routine check to which any patient is liable, or following a request from the Practice Board or a Family Health Services Authority. When it is noted that a fee has been claimed but the treatment apparently not provided, then further patients of the same practitioner may be examined. Recurrences of similar situations may then lead to an extension of the investigation with the facts obtained eventually being made known to the Director of Public Prosecutions. Conviction in the courts for such offences may lead to a fine and/or imprisonment and subsequently to the practitioner appearing before the Professional Conduct Committee of the General Dental Council. It is indeed a very sobering influence to attend court and see a colleague charged with fraud as a result of signing forms which claimed fees for the treatment of persons who never existed or for treatment never provided to persons who were patients. The 'Old Bailey' was the scene of such a hearing not long ago and the practitioner involved, a married man with a family, was sentenced to three years' imprisonment. In prison he met another colleague found guilty of similar charges only a few weeks previously.

No practitioner should sign NHS forms, requesting payment for treatment provided, on behalf of any other practitioner nor allow the reverse to occur, unless appropriate arrangements have been made with the Dental Practice Board. Having signed such a form the dentist is responsible for the claim made and must appreciate that whilst clerical errors will occur the authorities have a duty to investigate practitioners when such errors appear somewhat frequently, and invariably to the financial advantage of the practitioner.

Other situations which give rise to allegations of fraud are the issuing of cheques for the purchase of items when the practitioner is aware of a lack of funds to meet the payment.

As explained in Chapter 1, the police have a duty to inform the General Dental Council when a dental practitioner has been convicted in the courts of an offence other than a minor infringement of the law. The dentist, therefore, has always to consider two aspects in relation to misdemeanours, the legal and professional. In many countries outside the United Kingdom the procedure is precisely the same.

A *plea of guilty* should never be made, possibly at the suggestion of the police, as a means of 'getting it over with quickly and with the minimum fine', for then the dentist cannot usefully deny guilt of the offence at a hearing of the Professional Conduct Committee of the General Dental Council, or equivalent body overseas, as a court conviction is accepted as proof of guilt.

Drugs

The Misuse of Drugs Act 1971 (United Kingdom)

Dentists may become involved in offences against this Act either by personal addiction or from abuses of the privileges conferred upon them by this legislation. There are six schedules to the Regulations (1985) – not to be confused with the Schedules to the Act. Schedules 1–5 list controlled drugs subject to various requirements of the Regulations, while Schedule 6 gives the forms of Register to be maintained for obtaining and supplying controlled drugs.

Schedule 1. Possession and supply of these drugs is prohibited without specific Home Office authority; they include drugs such as cannabis.

Schedule 2. The drugs in this group are subject to the full controls relating to prescriptions, safe custody and the keeping and maintenance of registers (unless exempt in Schedule 6), and include drugs such as diamorphine, morphine, pethedine, amphetamines and cocaine.

Schedule 3. These drugs are subject to special prescription requirements but not to the safe custody requirements nor is there a need to keep a register. These drugs include barbiturates and pentazocine.

Schedule 4. These drugs are subject to a minimum amount of control. They are not subjected to Controlled Drug Regulations regarding prescription nor subject to safe custody requirements.

Schedule 5. Includes preparations not intended for administration by injection which contain only a small amount of a Controlled Drug and are therefore exempt from the Controlled Drug requirements.

Limited List Regulations

Since 1985, the range of drugs available for prescription on the NHS has been limited by the Government. The list can be found in the Dental Practitioners Formulary, but as it varies from time to time practitioners should ensure they keep themselves familiar with the updated list.

Registers

A dentist obtaining or supplying controlled drugs (Schedules 2 and 3) has to maintain registers and entries must be made when he administers a drug himself or causes it to be administered under his supervision. Schedule 6 gives the forms of Registers and these must be retained for at least 2 years after the date of the last entry.

Awareness of the Regulations

Dental practitioners should be aware, in particular, of the list of drugs in Schedule 2 and keep abreast of new regulations affecting controlled drugs. Failure to observe the legal requirements of the Act and Regulations could result in criminal proceedings being initiated.

Outside the United Kingdom

Most countries today have legislation relating to 'controlled' or 'dangerous' drugs and it is the obvious duty of practitioners to know of this and act accordingly. Not only might a failure to observe the law result in criminal proceedings but also in disciplinary action by the dental registration authority which could be that of removal from the register and thus the right to practise (see Chapter 11).

Criminal negligence

For the treatment of a patient to be deemed criminally negligent it must have been provided with a total disregard of the duty of care a practitioner owes to his patient, and to have caused death or very serious injury. In this manner it would create an offence against the State and be punishable by a criminal court.

Allegations against doctors or dentists of criminal negligence are extremely uncommon. The authors are aware of only a few cases involving dental practitioners where papers were forwarded to the Director of Public Prosecutions.

The case referred to resulted from the death of a young child following collapse during the administration of an intravenous anaesthetic. The dental practitioner was acting in the dual rule of operator/anaesthetist and had only one surgery assistant, who was young, inexperienced and untrained in the handling of such an emergency. No oxygen was available at the practice and a lack of appropriate drugs necessitated the assistant being sent to a local pharmacy on at least two occasions following the collapse, to obtain those required. The matter received considerable press publicity following the inquest and the parents initiated proceedings for a civil claim and lodged a complaint with the National Health Service authorities, which led to an investigation. One result of the latter was the referral of the papers to the Professional Conduct Committee of the General Dental Council, at a meeting of which the practitioner was found guilty of serious professional misconduct but the penalty of erasure from the Register was not inflicted. The dentist assured the Committee at the time that he had no intention of acting as operator/anaesthetist in the future. Today, it is unlikely that a practitioner would remain on the Register in similar circumstances.

As would be expected the whole affair, with the repercussions which went on for over a year, proved to be an extremely harrowing experience for the practitioner, and the knowledge of the involvement of the Director of Public Prosecutions did nothing to lessen the anxiety and stress he had to bear. The civil claim in negligence was handled by his protection organization and a settlement was effected. At his appearance before the General Dental Council he was legally represented, this also coming under the aegis of the same organization.

Some other aspects of involvement of dental practitioners with the criminal law are apparent from the abridged list of convictions, given on page 9, paragraph 15, and these have resulted in appearances before the Professional Conduct Committee of the General Dental Council.

Statements to the police

The police, on receipt of an allegation against a dentist involving a criminal act, are almost certain to visit the practitioner and request a statement. The practitioner is under no obligation to provide this and indeed, other than making an outright denial, is generally well advised to refuse to make a statement until he has contacted his solicitor or protection organization. It is well to remember, however, that any immediate reply may be quoted, or even misquoted, at a later date and therefore is best limited to a statement to the effect that, 'This is a very serious allegation and I wish, therefore, to obtain legal advice. In the circumstances I am not prepared to make any statement at this time.'

A practitioner cannot effectively *order* his staff not to assist the police but can, of course, ask them to defer making a statement until they have received advice. They are not, however, bound to accede to such a request.

Chapter 8

Professional ethics

The ethics of a profession are not imposed by legislation but self-inflicted and voluntarily accepted for the purpose of establishing and maintaining an honourable pattern of behaviour recognized both by its members and the community it serves.

For the most part dental ethics is an unwritten code but, of necessity, guidelines have been laid down for the information of members and potential members of the profession. Unethical behaviour can be of such a nature as to constitute serious professional misconduct and thus come within the disciplinary jurisdiction of the dental registration authority. For this reason the General Dental Council in the United Kingdom issues the booklet *Professional Conduct and Fitness to Practice* (see pages 7–16). This broadly indicates the type of behaviour of which the Council disapproves and which is likely therefore to lead to disciplinary action.

In view of this it seems opportune to remind the reader that the General Dental Council portrays the government of the profession by the profession and it is by his own colleagues therefore that a practitioner's conduct is judged.

Equivalent bodies overseas give similar guidance and in some areas the regulations under the Dentists Act include a Dental Code which may contain quite a considerable number of 'dos and don'ts'. Any breach of that code is then an action contrary to the Act and renders the offender liable to disciplinary procedures with possible erasure from the Register.

Undoubtedly it is an impossible exercise to conceive, and therefore to put into writing, positive guidance on all the potential ethical problems with which a practitioner may be faced. The British Dental Association produces a booklet *Ethical and Legal Obligations of Dental Practitioners*, and this very adequately advises on the more common problems arising in that field. The authors are indebted to the Association for permission to reprint in this book certain of the information and advice contained therein.

National dental associations, as well as the dental registration authorities, have a definite interest in ethical matters and on occasions this may be of a disciplinary nature with expulsion from membership of the association as a penalty for a serious breach of the code. The associations and the protection organizations are able to act as arbitrators or conciliators when members are in dispute over ethical matters, and equally to advise and assist individuals in an understanding of the ethics relating to specific circumstances. The protection organizations also can assist by undertaking legal proceedings when such are deemed necessary to safeguard a member's interests.

Dentistry being one of the healing arts, and thereby including in its practice many aspects of that of medicine, has derived its code of behaviour from the Hippocratic

Oath. After surviving for some 25 centuries this Oath was revised by the World Medical Association following the Second World War. Revision was considered necessary, not only because the wording had become archaic and some of the principles anachronistic, but also because of the numerous crimes which were perpetrated during the war against individuals, races and creeds. The object of the revised code, termed the 'Declaration of Geneva', was to unite all members of the medical profession throughout the world, and introduce an international code of medical ethics applicable both in peace and in war.

The Declaration of Geneva

This states:

At the time of being admitted as a member of the Medical Profession I solemnly pledge myself to consecrate my life to the service of humanity.
I will give to my teachers the respect and gratitude which is their due.
I will practice my profession with conscience and dignity.
The health of my patient will be my first consideration.
I will respect the secrets which are confided in me.
I will maintain by all the means in my power the honour and the noble traditions of the medical profession.
My colleagues will be my brothers.
I will not permit considerations of religion, nationality, race, party politics or social standing to intervene between my duty and my patient.
I will maintain the utmost respect for human life from the time of conception: even under threat, I will not use my medical knowledge contrary to the laws of humanity.
I make these promises solemnly, freely and upon my honour.

The International Code of Medical Ethics

Duties of doctors in general
A doctor must always maintain the highest standards of professional conduct.
A doctor must practise his profession uninfluenced by motives of profit.

Duties of doctors to the sick
A doctor must always bear in mind the obligation of preserving human life.
A doctor owes his patient complete loyalty and all the resources of his science. Whenever an examination or treatment is beyond his capacity he should summon another doctor who has the necessary ability.
A doctor shall preserve absolute secrecy on all he knows about his patient because of the confidence entrusted in him.
A doctor must give emergency care as a humanitarian duty unless he is assured that others are willing and able to give such care.

Unethical practices
1. Any self advertisement except such as is expressly authorized by the national code of medical ethics.
2. Collaboration in any form of medical service in which the doctor does not have professional independence.
3. Receiving any money in connection with service rendered to a patient other than a proper professional fee, even with the knowledge of the patient.

Intra-professional relations
A doctor ought to behave to his colleagues as he would have them behave to him.
A doctor must not entice patients from his colleagues.
A doctor must observe the principles of the 'Declaration of Geneva' approved by the World Medical Association.

The FDI principles

The Fédération Dentaire Internationale (FDI), since the publication of the Declaration of Geneva, has formulated 'International Principles of Ethics for the Dental Profession' (revised 1986).

Introduction
These International Principles of Ethics for the dental profession should be considered as guidelines for every dentist. They in themselves cannot cover all local or national traditions and circumstances.

The spirit and not the letter of the principles therefore must be the guide to the conduct of the dentist, who has many obligations in addition to those stated within the principles.

The essence of these principles is summarized by the phrase 'Do as you would be done by'.

The dentist has an obligation to work constantly for the progress of dental science by service to (1) the patient, (2) the community and (3) the profession.

1. *The patient*
   1.1 The primary duty of the dentist is to safeguard the health of patients irrespective of their nationality, sex, race, creed, political views or social and economic standing.
   1.2 The needs of the patient are the overriding concern and should be met by the dentist offering all possible treatment with, if necessary, the assistance of other professional colleagues.
   1.3 A dentist has the right to decline to treat a patient except in the case of emergencies or where, for humanitarian reasons, treatment should not be witheld. However, a course of treatment once commenced should not be discontinued except for exceptional reasons and then the dentist should cooperate in making alternative arrangements for its completion.
   1.4 The dentist should uphold the principle that the patient has a free choice of practitioner.
   1.5 Professional secrecy must be absolute, except where the laws of the country dictate otherwise. It is also the obligation of the dentist to ensure that auxiliary personnel observe this rule.
   1.6 The dentist must accept full responsibility for all treatment undertaken, including treatment carried out, on the dentist's instructions, by auxiliaries. No operation or service should be delegated to a person who is not qualified or is not permitted by the laws of the country to undertake that work.
   1.7 A dentist should refer for advice or treatment any patient considered to require a level of competence greater than that of that dentist.

2. *The community*
   2.1 The dentist should participate in dental health education and should promote and support accepted measures to improve the general and dental health of the public.
   2.2 Dentists may advance their professional reputations only through the medium of the professional services they provide to patients and to society.
   2.3 The dentist should assume a responsible role in community life.

3. The profession

3.1 A dentists should behave in all circumstances both within and outside professional life in a manner that will enhance the prestige, honour and dignity of the profession.

3.2 The dentist has a duty to maintain professional competence through continuing education keeping abreast of appropriate modern scientific knowledge and technical development.

3.3 A dentist should behave towards colleagues in a manner that respects the rules and etiquette of the profession and should be willing to assist colleagues professionally.

3.4 A dentist should not solicit patients of colleagues and when consulted by a patient of another dentist should attend to any condition constituting an emergency and then refer that patient back to the dentist concerned.

3.5 The dentist should not refer disparagingly to the services of another dentist. If the welfare of the patient demands that corrective treatment be instituted this should be carried out in such a way as to avoid any reflection on the previous dentist or on the dental profession.

3.6 A dentist has an obligation to support the advancement of the profession through membership of scientific and professional organizations locally, nationally and internationally and to observe their rules of ethics.

3.7 A dentist should make the results of research available to all when such results may be useful in protecting or promoting the dental health of the public

Final document approved by General Assembly A
Manila 1986

General advice

The dentist and his patients

Professional competence and experience*

A patient has a right to expect that treatment is undertaken by a practitioner whose competence and experience equips him to complete it to a satisfactorily high standard. Every dentist must ensure that his competence is adequate for all the techniques he undertakes and that his knowledge is kept up-to-date by frequent participation in postgraduate education. Unsatisfactory treatment or failure to exercise adequate skill and care may render a practitioner liable to civil actions for negligence, to investigation by a Family Health Services Authority and to allegations before the General Dental Council of serious professional misconduct. Postgraduate courses are regularly arranged by the BDA, the specialist societies and the regional postgraduate centres. The Association can put members in touch with the Societies and course organisers.

Acceptance of patients*

The importance of good communications with patients cannot be overemphasized. Relations should be friendly and dentists and their staff alike should take care to ensure that patients are put at ease and feel that they are taking an active part in

*These items are from Ethical and Legal Obligations of Dental Practitioners *(1988) and are reprinted here with the kind permission of the British Dental Association.*

their dental care. Good communications will help to avoid disputes over treatment or fees charged but, even if these do arise, at least they will minimize confusion and enable each side to put their cases clearly. Dental staff must be accessible, well trained and prepared to answer patients' questions clearly, accurately and promptly.

All patients have a right of free choice of general dental practitioner and the right to change their dentist (provided that the GDS requirements are met if a course of treatment has already begun with another dentist). Once a patient has been accepted for other than occasional treatment, under the GDS Regulations, a dentist must be prepared to carry out or arrange for all treatment necessary for dental fitness that the patient is willing to undergo. A dentist has a duty to ensure that the patient is provided with full information so that he understands the treatment to be carried out and the nature of the contract with the dentist, whether private or NHS. It is important that accurate cost indications are given at the outset and that any necessary changes to estimate or treatment plan are fully explained to and agreed by the patient.

Where a dentist refers a patient to another practitioner for specific items of treatment, it should be made clear to the patient the terms on which he is being accepted for that treatment – whether NHS or private – and the probable cost. Both the referring and the second practitioner in such cases have equal responsibility to ensure that the arrangements are acceptable to the patient. Patients should not find that what they thought was an NHS referral as part of the same course of treatment turns out to be a private arrangement at a cost they had not expected.

Practitioners should take care not inadvertently to accept for general treatment patients who are undergoing courses of treatment with another dentist or are the regular patients of another practice unless the patient expressly wishes to change dentist. Wherever possible, emergency care should be made available if patients are unable to contact their own dentist. In such cases, however, only such treatment as is immediately necessary should be undertaken except with the agreement of the patient's usual dentist.

Cases arise where a practitioner is consulted by a patient who was previously treated by him when he was an assistant or an associate in another practice. Where his contract made particular provision for such a circumstance, the practitioner should refer to it and, if such is the provision, make every reasonable endeavour to induce the patient to return to the former practice. Only after it has been ascertained that the patient would in any event not return to the previous practice should he accept the patient for treatment.

Considerable problems can face a departing assistant or associate if questioned by his patients about his future plans. The departing practitioner has a contractual obligation to make arrangements for the completion of any treatment commenced and, apart from in exceptional circumstances, it would be quite unacceptable for a practitioner to connive in an arrangement whereby a patient makes an appointment believing it to be with the former dentist only to find on arrival that the appointment is with another, perhaps unknown, practitioner. The precise details of arrangements for leaving must be left for agreement between the parties involved but it must be remembered at all times that with the exception of the assistant, the dentist who performs the treatment has the responsibility in law and under General Dental Service Regulations for the interests and the dental care of patients he has accepted for a course of treatment.

*Second opinions**

When a dentist sees a patient who has been previously examined or treated by a colleague, he should avoid, as far as possible, any word or action which might disturb the confidence of the patient in any dentist or in the dental profession as a whole. It is not unreasonable, however, and is becoming increasingly common, for patients to seek second opinions. Dentists should be mindful of current attitudes to patients' rights when considering whether or not to agree to give a second opinion. The interests of the patient should be the first concern, but the dentist, in some circumstances, may wish to make the first dentist aware of the approach made to him. It is possible that, as a result of a second opinion, a dentist might be called upon as a witness and be cross examined under oath.

*Emergency treatment and availability**

A dental surgeon has an ethical obligation to make adequate arrangements for the treatment of his patients in emergencies at times when his practice may not be attended. Patients should be made aware of what these arrangements are and the Association supports local initiatives in setting up rota systems. Schemes approved by the profession locally should be advertised in the press, as may a practitioner's individual arrangements. At the very least, arrangements should provide for a telephone number at which the dentist or someone who can act for him will be available. The telephone number of the private residence should not be ex directory if there is no such arrangement (see page 173: Terms of service).

*Practice leaflets**

An attractive leaflet is an excellent means of providing patients and those making enquiries about the practice's services and facilities with much-needed information. Detailed advice on the content of such leaflets is available from the BDA – in a leaflet.

*Changes in practice circumstances**

The sale of a practice or changes in practice personnel may be announced in the press, but it is customary for patients of the practice to be informed by letter if a practice changes hands. In these cases the retiring practitioner would advise patients of the change, introduce his successor, thank them for their past support and state that the sucessor will be pleased to see patients by appointment. It may be necessary to include arrangements for forward appointments, if any, but the option should always be available for patients not to return if they so prefer.

*Recall cards**

Recall cards may be sent informing a patient of the time which has elapsed since his previous appointment or offering a new appointment. They need not be sent under cover of an envelope.

*See footnote on page 108

*Use of dental health literature and commercial promotional literature**

It is becoming increasingly the practice for individual dentists to distribute their own dental health literature to patients. Promotional material prepared by manufacturers which is aimed at explaining a technique or, in particular, a branded product directly to the patient should be used with caution. It is the responsibility of the dentist, if he gives such material to a patient, to ensure that the statement and claims contained in the leaflets are accurate, applicable to the patient's clinical condition and do not mislead a patient from the point of view of suitability of the treatment, its availability either under the National Health Service or private contract, and the expectations of its performance. Practitioners should take care not to mislead a patient by making unjustified claims about the life expectancy of crown and bridgework in particular.

*Sale of dental goods**

There is no ethical objection to dentists selling items such as toothbrushes, toothpaste and other aids to prevention if such products are considered to be in the patient's interest. Practitioners should be particularly wary of selling mechanical aids which may prove to be faulty or unsatisfactory as the legislation which now controls trading is complex and far-reaching.

*Use of titles and descriptions**

The Dentist Act permits a registered practitioner to use the title dentist, dental practitioner, or dental surgeon. He must not use any title which suggests that he possesses any professional status or qualification other than one which is indicated by particulars entered against his name in the Dentists Register. Descriptions such as 'specialist' are not permissible and the use of the title 'Dr' unless appropriately qualified is by implication also precluded by the Act. Certificates should only be displayed in surgery or waiting room if they relate to registrable qualifications.

*Private contracts and charges**

The need for a clear understanding between practitioner and patient over the nature and cost of treatment has been discussed above (see 'Acceptance of patients). This is particularly important in private contracts and it is advisable to give patients written statements covering both treatment and costs, updating them in writing where necessary. A signed agreement to the estimate by the patient is preferable since this serves both as consent to treatment and as a contract for the treatment. A patient should know from the outset that treatment is to be carried out privately and there should be no coercion on the patient to accept a private arrangement. Practitioners should avoid misleading statements to patients on matters such as the range of treatment available under the NHS or regarding the life expectancy of crown and bridgework for example. Section 9.16 and 9.17 explains the requirements of the Supply of Goods and Services Act and the Consumer Protection Act regarding fees.

*See footnote on page 108

Mixing NHS and private treatment, although in certain circumstances permissible under the new NHS contract, can cause problems and practitioners run the risk of falling foul of their terms of service. The BDA will advise in individual cases.

Broken appointments

A practitioner who charges or wishes to charge for failed appointments should notify patients accordingly. This can be effected verbally, but it is preferable that it be in writing, and appointment cards are appropriate items to bear such information.

If a patient is left unaware that a fee is chargeable for a broken appointment then difficulty may ensue in the pursuit of such a fee by the practitioner. Disputes do arise from time to time when a dentist claims fees for broken appointments and the patient retaliates with reminders of the occasions he was kept waiting for not inconsiderable periods of time, having arrived at the appointed hour. Before sending in accounts for failed or 'late' appointments it is advisable, therefore to take any such situations into consideration. A patient has every right to consider that his or her time is of equal value to that of the practitioner and it is indeed unwise to 'wave a red rag at a bull'.

Dichotomy (fee-splitting)

It is quite unethical, as well as being illegal (Prevention of Corruption Act 1906), for any arrangement to be made between two practitioners, medical or dental, whereby a fee paid by a patient to one practitioner is then paid in part to another. Equally no payment in cash or kind (and this includes free treatment), should be made by a practitioner to any third party as an inducement to that party to recommend patients to a practice.

Confidentiality

See Chapters 3, 9, 10 and 12.

The dentist and his employees

A dental practitioner is free to advertise in the press when vacancies occur in his staff. It is ethically wrong deliberately to entice into employment staff employed by another practitioner.

Under current employment legislation, employers are required to give employees, not later than 13 weeks after employment has begun, written information about their main terms of employment. The BDA issues advice leaflets on this and other matters. The general Dental Services Regulations state that wages paid to dental technicians must not be less that the scale agreed for the time being by the National Joint Council for the Craft of Dental Technicians. A copy of the scale can be obtained from the Secretary of the Association.

The dentist and his professional colleagues

*Establishment in specialist practice**

A dentist who wishes to confine his practice to a particular branch of dentistry may inform other practitioners in the area of his intention. The communication is one between colleagues and is to an extent privileged. It should include all the essential facts, but the dentist is unlikely to achieve his objective if he refers to himself in too laudatory terms. A dentist may not refer to himself as a specialist either in a communication or in an advertisement, but may state that he restricts his practice to a given sphere.

*Dentists needing further dental opinion**

When a dentist requires another opinion it is desirable, if he is not to be present during the examiniation of the patient, that he should communicate in writing all relevant information concerning the condition upon which advice is sought to the dentist consulted, who should reply giving his conclusions. The dentist consulted may give to the patient such information as he judges appropriate to the occasion.

The dentist consulted should not attempt to secure for himself, or any other dentist, the care of the patient sent in consultation, nor should he treat the patient then or subsequently except with the consent of the dentist who referred the patient, unless the patient does not wish to return to the original dentist.

*Radiology**

When the patient is sent to a radiologist for radiographic examination the report and/or radiographs should be sent direct to the dental practitioner. Clinical advice should not normally be given to the patient by the radiologist. Radiographs are a diagnostic aid and remain the property of the practitioner or radiologist.

*General dental practitioners and general medical practitioners**

In the course of his practice a dental practitioner will frequently have to communicate with members of the medical profession and it is not necessary in this booklet to comment on the cordial relationship which should exist between the members of all professions. The doctor/dentist relationship, however, is of particular importance and the following rules for the conduct of doctors in relation to dentists have been prepared jointly by the British Dental Association and the British Medical Association:

1. When a patient, in the opinion of his medical attendant, needs dental treatment, the patient should be referred in all but exceptional circumstances to his own dentist. In the event of the patient having no regular dentist there is no objection to a doctor recommending a dentist of his own choice.
2. When a doctor needs dental advice concerning one of his patients, the doctor should communicate in the first instance with the patient's own dentist. In the

*See footnote on page 108

event of the patient having no regular dentist there is no objection to the doctor consulting the dentist of his own choice.

3. When the dentist has reason to believe that the patient has some constitutional disorder and considers some major dental procedure is necessary, he should consult the patient's doctor before carrying out such treatment. The dentist remains, however, entirely responsible for the treatment which he may undertake.

4. When there is a conflict of opinion between a doctor and a dentist concerning the diagnosis and/or treatment of the condition of a patient, they should consult with each other to reach an agreement which is satisfactory to both.

5. Where the conflict of opinion remains unresolved, the patient should be so informed and invited to choose one of the alternatives or assisted to obtain other professional advice.

6. On the completion of any dental operation and especially if there is any reason to think that post-operative complications may ensue, the patient should be advised to consult the dentist immediately if such complications arise and the dentist should take all reasonable steps to facilitate such consultation.

*Medical consultant needing dental opinion**

Normally the dentist consulted should ascertain if the patient has a dentist and should satisfy himself that the latter is cognisant and willing that the consultation should take place. The dentist consulted should subsequently notify the patient's dentist as well as the doctor or medical consultant regarding:

- his general opinion of the case
- any urgent treatment carried out or to be carried out by him, i.e. the dentist consulted
- his recommedations regarding further treatment; normally this further treatment should be carried out by the patient's usual dentist or by the dentist consulted in cooperation with the former.

The hospital service and university teachers

General principles of ethics are common to all spheres of practice. This section, however, covers some aspects specific to the hospital service and to those providing treatment in dental schools.

*Staff**

Consultants, including those holding honorary status, have patients referred to them by other dental and medical practitioners. Although they may delegate the treatment of such patients to more junior colleagues the overall responsibility for their care remains with the Consultant. In no circumstances should he or his staff criticise, either directly or by implication, the advice or treatment given by another practitioner. Neither should anything be said or done to undermine the confidence of patients in their own practitioners.

*See footnote on page 108

The referring dentist or doctor should be informed as soon as possible and preferably in writing of the result of the initial consultation and of the extent and timing of any proposed treatment. A further communication should be sent on the completion of hospital treatment when indicated for the continuity of patient care.

Treatment*

In the case of an in-patient in a general hospital, the dental officer to the institution should carry out any dental treatment related to the clinical reason for referral. Further dental treatment should not be undertaken without consultation with the practitioner concerned.

In the case of a patient attending the out-patient department of a general hospital, the dental officer to the institution should advise concerning any dental treatment necessitated by the patient's general condition: if treatment is required only that necessary for the patient's immediate welfare should be undertaken unless his usual practitioner has been consulted.

It is unethical for a hospital dental officer to use his position to influence patients to consult either himself or a colleague in his private capacity.

In all cases where treatment in hospital is given to a patient referred by another practitioner full information concerning that treatment should be passed on to the patient's own dentist.

Clinical research*

The protocol of all proposed clinical research projects should be submitted for approval to the appropriate Ethical Committee. It is suggested that before engaging in such research members may wish to contact the BDA for advice on the conduct of projects.

When a project involves the examination of patients singly or in groups, every effort should be made to acquaint the patient's usual dentist, if he has one, of the nature and purpose of the examination. It is undesirable that any comment concerning the result of the examination should be made to the patient as it might be liable to disturb the relationship between the patient and his regular dentist.

The dentist and the public

Press, television and radio*

A dental practitioner has a right and in fact a duty as a citizen to take his place within the community in which he lives and which he serves. Taking part in such activities is not of itself unethical but a dental practitioner should avoid publicity through the media of a nature which may be regarded as likely to bring the profession into disrepute.

It is increasingly common for a practitioner to be approached by press, radio or television in connection with his public activities or for comment on dento-political matters or on professional matters of public interest. The communications media are understandably reluctant to accept comment on professional matters without

*See footnote on page 108

being able to quote the authority for the comment. If a dentist declines to allow his name to be used an opportunity for publicity which could be advantageous to the profession may be missed, or an authoritative statement from the profession, issued in the interests of the general public, may not be broadcast. Publicity exceeding statements relating to the identity of the person interviewed and the giving of a professional opinion may be regarded as likely to bring the profession into disrepute.

The public takes an active interest in all aspects of life and it is therefore desirable that dentists' success and achievements in public affairs, sport, etc, should be known. However, unduly frequent publicity of any kind, whether or not it is likely to benefit the individual directly in relation to his practice should be avoided.

Articles written for the lay press should not appear to laud the writer. The practitioner concerned should be prepared to have his motives closely scrutinised. It is often easier to avoid complaints being made than to deal with them when they have been lodged.

One of the problems associated with newspaper publicity arises from interviews with the press. It is often better to offer a prepared statement than to accept a promise that the proof will be submitted for scrutiny. Members acting as official spokesman for the Association or for Branches and Sections should give the press only their name and spokesman position.

No exception is likely to be taken to a dentist's name being published in reports of social occasions or gatherings. Care should, however, be taken in this connection.

Lectures to lay audiences

While there is no objection to a dental practitioner delivering lectures to lay audiences, he should take all reasonable steps to see that in any preliminary announcement or subsequent press report of the lecture his professional qualifications and/or ability (as distinct from the subject-matter of the lecture) are not made the subject of laudatory references.

Parliamentary and local Government elections

A dentist may wish to stand for election to Parliament or to a local council. In so doing he is bound to obey the law relating to elections generally. It will be necessary for him to state his name, address and profession and these details must inevitably appear in official notices concerning the election. It could not be considered wrong, therefore, if in his election address reference was made to the fact that he was a dental surgeon, but again this should not be in laudatory terms.

Advertising and canvassing

Freedom to advertise*

The General Dental Council first relaxed the absolute restriction on advertising in November 1985 and this was followed by more extensive freedom to advertise in

*See footnote on page 108

May 1988. The Council's booklet, 'Professional Conduct and Fitness to Practice' describes the rules in detail (paragraphs 37–45). In general, however, the only restrictions are that advertisements should be legal, decent and truthful, have regard for professional propriety and should not be of a character that could reasonably be regarded as likely to bring the profession into disrepute. They should not contain any reference to the efficiency, skills or knowledge of any other dentist or practice nor make claims which are not capable of substantiation or which suggest superiority over any other dentist or practice.

No publicity or advertising materials should indicate that a dentist has specialist expertise but it may state that a practice is wholly or mainly devoted to particular types of treatment.

There is no size restriction on advertisements and they may contain dental health messages and practice logos, mention the availability of specific items of treatment, services and facilities, for example the service of a hygienist or a children's health club, and include fees.

Signs*

The professional plate is the standard means of indicating to those seeking it the existence of a dental practice on the premises. The General Dental Council disapprove of a registered dental practitioner carrying on a dental practice in a name other than the name in which he appears in the Dentists Register. The object of the plate is to indicate those practitioners in regular attendance and the plate of a predecessor in a practice may be shown for a period not exceeding 3 years but it must be plainly preceded by the word 'late' or 'formerly'. Nothing must be used by way of initials or otherwise which may mislead the public. Only those initials used in the Dentists Register should appear – for example it is not considered ethical to display the abbreviation 'Hons' after a qualification as this may mislead. It is not permissible to include the names of hygienists or other auxiliary staff on a plate, which should include name(s), registered qualifications, the title 'dentist', 'dental practitioner' or 'dental surgeon'.

There are no prescriptive guidelines for the nature of other practice signs, but further information might include the telephone number of the practice, hours of attendance and a telephone number for use in emergencies.

Commercial interests*

A dentist should take care that there is no connection between his practice and any other commercial interests he may have. If for example, he owns a retail or other business next door to the practice, the public should not be encouraged to consider the two as one business and no attempt should be made to refer a person to one business from another. The business should at all times be wholly independent of any other business.

The promotion of products*

A practitioner must ensure that he does not promote one particular product for gain or prescribe treatment for a patient which is not suitable for the clinical condition of a patient.

*See footnote on page 108

*Professional consultancies**

Any professional consultancies, commercial research funding or interests in a commercial venture should be disclosed to interested parties where they might have a bearing on any other activity of the dentist.

*Patents**

Where a dentist may be considering applying for a patent, he should be mindful of the fundamental ethical principle that a practitioner should, at all times, prefer his patient's interest to his own. The following statement has been agreed between the Association, the General Dental Council and the Protection Societies:

No dentist who obtains a patent on either an instrument or a remedy should attempt to retain the monopoly of that patent.

While ideally an invention or discovery should be shared freely among the profession, it is recognized the the inventor or discoverer may reasonably expect to receive a financial reward from his efforts (although this may be controlled by his terms of employment).

A dentist holding a patent in respect of an invention or discovery in the dental field should ideally dispose of his interest in the patent, either by assigning it to the National Research Development Corporation, through whom an award may be claimed, or in the case of instruments, by selling his interest outright to a commercial firm. In the latter case it is appreciated that a ready purchaser may not always be found in the first instance. Thus until the saleability of the invention is proved no objection can be raised to the dentist receiving royalties on its sale to start with.

*Windows**

Windows should be adequately screened.

*Naming of premises and practices**

Dentists should practice under their own name (see 'Signs' above), but some use a business name for convenience in dealings with suppliers, etc. While there is no longer a statutory requirement to register business names, Statutory Instruments No. 1685 of 1981 prescribes a list of sensitive and prohibited names which may only be used by permission of the Secretary of State if a letter of non-objection is obtained from a 'relevant body'. The words 'dental' and 'dentistry' are included in this list and if a practitioner intends to practice in a name other than his own which includes such a word, he must first consult the General Dental Council and thereafter obtain consent to its use from the Secretary of State.

*Canvassing**

A dentist should not enter into or connive at any financial arrangement by which patients are referred to him. The use of unsolicited telephone calls to promote a

*See footnote on page 108

practice would be likely to diminish public confidence in the profession and bring the profession into disrepute. Unsolicited mailings or practice leaflets are acceptable, however.

A dentist may offer his services to the residents of public or private nursing, old peoples', children's and other homes through their administrators and to personnel employed at workplaces through managers, provided that the terms of any arrangement do not require that treatment may be obtained exclusively from that practitioner.

Chapter 9

The practitioner and his staff

The reader will already be aware (Chapter 4) of an employer's vicarious liability for employees' misdeeds. A practitioner's supervisory duties and other responsibilities to dental hygienists are dealt with in Chapter 10. This chapter summarises a dentist's rights and liabilities as an employer.

Laws and Regulations

The following Statutes and Regulations in the United Kindom concern dentists and staff. Employment law changes rapidly and is stated here as at May 1990. Statutes applying to dental employees are now listed.

The Dentists Act 1984
The Dental Auxiliaries Regulations 1986
The Employment Protection (Consolidation) Act 1978
The Employment Acts 1980–88
The Occupiers Liability Act 1957
The Factories Act 1961
The Defective Premises Act 1972
The Employers Liability (Compulsory Insurance) Act 1969
The Employers Liability (Defective Equipment) Act 1969
The Law Reform (Personal Injuries) Act 1948
The National Insurance (Industrial Injuries) Act 1946
The National Health Service Acts
The National Insurance Acts
The Offices, Shops and Railway Premises Act 1963
The Health and Safety at Work Act 1974
The Data Protection Act 1984
The Consumer Protection Act 1987
The Income Taxes Management Act 1988
The Race Relations Act 1976
The Sex Discrimination Act 1975
The Social Security Act 1986

The Dentists Act 1984

This Act makes the practice of dentistry illegal other than by registered practitioners and enrolled auxiliaries, and by its professional conduct procedures oversees the conduct of the profession (see page 2)

The Dental Auxiliaries Regulations 1986

These include the provision of separate Rolls to be kept for dental hygienists and dental therapists; they also stipulate the requirements for enrolment, the limitations of treatment to be provided by each class and the diciplinary procedures when an auxiliary is convicted in the courts or alleged to have been guilty of misconduct.

Employment legislation

Contracts of employment

The Employment Protection (Consolidation) Act 1978 requires employers to give employees, not later than 13 weeks after employment has begun, written information about their main terms of employment, i.e. pay, hours of work, holidays and holiday pay, sickness and sick pay, pension arrangements and notice. Information given to employees has to be kept up to date. Written information is not required to be given to part-time employees normally working for less than 16 hours per week.

Specimen form of notice to employees

The notice to employees must cover the main terms of employment referred to above, but no statutory form is provided. The wording of a possible form of notice is given subsequently, but it is emphasized that this is no more that an indication of a form which might be used, as variation to meet individual circumstances will be necessary at the discretion of the employer.

Rights to notice

The Act lays down minimum periods of notice of termination of employment. In the case of an employee who has served continuously for four weeks or more, at least one week's notice must be given by the employer. After service of two years or more, the minimum notice is two weeks. After service of five years or more, the minimum notice is four weeks.

The notice required to be given by an employee to the employer is at least one week if the employee's length of service has been four weeks or more; longer service does not necessitate longer notice being given.

It is permissible for employer or employee to waive their right to notice or to accept payment in lieu of notice. The right of either party to terminate the contract without notice if the behaviour of the other party justifies it is unaffected.

Effect on contracts

In the event of a contract of employment for a fixed term, rights to notice will not generally apply. There is an exception: where an employee is under contract for a fixed term of four weeks or less, but has been employed for 13 weeks or more, the contract has to be regarded as if it were for an indefinite period, the mimimum rights to notice then being applicable. Minimum rights to notice do not apply when a longer period of notice is provided for under any agreement between employer and employee.

Definition of 'employee'

If a person is paid net with tax deducted under Schedule E then they are certainly employees. A person may ostensibly be self-employed, paid gross and liable to pay their own Income Tax under Schedule D. Even so, the Inland Revenue are increasingly strict and will regard them as employees unless they have full independent responsibility for controlling their own work, arranging their absences and being responsible for (and paying for) their own substitutes at times of absence. Dental hygienists who work under the direct control of a dentist will almost certainly be employees of the principal or partners of that practice. Associate dentists who control their own work within a principal's practice are likely to be self-employed.

Day of giving notice

Notice can be given on any day. Normally the period of notice will run from the start of the following day so that a week's notice given on a Monday would expire at the end of the following Monday. The position may be affected by the conditions of any contract between employer and employee.

Pay during notice

An employee working as usual during the period of notice will receive what they earn. If an employee does not work for some or all of normal hours during the notice period, their pay is safeguarded if the reason is either failure by the employer to make work available, sickness or injury, or holidays. There is no statutory minimum pay in lieu of notice.

An employer or employee who claims to have incurred loss because the notice provided for under the Act has not been given can bring an action for damages. An employee can claim if not paid during a notice period.

Draft form of notice of terms of employment

To: (*employee's name*)
From: (*employer's name*)

I advise you that the terms and conditions of your employment, which began on ....
(*date*) are as set out below

1. Your basic duties will be ....
2. Your salary remuneration/wages will be £......... per week/month.
   Your remuneration will be calculated as follows:...
   (*Delete whichever of the above alternatives is inappropriate.*)
3. Your normal hours of work will be from .... a.m. to .... p.m. on Monday–Friday
   and .... a.m. to .... p.m. on Saturday, totalling .... hours in all.
   As the welfare of the patients of the practice is of primary importance, some overtime
   may be necessary which will be paid at the rate of .... per hour.
4. Your will be entitled to .... weeks holiday and to payment during such periods at
   your normal rate.
5. During periods of absence, owing to sickness or injury, your pay entitlement will be [*State
   if SSP only or if any enhanced scheme applies*].
6. Your employment is contracted in [or contracted out] for the purpose of the State
   Earnings Related Pension scheme.
7. You are entitled to receive .... weeks notice of termination of employment.
8. Failure to observe the normal code of conduct within the practice could render you liable
   to dismissal without further notice.
9. If your have reason to complain at any time with regard to your working conditions then
   this should be referred to ....

Unfair dismissal

Employees, except for those excluded by statute (see below), have the right not to
be unfairly dismissed. The remedy for unfair dismissal is by complaint to an
Industrial Tribunal and dismissal occurs if one of the following takes place:

1. The employer terminates the contract with or without notice.
2. The employee is employed under a contract for a fixed term and the term
   expires without being renewed under the same contract.
3. The employee terminates the contract with or without notice in circumstances
   such that they are entitled to do so without notice by reason of the employer's
   conduct. This is known as constructive dismissal, that is, where the employer is
   guilty of a fundamental breach of obligation to the employee.

The right not to be unfairly dismissed is excluded until an employee has been
continuously employed for a period of not less than 104 weeks ending with the
effective date of termination, but this only applies to those who work at least 16
hours per week (or eight hours if the employee has been employed for at least five
years). Employees working less than eight hours a week cannot acquire protection.

However, an employee cannot claim unfair dismissal if they have attained on or
before the effective date of termination the normal retiring age for their position.
The normal retiring age should be the same for men and women.

The employer has to show the dismissal was fair, to confirm the reason for the
dismissal and to show that this was a reason which the law regards as acceptable.

Acceptable reasons for dismissal are limited to redundancy and substantial reasons related to conduct, capability or qualifications.

The Tribunals also take into account the circumstances including the size and administrative resources of the employer's business in deciding whether or not a dismissal was unfair. The Tribunal itself decides whether or not the employer has acted reasonably.

The Advisory Conciliation and Arbitration Service (ACAS) exists to promote settlement in cases of alleged unfair dismissal by means of persuading the employer to re-engage the employee or to pay compensation. A complaint of unfair dismissal must be presented to the Industrial Tribunal before the end of three months beginning with the effective date of termination or within such further period as the Tribunal considers reasonable in a case where it is satisfied that it was not reasonably practicable for the complaint to be presented within the period of three months. If a Tribunal finds that there has been an unfair dismissal it must ask the successful applicant whether they seek reinstatement or re-engagement, and the Tribunal may make an order subject to certain conditions being satisfied. If an employer refuses to reinstate or re-engage the employee despite such an order, a financial penalty may be imposed. The tribunal must consider if reinstatement or re-engagement is practical before making an order.

An award or compensation may be made in any event, and is in two parts, a basic and a compensatory award. The basic award is calculated by taking the date of the termination and reckoning backwards the number of years falling within the period of employment and allowing one-and-a-half week's pay for each year when the employee was over 41, one weeks' pay for each year between 22 and 41, and half a week's pay for each year below 22. The maximum basic award is 20 weeks' gross pay with a maximum of £157.00 per week. The maximum compensatory award is £8500.00. Both awards can be reduced to take account of the employee's conduct during employment. This reduction can be made even if evidence of misconduct does not emerge until after dismissal. A dismissed employee has a duty to try immediately to find other employment to lessen any financial damage following the dismissal (this is known as 'mitigation of loss').

The employer has a common law right to dismiss an employee without notice on the ground of the employee's serious misconduct. Great care must be taken in exercising this right. Proper practice is to suspend an employee on full pay while urgent enquiries are made before the decision to dismiss is reached.

Examples of serious misconduct are wilful disobedience to lawful and reasonable instructions or where the employee is found guilty of fraud or dishonesty in connection with the employer's business.

Every employer should have a grievance and discipline procedure which provides for warnings and counselling to be given in case of misconduct during employment. When an employer gives an employee a warning this should be done only after the employee has been given a chance to state their case. A careful record must be kept by the employer especially if the warning is oral only.

If a second warning has to be given or if the employee has done something very serious then the warning should be in writing. A warning should not remain on an employee's record for more than two years, after which the record should be given to the employee to destroy. If an employee is dismissed then this should be done only after a hearing at which the employer should ensure there is another member of the management staff present as a witness. Again, a careful record must be kept and the employee given a written notice of the reasons for dismissal.

Maternity Rights

Women employees who are pregnant have four rights:

1. Not to be dismissed because of pregnancy.
2. To have paid time off for antenatal care.
3. To receive statutory maternity pay or maternity allowance.
4. To return to work after the baby has been born.

1. Dismissal because of pregnancy is unfair unless pregnancy has made the woman incapable of doing her job adequately or the job is one which it is illegal for a pregnant woman to do. It may be illegal for a woman employee to work with X-ray equipment during pregnancy but a dentist would probably have to show that it was impractical to relocate a woman employee in a practice during pregnancy to avoid her having to become involved with X-rays.

2. A woman who has had medical or midwifery advice to have antenatal care sessions is entitled to paid time off to attend pre-booked appointments.

3. Statutory Maternity Pay (SMP) is payable by an employer to any woman employee who is pregnant and at the fifteenth week before her expected week of delivery has worked for not less than 26 weeks continuously in that employer's business.

SMP is payable for a total of 18 weeks. If a woman has been employed in a business for at least two years by the time she reaches the fifteenth week before the expected week of confinement then the first six weeks of SMP are at the higher rate. This basically is nine-tenths of a week's pay at the fifteenth week before confinement. She is then entitled to a further 12 weeks at the lower rate. These rates are published annually by the Department of Social Security (DSS).

A woman who has worked for less than two years but who qualifies under the 26 week rule will be entitled only to lower rate SMP throughout the 18 week period. The employer is legally obliged to make the payments and must deduct tax and National Insurance contributions from them. The payments themselves are recovered by the employer when accounting to the Inland Revenue with National Insurance contributions and Income Tax.

A woman employee who does not qualify for SMP (that is she has not been employed for more than 26 weeks) may qualify for maternity allowance which is paid to her direct by the DSS and she claims this direct by applying at the local DSS office.

4. An employee who had been employed in the business for two years at the beginning of the 11th week before her estimated date of delivery can then leave and may return to work as now described. Up to 29 weeks after her estimated date of delivery a woman who qualifies as just described has the right to return to work with pay and conditions of employment as favourable as if she had not been absent. An employer can fill a woman's post with a temporary replacement and broadly, so long as the replacement has been told that the post is a temporary one during absence of the permanent employee, then dismissal of the temporary employee will be fair. If the woman's previous job has disappeared then the employer's obligation is to provide suitable alternative work.

If the employer can show that it is not reasonably practicable to offer the woman her former job or suitable alternative employment or else if the business is a small one employing five or fewer employees, then the employer can refuse to allow the woman to return to work. Any dentist who contemplates refusing to allow a woman employee to return to work after childbirth should take professional advice before implementing the refusal.

The woman must tell her employer in writing when she leaves work that she proposes to return after having her baby. Department of Employment Legislation Leaflet No. 4, 'Employment Rights for the Expectant Mother', explains notices which must be given during the period of absence to enable a woman to qualify for return.

Statutory Sick Pay

This is a complex topic on which comprehensive leaflets are issued to employers by the Department of Social Security.

For a maximum period of 28 weeks an employee is entitled to receive Statutory Sick Pay (SSP) from the employer because of absence from work due to sickness or disablement. Female employees under 60 (and male under 65) are entitled to SSP. European Community law is likely to standardize retirement ages for both sexes.

SSP is payable only after the employee has been absent for three days, known as 'waiting days', and pay is then due at a rate which is set annually and published by the DSS. When making the payment the employer must deduct National Insurance contributions and Income Tax. The employer reclaims SSP payments in full by deducting the gross amount from National Insurance contributions before paying them over to the Inland Revenue. Employers' National Insurance guides explain the procedures.

It is important for the employer to have a system requiring the employee to notify sickness and to make that procedure known to the employees. It is common to require employees to 'self-certify' for the first week of absence and for any absence after that to provide medical evidence by way of a doctor's certificate.

Redundancy

Redundancy payments to employees are governed by the Employment Protection (Consolidation) Act 1978. A redundancy occurs where the reason for dismissal is that the employer's need for the employee to do work of the particular kind or at a particular place has diminished or ceased. An employee dismissed for redundancy is entitled to a payment if they have worked for not less than two years so long as they have worked for at least 16 hours a week (or eight hours a week if they have more than five years' service).

If an employer offers appropriate alternative emloyment which is refused unreasonably there is no entitlement to a redundancy payment.

A redundancy payment is calculated in the same way as a basic award for unfair dismissal (see page 123) and so is dependent on length of service.

Employers' responsibility for the acts of employees

Vicarious liability (see Chapter 4, page 56) imposes responsibility on the employer for paying damages to a person injured through an employee's fault. That is because, as a matter of public policy, the courts want to see injured people compensated. Employers generally are insured where employees are not, and so certainty of payment is increased.

As a practitioner has liability for the negligent acts and omissions of staff committed in the course of employment, it is vital to ensure that employees are adequately instructed in their duties and that no duty is delegated to someone insufficiently trained or experienced to perform it. Dental receptionists and surgery assistants speak for the employer and thus instructions given or entered into by these members of staff with patients may be legally binding on the dentist.

Lay staff should not accept a patient on behalf of the dentist, even on the telephone, for any particular dental operation other than an examination. Equally a receptionist should not, even by implication, accept a patient for treatment within the National Health Service. When asked if the dentist takes NHS patients they should reply, if the dentist does accept them, that this is so, but any arrangement must be decided by the dentist after discussion with the patient. To state positively that the dentist accepts NHS patients and then to give an appointment can imply acceptance of the patient by the dentist for treatment within the NHS. Such instances can lead to Service Committee procedures or to refusal by patients to pay private fees – or both. Practitioners should ensure that employees, be they DSAs, hygienists or technicians, do not act in any way that could be construed as the practice of dentistry which might contravene section 38 of the Dentists Act 1984.

On the subject of covering, see page 12, paragraph 31.

Engagement of employees

By virtue of the Sex Discrimination Act 1986 and the Race Relations Act 1976 it is illegal for employers to discriminate by reference to gender and/or racial origin in advertising for and recruiting staff.

Difficulties in obtaining experienced staff, both qualified and lay, mean that some practitioners do not ask for references or follow up those obtained. Many a practitioner has regretted this when a quick word with the previous employer might have indicated that no job offer should be made. Often when practitioners have engaged staff, qualified or lay, they have proved bad employees and have even been fraudulent.

An employee is not entitled as a right to a reference from a former employer, but if one is given then it must be fair and honest or the employee may have a right of action in defamation. A new employer misled by an inaccurate reference may claim damages against the referee for negligent mis-statement.

Occasionally a practitioner employs someone, arranges a date to start and then fills the position with another applicant considered more appropriate. The original employee can claim against the employer for breach of contract but must show financial loss. The disappointed applicant must take all reasonable steps to find new employment. The measure of damages is pay lost and expenses incurred between the erstwhile starting date and the start of an alternative job, and in addition continuing loss if the new job is at lower pay.

Obligations of employees

An employee's contract, verbal or written, contains an implied obligation to serve the employer faithfully. There is also an obligation to obey all lawful instructions given by the employer within the scope of employment and not to divulge any of the employer's business secrets. An employee who wilfully disobeys a lawful instruction is liable for dismissal. A former employee is not entitled to remove any papers or documents belonging to the employer.

A dentist's duty of confidentiality to patients equally extends to staff. Failure to maintain confidentiality and other aspects of the ethical code of the profession could provide reasonable grounds for dismissal.

Where patients' records are maintained on computer the Data Protection Act 1984 gives the data subject (the patient) a right to have the data kept confidential. If there is any unlawful disclosure of computerized data then the patient, as data subject, has a right to claim damages against the data user, that is the dentist who runs the computer, even where the unauthorized disclosure has been carried out by an employee.

Absenteeism

An employee is under an obligation to attend the workplace on the agreed days and times. Absence without good reason entitles the employer to dismiss, but an employer should not take such action unless an employee has failed to respond to earlier warnings to improve performance. Where an employee is frequently absent through ill-health the employer should obtain a medical report on the employee before considering dismissal. Advice should be obtained before dismissing for ill-health.

Employer's liabilities

Occupiers Liability Act 1957
Defective Premises Act 1972

An occupier of premises must take reasonable care to ensure that lawful visitors are safe in using them. Adequate lighting, safe stairways, non-slippery floors, properly fitted and unworn carpets need to be considered. Insurance cover against claims from such accidents is a wise investment. Defence Society membership does not cover this risk.

The Employers Liability (Compulsory Insurance) Act 1969

Under this Act all employers carrying on a business in the United Kindom must insure under an approved policy with an authorized insurer against liability for injury or disease sustained by their employees during the course of employment. This duty to insure extends only to injury or disease sustained in the course of employment and for which the employer is liable and thus not to any injury or disease suffered by an employee. Defence Society membership does not cover this risk.

The Employers Liability (Defective Equipment) Act 1969

This Act makes further provision in respect of the liability of employers for injury to employees which is attributable to any defect in equipment provided by the employer for the purpose of the business.

When an employee suffers personal injury in the course of employment because of the defect in equipment provided by the employer and the defect arises wholly or partly from the fault of a third party, the injury is deemed also attributable to employer's negligence. It is in the interest of dentists to ensure that all equipment is soundly constructed, installed and maintained.

Even if equipment has a latent defect due to manufacturing error, the employer is deemed liable. It is then up to the employer to pay damages to the injured employee and then to recover an indemnity from the third party, who might be an overseas manufacturer.

The Law Reform (Personal Injuries) Act 1948

This renders an employer vicariously liable in the event of an injury to one employee being caused by the negligent act of another employee.

The National Insurance (Industrial Injury) Act 1946
The Social Security Act 1975

Employees sustaining an industrial injury are eligible by the provisions of these Acts for immediate payment of a weekly sum, and no element of fault need be proved.

The National Health Service Act 1977

Practitioners working in the National Health Service as general practitioners in contract with Family Health Services Authorities (in England and Wales) and Health Boards (in Scotland) must be familiar with their Terms and Conditions of Service which form their contract with the National Health Service. The 1990 dentists' contract has not been finalized at the time of writing.

Social Security and Income Tax Acts

An employer must deduct both employer's and employee's National Insurance contributions from wages and pay them to the Collector of Taxes each month along with PAYE Income Tax. Detailed guides are issued to employers by the Inland Revenue.

Factories Act 1961
Offices, Shops and Railway Premises Act 1963
Health and Safety at Work Act 1974

Dental surgeries (including those which have laboratory facilities) fall within the scope of these Acts. They prescribe standards of cleanliness, levels of occupation, temperature, ventilation, lighting, drainage of floors and the provision of sanitary facilities. The Factories Act requires the provision of breathing and resuscitation apparatus as a safety precaution where dangerous fumes are liable to be present. Protective eyewear should be available to employees whose work involves 'a special risk' of injury to the eyes from particles or fragments thrown off in the course of the working process. Employers must ensure that these minimum standards are kept.

Certain precautions must be taken by users of air compressors and autoclaves to avoid risk of injury. Air receivers (tanks) have to be inspected by a 'competent person' at least once every 26 months and steam generating autoclaves at least once every 14 months.

In view of the potential dangers from such items of equipment the practitioner is advised to ensure appropriate and adequate insurance cover. This should be included in a comprehensive practice insurance policy but cannot be taken for granted. A check on the policy is therefore advisable.

An employer is under a duty to ensure that the health, safety and welfare of his employees are safeguarded. Mimimum standards are prescribed in respect of the cleanliness, temperature, ventilation and lighting of the business premises. Furthermore the employer is required to provide 'suitable and sufficient' sanitary and washing facilities for his employees.

The Health and Safety at Work Act 1974 exposes an employer to criminal prosecution for any failure to discharge responsibilities for the safety of employees, patients and other persons using practice premises. The dentist's general duty as an employer is to ensure, so far as is reasonably practicable, the health, safety and welfare at work of all employees.

The dentist must provide and maintain safe equipment and systems of work, ensure safe handling and storage of any potentially harmful substances, maintain entrances and exits in a safe condition, provide a working environment for employees without risk to their health and such instruction, training and supervision as is necessary to ensure health and safety.

Where five or more people are employed a written statement of the employer's general policy with respect to health and safety must be brought to the notice of all employees.

The Health and Safety Executive has the duty to enforce legal requirements and provide advisory services. Inspectors have the power to enter premises and investigate accordingly. An inspector identifying any risk to health and safety may issue a Prohibition Notice preventing the continuance of the risk activity until specified remedial action has been taken, or issue an Improvement Notice requiring action within a specified time and/or prosecution of the offender. (See also BDA Advice Sheet 19.)

Control of Substances Hazardous to Health Regulations 1988 (COSHH)

The COSHH Regulations came into force on 1 October 1989. While the Health and Safety at Work Act 1974 places a general responsibility on employers to do all that is 'reasonably practical', to ensure the health and safety of employees, and a sub-section of this Act extends this responsibility to protection from harmful substances, the COSHH regulations are more specific. For certain substances there are Occupational Exposure Limits (OELs) and Maximum Exposure Limits (MELs). In dentistry the substances concerned include mercury, methylmethacrylate, glutaraldehyde, iodine, phenol and trichloroacetic acid. There is an onus therefore on the practitioner, as an employer, not only to make a risk assessment on hazardous substances, but also to take action to reduce any identifiable risk as much as possible.

Notification of Accidents and Dangerous Occurrences Regulations 1980

These Regulations (SI 1980/804) require employers to notify the Health and Safety Executive of accidents causing death or major injury to any person or in case of 'dangerous occurrences' regardless of whether death or injury is caused.

Notification must be made with minimum delay (by telephone if possible) to the Health and Safety Executive (HSE). Addresses of HSE area offices are given below. If the correct address cannot be determined, the British Dental Association Headquarters can help.

The HSE requires a report on a standard form (Form 2508) available either from Her Majesty's Stationary Office or else from BDA headquarters. Occurrences in a dental practice covered by the Regulations include compressor or autoclave explosions and mercury spillages.

The Regulations require employers to keep a record of notifiable accidents and dangerous occurrences and to make it available to the HSE or to a staff safety representative. A full explanatory booklet about these Regulations can be obtained from HMSO.

Health and Safety Executive area offices

South West: Inter City House, Mitchell Lane, Victoria Street, Bristol BS1 6AN (Tel: 0272 290681)

South: Priestley House, Priestley Road, Basingstoke RG24 9NW (Tel: 0256 473181)

South East: 3 East Grinstead House, London Road, East Grinstead, West Sussex RH19 1RR (Tel: 0342 326922)

London North: Maritime House, 1 Linton Road, Barking, Essex IG11 8HF (Tel: 081–594 5522)

London South: 1 Long Lane, London SE1 4PG (Tel: 071–407 8911)

East Anglia: 39 Baddow Road, Chelmsford, Essex CM2 0HL (Tel: 0245 284661)

Northern Home Counties: 14 Cardiff Road, Luton, Beds LU1 1PP (Tel: 0582 34121)

East Midlands: Belgrave House, 1 Greyfriars, Northampton NN1 2BS (Tel: 0604 21233)

West Midlands: McLaren Building, 2 Masshouse Circus, Queensway, Birmingham B4 7NP (Tel: 021–200 2299)

Wales: Brunel House, 2 Fitzalan Road, Cardiff CF2 1SH (Tel: 0222 473777)

Marches: The Marches House, Midway, Newcastle-under-Lyme, Staffs ST5 1DT (Tel: 0782 717181)

North Midlands: Birkbeck House, Trinity Square, Nottingham NG1 4AU (Tel: 0602 470712)

South Yorkshire: Sovereign House, 40 Silver Street, Sheffield S1 2ES (Tel: 0742 739081)

West and North Yorkshire: 8 St Pauls Street, Leeds LS1 2LE (Tel: 0532 446191)

Greater Manchester: Quay House, Quay Street, Manchester M3 3JB (Tel: 061–831 7111)

Merseyside: The Triad, Stanley Road, Bootle L20 3PG (Tel: 051–922 7211)

North West: Victoria House, Ormskirk Road, Preston PR1 1HH (Tel: 0772 59321)

North East: Arden House, Regent Centre, Gosforth, Newcastle-upon-Tyne NE3 3JN (Tel: 091–284 8448)

Scotland East: Belford House, 59 Belford Road, Edinburgh EG4 3UE (Tel: 031–225 1313)

Scotland West: 314 St Vincent Street, Glasgow G3 8XG (Tel: 041–204 2646)

Chapter 10

Dental therapists and hygienists in the United Kingdom

The involvement of dental auxiliaries with the Dentists Act 1984 and thereby the General Dental Council has been outlined in Chapter 1. Practitioners supervising auxiliaries should be aware of the following information in the interests of themselves, the auxiliaries and their patients.

Enrolment

Enrolment with the General Dental Council is essential before a person in the United Kingdom can legally practise as a dental therapist or dental hygienist. This is effected by the person concerned showing, to the satisfaction of the Registrar, that he or she is of good character, holds a certificate indicating that an acceptable course of training and examinations has been satisfactorily completed, and by payment of the appropriate fee. Enrolment terminates on 31 December each year, and, when required, should therefore be renewed, prior to that date, for the ensuing 12 months. To provide treatment when not currently enrolled is an offence against the Dentists Act 1984.

All too frequently, the authors have had the unhappy task of advising and assisting dental auxiliaries, usually hygienists in general practice, who have been instructed to cease practising by the General Dental Council because they were unenrolled. It is not difficult to envisage the disruption to a practice in such circumstances. The most common reason is a failure by the dental auxiliary to notify the General Dental Council of a change of address as a result of which the reminders to pay the annual retention fee are not received. It is the responsibility of dental hygienists to ensure they pay their annual retention fee. It is, however, obviously prudent for practitioners who employ dental hygienists to satisfy themselves that the enrolment requirements have been met, even to the extent of asking to see the current enrolment certificate.

Disciplinary procedures

These essentially are similar to those involving registered dental practitioners, the main difference being that the Committee concerned may be either the Dental Auxiliaries Committee or its disciplinary sub-committee.

Titles

A person enrolled in the Roll of Dental Hygienists is authorized to use the title 'dental hygienist' and the letters EDH after their name. A person enrolled in the Roll of Dental Therapists is authorized to use the title 'dental therapist' and the letters EDT after their name. No other titles may be used 'which might reasonably be taken to suggest that they possess a status or qualification connected with dentistry unless it is entered in the Roll in respect of them'.

Dental hygienists

Dental hygienists are permitted to carry out dental work of the following kinds only:

1. Cleaning and polishing teeth.
2. Scaling teeth (that is to say, the removal of deposits, accretions and stains from those parts of the surfaces of the teeth which are exposed or which are directly beneath the free margins of the gums, including the application of medicaments appropriate thereto).
3. The application to the teeth of such prophylactic materials as the General Dental Council may from time to time determine (these include solutions, gels and sealants).

The provision of any other treatment amounting to the practice of dentistry is not permitted. (Section 37 of the Dentists Act 1984, sub-section (1), is given in full in Chapter 1, page 2.)

Field of employment

Dental hygienists in the United Kingdom may provide treatment within the community health services, the armed forces, and in general dental practices, within the aforestated limits.

Authority to provide treatment

Dental hygienists may provide treatment only when under the direction of a registered dentist and after the latter has examined the patient and indicated, to the hygienist, the course of treatment to be provided in that instance. A written prescription for the treatment is not required under the terms of the Dental Auxiliaries Regulations 1986.

Supervision

Except when employed in the community health service, a dental hygienist shall only provide authorized treatment when under the direct personal supervision of a registered dentist, who must be on the premises at the same time.

Dental therapists

Dental therapists are permitted to carry out dental work of the following kinds:

1. Extracting deciduous teeth.
2. Undertaking simple dental fillings.
3. Cleaning and polishing teeth.
4. Scaling teeth (that is to say, the removal of deposits, accretions and stains from those parts of the surfaces of the teeth which are exposed or which are directly beneath the free margins of the gums, including the application of medicaments appropriate thereto).
5. The application to the teeth of such prophylactic materials as the General Dental Council may from time to time determine.
6. Giving advice within the meaning of sub-section (1) of section 37 of the Dentists Act 1984 (see page 2) such as may be necessary to the proper performance of the dental work referred to above.

Dental therapists are permitted to carry out treatment set out in 1, 2, 4 and 5 above, under local infiltration analgesia administered by the dental therapist, or under any local or regional block analgesia administered by a registered dentist.

Field of employment

The health authority services only.

Authority to provide treatment

Dental therapists may only provide authorized treatment under the direction of a registered dentist and following the examination of the patient and compilation of a treatment plan (prescription), in writing, by a registered dentist.

Supervision

'Under the direction of' does not imply personal supervision and it is therefore for the directing dental surgeon to determine the degree of supervision necessary in individual cases. This will vary with the type of treatment to be provided and the skill and experience of the therapist concerned. When no dental surgeon is on the premises at a time when a dental therapist is providing treatment, then one should be readily available should an emergency arise, i.e. within a reasonable distance and able to be contacted easily, if necessary by telephone. It is recognized that employing authorities can expect registered dental practitioners and their staffs to accept the supervision of dental auxiliaries as part of their normal duties.

Professional associations

Membership of a professional organization is recommended to all dental auxiliaries as a means of participating fully in their chosen profession. The appropriate associations are:

- The British Dental Hygienists Association, 64 Wimpole Street, London W1M 8AL
- The British Association of Dental Therapists, c/o The Principal, Dental Auxiliary School, London Hospital Medical College, 6–8 Walden Street, London E1 2AD.

Professional indemnity

Dental auxiliaries, by the very nature of their work, are liable to the problems inherent in the practice of dentistry generally, many of which have been detailed in earlier chapters. Whilst the employer and/or the supervising practitioner will have a vicarious liability for some incidents that may arise, there is nothing to prevent an aggrieved patient taking legal action directly against an auxiliary, or the auxiliary being joined in such action or involved subsequently. Allegations of improper behaviour from patients and/or employers are also hazards to be faced by dental auxiliaries, and these could lead to disciplinary or even legal procedures being initiated. A form of professional indemnity is therefore advisable. The protection organizations offer associate membership of both hygienists and therapists who are on the Rolls of the General Dental Council and to certain auxiliaries overseas. Associate membership provides complete professional indemnity in all non-Health Authority cases, and also confers the advantages of advice and assistance upon all matters relating directly to professional activities and to legal representations, when considered necessary by the Society, before disciplinary committees, including that of the General Dental Council and equivalent overseas authorities.

Standards of conduct

The behaviour and standards of conduct expected of dental auxiliaries, as with the ethical code of the dental profession, cannot readily be put into writing but must follow certain basic principles, which are:

1. The primary consideration of dental auxiliaries must at all times be the welfare of the patients entrusted to their care.
2. Dental auxiliaries are under an obligation to carry out the lawful and reasonable directions concerning the care and treatment of patients given by the registered dental practitioner under whose direction and/or supervision they are working.
3. Dental auxiliaries must recognize not only the responsibilities but also the limitations of their functions.
4. Dental auxiliaries who give advice on matters relating to oral hygiene, whether on an individual or group basis, should be fully aware of their ethical and legal obligations towards the patients or people concerned; oral hygiene advice should be given with special regard to the dental auxiliary's state of dental knowledge and professional competence.
5. Dental auxiliaries who commit any immoral, dishonest or otherwise improper act involving abuse of the relationship in which they stand to a patient in their care are liable to erasure from the Roll.
6. Dental auxiliaries must never disclose information of a personal or confidential nature acquired in the course of their work, whether related to the patient or to

the practice or clinic in which they are employed, except to the registered dental practitioner under whose direction or supervision they are working, and then only in matters relating to their work.

7. Dental hygienists may not advertise or canvass for the purpose of obtaining patients for any dental practice, whether or not they are employed in it. Their names may not be displayed on signs outside the premises of the practice where they are employed.

8. It is permissible for dental auxiliaries to advertise for employment, either by means of a notice in a newspaper (which should be restricted to the name, title, private address or box number, telephone number, and a statement of the post required), or by calling upon or writing to a registered dental practitioner (dental hygienists only) or the authorities of a hospital or public health authority.

9. A dental auxiliary may not permit the use of the title 'dental therapist' or 'dental hygienist' or the qualification Enrolled Dental Therapist (EDT) or Enrolled Dental Hygienist (EDH), directly or indirectly, in the sale or advertisement of a commercial product or service. Nor should he/she advise the use, except on purely clinical grounds, of any dental product, or improperly promote the sale of any product in the course of his/her work as a dental auxiliary.

Note. It is permissible for enrolled dental auxiliaries to engage in dental health education work for a commercial company provided that they do so in a private capacity, using a title such as 'dental health educator'. The title 'dental hygienist/dental therapist', which is subject to statutory restriction, should not be used in this connection.

When judging the behaviour of a dental auxiliary in the ethical context, similar considerations would undoubtedly be applied to those which would appertain to a registered dental practitioner in similar circumstances (see Chapter 8, page 105). A dental surgeon directing or permitting an enrolled auxiliary to practise dentistry outside the limits laid down in the Dental Auxiliaries Regulations 1986 renders himself liable to disciplinary action by the General Dental Council for 'covering' (see Chapter 1, page 12).

Problems relating to the employment of, and provision of treatment by, auxiliaries have come to the notice of the Medical Protection Society. Treatment 'incidents' have related mainly to damage of soft tissues and ingestion by patients of foreign bodies. A number of requests for advice have been received from practitioners unaware of their own position regarding the supervision of these persons and/or of their liability. This is dealt with in Chapter 4 (see page 57).

Chapter 11

Notes on Australia, Republic of Ireland, Hong Kong, Singapore and Malaysia

Much of the general content of this book is applicable to those areas outside the United Kingdom where English-based law operates. There are, however, certain variations in the Dentists Acts, in other relevant statutes and in the structure of the courts.

Australia

There are Federal, State and Territory laws. There is no Federal equivalent to the United Kingdom Dentists Act and nor, therefore, to the General Dental Council.

There are separate Dental Acts for each State and Territory and thus individual Dental Boards having similar duties to the General Dental Council, i.e. registration of dentists and certain auxiliaries, determination of acceptable academic and other qualifications for registration and the appropriate fees, education and discipline.

A important difference is that in the United Kingdom there are no regulations stipulating specific ethical requirements, whereas a number of 'shall and shall nots' are included in the Conduct of Practice Regulations made under the provisions of the Australian Dental Acts.

The General Dental Council has currently (1990) no power to impose fines, only to suspend or erase, but the Dental Boards in Australia have these three prerogatives, and the actual amounts of fines for certain breaches are included in the Regulations.

Dental Acts must, of necessity, define dentistry, and these definitions do vary, although in the ultimate all convey the same message. In Australia the conditions under which dental auxiliaries are permitted to practise are specified and so far as hygienists and therapists are concerned these are somewhat similar to those in the United Kingdom.

General practice in Australia

Before commencing practice in Australia, the newly arrived graduate should discuss the requirements of practice with the relevant Australian Dental Association State Branch. Certain dental practitioners are approved by the Minister of Health to provide treatment under Medicare. The practitioner will be provided with a schedule of fees based on the medical Benefits Schedule. Other patients will belong to private health funds which frequently offer dental insurance. There are many of these funds; the requirements are precise and should be clearly understood. Errors can prove to be costly, and as practitioners themselves are totally responsible for the accuracy of their claims, any delegation of administration to practice staff should be checked with the greatest care. It is important that practitioners are familiar with the correct method of setting out a treatment account, which should clearly show the date the treatment was provided, the relevant item number, a brief description of what the treatment comprised, and the appropriate fee. Duplicate accounts must not be issued unless clearly marked as such. Some patients will seek treatment following accidents in the workplace (Workers Compensation Jurisdiction) or arising out of road traffic accidents (third party jurisdiction), and again scrupulous accuracy with regard to treatment details and reportage is essential. Practitioners should not provide complicated or expensive treatment without the prior agreement of the insurers. It is not unknown for settlement of such claims to take an inordinately long time.

If a practitioner should be unfortunate enough to receive a letter from a Complaints Unit seeking observations upon a complaint by a patient, it would be prudent for that practitioner to seek advice before replying.

Dental legislation in Australia*

Preamble

The law relating to dentistry in Australia is similar to that of other nations of comparable development. There are, however, significant differences – and of these differences those seeking registration should be aware.

Historical

The basic foundation of the legal system of Australia is a large body of law introduced from England. When Australia was colonized it was an accepted principle of English law that British settlers took overseas with them such of the laws of England as could reasonably be applied to the circumstances of the new colony.

Today, over 200 years later, Australian institutions and law have a distinct character of their own. The difference between British and Australian institutions are at least as pronounced as are their similarities. Nevertheless, the British background is still there and it is only the light of such that much of Australia's legal system can be understood.

Australian administration

For administrative purposes Australia is divided into six States (and two Territories) and each State is divided into a large number of cities, towns, boroughs and shires. Thus Australia has a three-tiered system of government – Federal, State and Local Government.

With three such bodies, a certain amount of duplication of activity is inevitable – particularly in the fields of social services and health. However, dental legislation and dental health are primarily matters for the States – thus there are in Australia eight Dental Acts and eight Dental Boards.

The State Dental Acts

Throughout Australia parliamentarians have differed in their concept of an adequate dental service and the means by which this should be achieved. As a result, there are eight Dental Acts in which even the definition of dentistry varies.

*From a paper prepared for the Expert Panel in Dentistry of the Australian Committee on Overseas Professional Qualifications by John Wark CBE, by kind permission of the Committee.

As an example, the following is an extract from the current New South Wales Dental Act:

For the purposes of this Act 'the practice of dentistry' includes:

(a) the performance of any operation and the treatment of any diseases, deficiencies, deformities or lesions on or of the human teeth or jaws or associated structures; and
(b) the correction of malpositions of the human teeth or jaws or associated structures; and
(c) the performance of radiographic work in connection with the human teeth or jaws or associated structures; and
(d) the administration of an anaesthetic agent in connection with any operation on the human teeth or jaws or associated structures; and
(e) the mechanical construction or the renewal or repair of artificial dentures or restorative dental appliances; and
(f) the performance of any operation on, or the giving of any treatment, advice or attendance to any person, as preparatory to, or for the purpose of or for or in connection with the fitting, insertion, fixing, constructing, repairing or renewing of artificial dentures or restorative dental appliances; and
(g) the performance of any such operation and the giving of any such treatment, advice, or attendance as is usually performed or given by dentists.

Delegated legislation

In English law, the parliament has the power to delegate to various statutory bodies the authority to make laws and every Australian Dental Board has been accorded the right to institute or make regulations with regard to the adminstration of its Act and the practice of dentistry in its area.

The laws made through delegated legislation are generally known as Regulations (or maybe Rules, Orders, Ordinances, Warrants or By-laws). The delegation of legislative power enables Parliament to concentrate upon principles rather than detail – it affords more flexibility in the light of change and it permits highly technical matters to be handled by those competent in that field.

The regulations which have been made under the provisions of the Dental Acts of the six States and two Territories also vary. In the fact their variation is far more significant than the variations in the Acts themselves.

Registration as a dentist

Registration as a dentist is mandatory in order to practise dentistry in Australia. A person applying for registration in any state or territory must satisfy its Dental Board that he has an appropriate academic qualification, that he is of good character and that he has an adequate command of the English language. He must appear at the office of the Board in person, present his credentials, establish his identity, sign a statutory declaration and pay the usual fees.

Registration is on a State basis and the fact that a person is registered in one State will not entitle him to practise in another. However, whereas full-time dental officers of the Australian Defence Forces must be registered in one State, this need not be of necessity the State in which they are serving.

The academic qualifications for registration in the various States are now reasonably standard. These have been set out in a booklet entitled *Dentistry in Australia*, produced by the Committee on Overseas Professional Qualifications of the Department of Immigration and Ethnic Affairs.

Registration as a specialist practitioner

Certain of the Dental Boards are now empowered to register dentists as specialist practitioners (or specialists) in the fields of orthodontics, oral surgery, oral and maxillo-facial surgery, paedodontics, periodontics, endodontics and prosthodontics. Generally speaking the boards require that an applicant has a degree, diploma or award of high standing and relevant to the field in which he seeks to be registered. Further that he has had this qualification for a reasonable period of time and that he is practising in the field exclusively or under such circumstances which, in the opinion of the Board, warrant his being recognized as a specialist practitioner.

Any registered dentist may practice every aspect of dentistry – he may also restrict his practice to any particular field. However, no person shall hold himself out to be a specialist practitioner in a special branch of dentistry unless he is registered as such with the Dental Board of that state.

Temporary registration

Temporary registration may be granted by some Boards to a dentist who wishes to come to its State in some capacity connected with postgraduate study or with teaching or with research or dental science. A certificate of temporary registration is granted subject to such conditions and limitations as the Board may specify.

Provisional registration

The Dental Boards of New South Wales, South Australia and Queensland may grant a form of restricted registration to persons whom in its opinion do not fulfil specifications. Such individuals are permitted to practise under supervision as employees of certain institutions.

Privileges and responsibilities of the registered dentist

The registered dentist has certain rights. He can practise any aspect of dentistry and may have in his possession and use or prescribe any drug, poison or deleterious substance in the lawful practice of his profession as such.

He is entitled to call himself a dentist or a dental surgeon or a surgeon dentist; he can charge for his services and take legal action to collect his fees. He can practise independently or as an assistant or in partnership with another dentist. He can accept a salaried position with a government institution or with a hospital or university. He can conduct or manage to be in charge of a dental laboratory.

Privilege entails responsibility and for the registered dentist this responsibility is threefold:

1. To observe the basic ethical rules which the profession has adopted over the years.
2. To abide by the provisions of the Dental Acts, the Poisons Acts and any other Act relevant to the practise of dentistry and by any regulations made under the provision thereof.
3. To conform to the principles of common law applicable to dental practice.

The first of these three duties is to a degree voluntary; the second and third are obligatory.

Statutes relating to dental practice*

The practice of dentistry is governed by the provisions of the Dental Acts and the Regulations made thereunder. In addition, it is effected by the relevant portions of a large number of other Acts including the Dental Auxiliaries Act, the Acts relating to Paradental Personnel, the Poisons Act, the Radiation Hygiene Act, the Psychological Practices Act, the Taxation Act and the Labour and Industries Act.

The Dental Acts

The obligations of the dentist under the State Dental Acts are few and may be enumerated as follows:

1. To advise the Dental Board of a change of address and to pay the annual registration renewal fee.
2. Not to assume any title, description or qualification other than permitted under the Dental Act or in the Dentists Register.
3. Not to authorize or permit any employee to practise any branch of dentistry unless that employee is legally entitled to so practise.
4. To continue to be of good character. (N.B. A dentist who is convicted of a serious offence or who in the opinion of the Dental Board has been guilty of dishonest, fraudulent, immoral or infamous conduct in connection with his practice, may be deprived of his registration.)
5. To conform to the Conduct of Practice Regulations made under the provisions of the Act.

Conduct of Practice Regulations (or Ordinance)

Regulations made under the provisions of the Act may appear to have more direct effect upon the average practitioner than has the Act itself. In some States these Regulations are much more comprehensive than in others, but all include:

1. A maximum dimension for name plates.
2. A limitation of signs to that necessary to enable patients to locate the dentist's premises.
3. The restriction of advertising.
4. The prohibition of the soliciting of patients.

Throughout Australia it is the considered view of the dental profession that professional goodwill should be built up by the opinion of those who know at first hand a practitioner's skill – his patients and his colleagues. Whereas advertising and showy display are accepted procedure in commerce and industry, they have no place in dentistry.

In some of the States and in one Territory the ordinance has been expanded to include the relationships between the dentist and his patients and the dentist and his colleagues. The writer is of the opinion that such matters are better placed in a professional Code of Ethics.

The Australian way of life is based upon the principle of free enterprise and the freedom of choice. The patient has the undeniable right to choose his dentist and to change his dentist, even during the course of treatment. This principle must override any ethical rules concerning the relationship of one dentist to another.

*See footnote on page 139

Third parties in dentistry

The advent of contract dentistry and of pre- and post-payment schemes has resulted in a substantial increase in the administrative procedures for those engaged in private practice. In Australia these services include the Department of Veterans' Affairs, Local Dental Officers Scheme; the State Governments service for pensioners, orphans and accident victims and the dental benefits provided by Friendly Societies and Health Insurance Associations.

The conditions and scope of these services vary considerably and it is not possible to provide a brief and accurate analysis thereof. Before embarking upon treatment for any 'subsidized or insured patient' a dentist should ensure that both he and the patient are fully aware of the rules relating to the scheme in question.

Third parties serve an important role in the provision of health services and the future of private practice is to a degree dependent upon their survival. However when one body incurs the expense, another provides the service and a third pays the account, problems and misunderstandings are bound to arise.

A third party which meets some or all of the cost of the dental service is entitled to a voice as to how its funds are expended. The problem has been to equate this fact with the principles of ethics and practice management in dentistry.

Auxiliary and paradental personnel

Prior to 1958 the only dental workers in Australia were the dentist, the dental technician and the dental chairside assistant. Furthermore, the technician and the chairside assistant had no clinical status whatsoever. The profession had always maintained that none other than a registered dentist was competent to treat patients and had successfully opposed any move to the contrary.

Gradually it was realized that the situation was not realistic, economic or necessary, and legislation was enacted to permit the introduction of dental auxiliary personnel. The licensing of auxiliaries is still in the development stage and the position varies in the different States and Territories. The following is an outline of the position as at 30 June 1990.

School dental therapists (New Zealand type) have been introduced into every Australian State and Territory. They are trained to practise a wide range of children's dentistry as employees of the Department of Health *but not otherwise* except in Western Australia. Whilst working for the Government these therapists can maintain a high standard of service but it is doubtful if they could do so under the economic stress of private practice.

Dental hygienists

Dental hygienists are being trained in the Adelaide School of Technical and Further Education and are licensed to practise by the Dental Boards of all States and Territories except Western Australia and Tasmania. Nevertheless there is considerable variation throughout Australia in the range of activities which the hygienist may undertake.

The duties listed in the original South Australian Act followed the traditional pattern, i.e. dental health measures and the scaling and prophylaxis of teeth. However, when the issue was under consideration by the other States, various specialist groups made representation for the inclusion in the hygienists' duties of matters relating to their own particular discipline, and this was usually accepted in principle.

The result is that in the various Australian States and territories there is no uniformity in the duties which may be delegated to hygienists by dentists. The situation is very similar to the position which exists in America, and hygienists who propose to go to Australia on a working holiday should check in advance upon their eligibility to be licensed.

Dental technicians with chairside status

Despite opposition from the profession, legislation has been enacted in five States to permit certain dental technicians to undertake the clinical aspects of prosthetic dentistry, and to construct and supply dentures direct to the public.

The State legislation which applies to such personnel is by no means standard – and even the terminology varies. The Dental Prosthetist of New South Wales and the Registered Dental Mechanic of Tasmania are both authorized to construct, fit and repair all forms of removable dental appliances – other than those designed for orthodontics.

In Victoria, the work of the Advanced Dental Technician is restricted to the making, fitting and repairing of full dentures and mouth guards. The chairside duties of both the South Australian 'Clinical Dental Technician' and the Western Australian 'Dental Prosthetist' are restricted to the making and the repair of full dentures.

Contract dental laboratories

The development of the dental laboratory industry has enabled dentists to provide a wide range of services to their patients. It has also given rise to a number of legal issues, some of which have still to be clarified.

Laboratory proprietors maintain that they can be no longer regarded as dental auxiliaries (or helpers), but that they are a light industry in their own right which constructs and sells prostheses to dentists and to other laboratories.

Additional status involves additional responsibility, both for the success or the failure of any item. A problem arises regarding the responsibility for an unsatisfactory prosthesis, since both the dentist and the technician have been involved in its production. The laws relating to contractors and sub-contractors can be applied only in the light of the circumstances of each particular case.

Failures in dental prostheses sometimes occur and it would be unjust to blame the technician in every case. The problem is magnified when a large sum of money is involved. In Australia the trend is to regard the dental laboratory proprietor as a 'professional colleague' and it is only upon this basis that an equitable solution will be reached.

Dental laboratory technicians

In New South Wales, Victoria and Tasmania, legislation has been passed to license the dental laboratory technician as such. Throughout Australia the number of technicians who are employed by individual dentists is now relatively few – most practitioners preferring to utilize the services of a contract dental laboratory.

Chairside assistants, secretaries and receptionists

As these workers do not practise dentistry in their own right, they do not come within the jurisdiction of the Dental Act. However, as with all employees, their conditions of employment have been defined by a Wages Board determination.

The legal position of a dental nurse (dental chairside assistant) employed in four-handed dentistry can be clarified in the light of two basic facts. Firstly, not more than one person can practise dentistry on a patient at any time, and secondly, a dentist cannot practise dentistry on more than one patient at the one time.

Accordingly when a dentist is attending to a patient, the person acting as his chairside assistant is not contravening the law, provided always that the assistant is never permitted to assume the principal role or engage in operative dentistry. In such circumstances the dental nurse (dental chairside assistant) would be practising dentistry and the dentist acting as the assistant.

Unless a dentist is working at the chairside it is illegal for a dental nurse (dental chairside assistant) to undertake any intra-oral service for that patient.

The Poisons Acts

The prescribing of drugs by dentists is controlled by the Poisons Acts of the various States and Territories. Generally speaking these Acts are identical and are based upon the recommendations of the National Health and Medical Research Council of Australia.

Under the provisions of the Poisons Act a dentist may have in his possession and use or prescribe any poison or deleterious substance *in lawful practice of his profession as such*. The following points should be noted:

1. A dentist is not permitted to sell any poison or deleterious substance.
2. A dentist is not permitted to prescribe amphetamines unless he has obtained a special permit from the State Health Department.
3. Prescription of drugs listed in Schedule 8 (Drugs of Addiction) must be endorsed 'For dental purposes only'. Repeat prescriptions of such drugs are not permitted.
4. Dangerous or restricted drugs, if sent through the post, must be packaged securely, labelled 'Poison' and despatched as registered or certified mail.
5. A dentist should never prescribe a dangerous drug for himself. Contravention of dangerous drugs regulations can be the subject of criminal proceedings.
6. Under the Australian Government's Pharmaceutical Benefits Scheme, a dentist may prescribe certain antibiotic drugs for issue to a patient at a reduced cost. The list of such drugs and the prescription books are available from a Commonwealth Director of Health.

Psychological Practices Act

In Australia, hypnotism is not greatly used by practising dentists and the subject is not included in the curriculum of any dental school. In some States there is no restriction upon a dentist practising hypnotism on his patients provided always that he fulfils the common law requirements of any service rendered.

However, in Victoria a registered dentist may not practise hypnotism in the course of his practice of dentistry, except with the approval of the Victorian Psychological Council. A severe penalty may be imposed for the infringement of this law.

Radiation Hygiene Act

A Code of Radiation Hygiene in Dentistry has been drawn up by the National Health and Medical Research Council and is available from the Department of Health, Canberra, ACT 2065.

The State Acts require that either the radiograph machine or the person who operates the machine shall be licensed. They also provide that no person of less than 16 years shall be employed in work involving irradiating apparatus.

Labour and Industries Act

The conditions which apply to employed labour in Australia are, by world standards, generous. Any person who employs another individual must conform to the relative sections of the Labour and Industries Act and the Wages Board determination of that particular industry.

In each State the Dental Employees Wages Board has issued a determination relating to the employment of dental staff and this determination includes matters such as a minimum wage, hours which may be worked, overtime rates, annual leave, sick leave, long service leave, etc. A copy of this determination is available at the Government Printing Office.

The Taxation Act

The self-employed practitioner is immediately affected by many of the provisions of the Taxation Act, particularly with regard to his records, the provision for his retirement, the permissible rates for the depreciation of equipment and the taxation contributions of his staff. A professional accountant, who is an essential adjunct to a dental practice, will advise upon such matters.

In some states dentists are legally permitted to incorporate their practices and such arrangements are accepted by the Taxation Commissioner, provided they are not aimed at tax avoidance.

The Ethical Code

As already stated, the United Kingdom Dentists Act and the Regulations under the Act do not include a code of conduct. The General Dental Council does issue a booklet (see pages 6–16), and any breach of the 'guidance' given therein may well lead to disciplinary procedures. In Australia, however, the Dental Board Regulations cover matters such as advertising, signs and the soliciting of patients. These, therefore, are statutory and any breach of such requirements is a breach of the law.

The Branches of the Australian Dental Association have each adopted a Code of Ethics which is binding upon each of their members. These Codes deal specifically with the dentist's duty to his patients, his colleagues, the third parties in dentistry and to the public as a whole. However, dentists who are not members are in no way bound by these provisions.

Legal processes in Australia

These vary from State to State, but all bear a similarity to those in England and Wales. There is, obviously, the distinction between civil and criminal actions, but some courts are empowered to deal with both.

The collection of fees

Since private practice is responsible for most of the dental service of Australia, the collection of dental fees is basic to the future. It has been said that 'Good patients seldom leave good dentists – and a good dentist is not merely one who does good work. He is a dentist who also collects his fee for that good work and who does so in a fashion which retains for him the respect and the goodwill of the patient'.

The primary obligation of a dentist to his patient should be to give value for money, and to convince the patient that his service has been worth the amount charged. In most instances this can be achieved by providing a good service together with good communication and, in the assessment of the fee, good common sense.

The laws relating to debts and debtors are amongst the oldest in the statute book. They are designed to protect the interests of both parties and the procedure as laid down is fairly specific.

Under the provisions of the Dentists Act a dentist is entitled to charge a fee for any service he may render, and the size of that fee he alone will determine. There are, of course, certain factors which the prudent practitioner will assess in determining his fees – including an adequate return for himself and the satisfaction of the patient. Obviously he will wish his patients to feel that they have received good value for their money so that they will come back again, or maybe refer others.

The patient also has certain rights – he can request a detailed account, he can request that the account be discussed or reviewed, he can refer the account to the Consumer Affairs Authority for an opinion or in some States he can lodge a complaint with a Fees Tribunal. Finally, he can formally refuse to pay the account and invite the dentist to take the matter to court.

If a person is owed a debt, he can at any time send an account, issue a summons and take the matter to court seeking an order that the debt be paid forthwith. However, in court the other party will have the right of defending himself and, in the dental field, this defence may be that the work was never authorized, or that the work is unsatisfactory, or that the fees are excessive. Generally speaking, if unsatisfactory work is claimed, it falls on the patient to prove this case. However, on the question of fees, the onus falls upon the dentist to prove that his fees are fair and reasonable.

Age of consent to treatment

Unless there is an Act to the contrary, the age of majority is deemed to be the age of consent – usually 18 years. However, whilst it may be expected that the courts would accept as valid the informed consent of a mentally normal person of 16 years, problems could arise. This is a grey area which should be approached with caution.

Firstly, the courts must be satisfied that in giving consent the child realized what the dentist had in mind and understood the consequences of that to which he was consenting; also that he was capable of assessing the facts and of making a logical decision.

Secondly, it must be realized that a child cannot pledge the credit of his parents and, if the child himself has not the money and the parents refuse to meet the cost, the dentist could be left with an unpaid account upon his hands.

The Australian Dental Association

The national professional body of dentists in Australia is the Australian Dental Association, founded in 1928. It has a branch in each State and a membership of approximately 6500.

The Association aims to improve public health and to promote the art and science of dentistry.

Membership of the Association is achieved by joining a State Branch which automatically confers membership of the national Association. Any registered dentist in Australia may apply for membership of the branch in the State in which he has registered.

There is also a provision for limited membership for students, admission being restricted to dental students in the final 2 years of undergraduate study.

The Association publishes a scientific journal six times per annum, and a monthly News Bulletin. The *Australian Dental Journal* is supplied to members as a component of their membership subscription. Also, each State Branch distributes to its members a monthly Newsletter.

The national body of the ADA deals with Federal Government, Association policies and international affairs.

State Branches deal with State Governments, arrange defence cover and negotiate wage and salary awards and determinations.

Governing bodies
Federal Council and Secretariat: 75 Lithgow Street, St Leonards, NSW 2065 (PO Box 520 2065). Tel: 02.906.4412. Fax: 02.906.4676.
New South Wales Branch: Level 3, 123 Clarence Street, Sydney NSW 2000 (GPO Box 4319, 2001).
Victorian Branch: 49 Mathoura Road, Toorak, VIC 3142 (PO Box 434).
Queensland Branch: 61 Brookes Street, Bowen Hills, QLD 4006 (PO Box 455 Fortitude Valley) 4006.
South Australian Branch: Unit 2, 62 King William Road, Goodwood, SA 5034 (PO Box 858 Unley 5061).
Western Australian Branch: 14 Altona Street, Perth, WA 6005.
Tasmanian Branch: 161 Macquarie Street, Hobart TAS 7000.
Northern Territory Provisional Branch: 48 Mitchel Street, Darwin, NT 5794 (PO Box 4496).

Standing committees
Congress Manual Committee
Constitution Committee
Dental Auxiliaries Committee
Dental Health Services Committee
Education Committee
Legislation Committee
National Dental Health Week Co-ordinating Committee
Oral Health Education Committee
Practice Promotion Committee
Schedule Committee
Therapeutics Advisory Committee
Tariffs, Instruments, Materials and Equipment Committee

Australian Dental Journal
75 Lithgow Street, St Leonards, NSW 2065 (PO Box 520 2065).

Republic of Ireland

The Dentists Act 1928 and The Dentists Amendment Act 1983 have now been repealed and replaced by the Dentists Act 1985. This Act provided for the establishment of a Council to be known as The Dental Council whose function is to provide for the registration and control of persons engaged in the practice of dentistry and to provide for other matters relating to the practice of dentistry and the persons engaged in such practice. The Act prohibits any person from practising dentistry unless he is a registered dentist or a registered medical practitioner. An auxiliary dental worker may undertake such class or classes of dental work as may be specified by the Council and a student of dentistry or medicine may practice dentistry under the supervision of the registered dentist in certain circumstances.

The Council has power, on the recommendation of the Fitness to Practice Committee or on failure by a registered dentist to pay a retention fee charged by the Council, to erase the name of such person from the Register. Appeals against erasure are made to the High Court.

Other relevant legislation

Social Welfare (Consolidation) Act 1981 (as amended)

Covers matters relating to Social Insurance, occupational injuries and treatment benefit including dental treatment.

Health Act 1970

Amends and extends previous Health Acts and provides for the establishment of bodies for the adminstration of the Health Services (Health Boards).

Safety in Industry Act 1980

This is relevant to dental laboratories and makes provision for cleanliness, temperature, overcrowding, ventilation, lighting, and sanitary conveniences.

Office Premises Act 1958

Provides for the health and safety of persons employed in offices and thereby affects dental practices which have 'office' staff.

Payment of Wages Act 1979

Stipulates the methods by which employees may be paid.

Unfair Dismissals Act 1977

Provides redress for employees deemed unfairly dismissed from their employment.

Minimum Notice and Terms of Employment Act 1973

Stipulates minimum periods of notice and that a written statement of terms of employment be given to employees.

Redundancy Payments Act 1967–1979

Provides for redundancy payments to employees, establishment of a fund and rebates to employers making such payments.

Employment Equality Act 1977

Prohibits discrimination in employment, training and promotion of employees on grounds of sex or marital status.

Protection of Young Persons (Employment) Act 1978

Protects male and female employees in the 15–18 age group and sets standards for conditions of employment.

Sale of Goods and Supply of Services Act 1980

Contains provisions protecting recipients of services and sets out in statutory form implied undertakings as to the quality of services including those provided by the professions.

Consumer Information Act 1978

Aimed at ensuring all information about goods and services given to consumers/ patients is neither false nor misleading and that essential information is not withheld. Dental prostheses can be deemed as 'goods'.

Misuse of Drugs Act 1984

Controls and regulates production, supply and possession of dangerous drugs. Dental practitioners clearly should be aware of their duties in relation to the Act.

All of the Statutes referred to are relevant to dental practitioners, whether employer or employees. They must therefore ensure that they act in accordance with these laws as failure to do so could result in proceedings being initiated.

Republic of Ireland legal procedures

The Coroner's Court

Operates similarly to that in England and Wales (see page 46).

The District Court

Presided over by a District Justice who is addressed as 'Justice'. Civil claims up to £2500 are heard and criminal cases of a minor nature are dealt with.

The Circuit Court

Presided over by the President of the Circuit Court and other circuit court judges referred to as 'Your Honour'. Civil and criminal cases are heard. The jurisdiction in civil cases is currently £15 000. Hears appeals from the District Court. There is no right of appeal in such a case to the High Court except on points of law.

The High Court

Presided over by the President of the High Court and other high court judges. Hears civil cases with or without a jury, depending on the nature of the case. This court hears appeals from the Circuit Court in civil matters.

The Central Criminal Court

Presided over by a judge sitting with a jury. This is the criminal branch of the High Court and deals with serious offences.

The Special Criminal Court

Presided over by the three judges sitting with a jury. Hears criminal cases and deals with mainly political offences.

The Court of Criminal Appeal

Presided over by three judges sitting with a jury. Hears appeals from the Circuit Court in criminal matters and from the Central Criminal Court.

The Supreme Court

Presided over by the Chief Justice and the court sits with either three or five judges of the Supreme Court. This is the court of final appeal.

The Community Dental Service

Dental services are provided by Health Boards, free of charge, to the following persons:

1. Pre-school children and pupils of national schools (generally 4–12 years of age) following examinations arranged by the Health Board.
2. Persons with full eligibility for health services and their dependants. Persons with 'full eligibility' are those unable to provide primary medical care services for themselves and their dependants without undue hardship. Generally speaking, they are persons whose incomes are within guidelines adopted by the Health Board which provides the service.
3. Persons not within the foregoing categories who are regarded by the Health Boards as being unable on grounds of undue hardship to provide dental services at their own expense.

There are eight Health Boards. The Boards are responsible for the organization and provision of health sevices for persons who are eligible for such services under health legislation. Until recently the health board dental service was, in the main, provided by a full-time public dental staff. However, Health Boards are authorized to make agreements with private practitioners to treat eligible persons on a fixed fee basis.

Dental Services for Insured Persons

Persons insured under the Social Welfare Acts who satisfy prescribed insurance contribution requirements are eligible for dental services under the Treatment Benefit Scheme operated by the Department of Social Welfare. Insured persons, with very few exceptions, include employees aged 16 years and over and certain persons who have retired from employment. Eligible persons are entitled to dental services from a dentist of their choice who has entered into an agreement to provide services under the scheme. Dentists are paid on a fixed fee basis for treatments other than the provision of crowns, inlays, bridges and chrome cobalt dentures. Eligible persons are provided with services such as fillings, extractions scaling and polishing, free of charge. They pay a proportion (two-thirds) of the cost of dentures and, in the case of crowns, inlays and bridges, they pay the balance of the cost in excess of the subvention paid by the Department of Social Welfare. This scheme does not apply to dependants of insured persons. Practioners participating in the scheme are subject to certain rules and regulations and disciplinary procedures. As ever, they should be fully aware of their obligations and avoid any situation likely to result in a breach of contract.

National Association

This is The Irish Dental Association, 29 Kenilworth Square, Dublin 6, which publishes the *Journal of the Irish Dental Association*. The Journal keeps members informed of relevant legislation as well as including the usual type of scientific articles, and news items from the Branches.

Hong Kong

The Dentists Registration Ordinance corresponds to the Dentists Act in the United Kingdom, and the Dental Council, set up by that Ordinance, is the equivalent of the United Kingdom Dental Council and has similar duties and powers. Appeals against an order of the Council for removal from the Register are heard by the Hong Kong Court of Appeal whose decision is final.

The Ancillary Dental Workers (Dental Hygienists) Regulations, made under the Dentists Registration Ordinance, control the practice of dentistry by ancillaries and are similar to those in the United Kingdom.

The courts

Coroner's Court

This is similar in function to that in England and Wales (see page 46). Coroners have to be qualified in the law and it is for them to decide whether or not an inquiry is to be held with or without a jury.

Small Claims Tribunal

Claims, currently, of up to HK$8000 can be pursued in this court. (A recommendation to increase this to $15 000 has been made.) There is no legal representation of the parties involved.

The District Court

Hears both civil and criminal cases. Presided over by a district judge, addressed as 'Your Honour'. There is no jury. Civil claims up to HK$60 000 can be pursued. (A recommendation to increase this to HK$250 000 has been made.)

In criminal cases, the maximum sentence which can be imposed is imprisonment for seven years.

The High Court

Presided over by a high court judge addressed as 'My Lord'. A jury is called in criminal cases and in some civil ones. The court has unlimited civil and criminal jurisdiction.

The Court of Appeal

Presided over by three judges and empowered to hear appeals from any court including appeals against removal from the Dental Register.

Ordinances relevant to dental practice

Time limits for actions in negligence

These are fixed by the Limitations Ordinance. For personal injury cases arising from negligence or breach of duty the limitation period is three years from date of incident or from when the plaintiff became aware of a cause of action. As in the United Kingdom the Court has the power to override the time limit where this is deemed equitable in the circumstances.

Age of majority

This is 21 years.

Age of consent

There is no statutory provision similar to that in the United Kingdom, and no precedents yet established in the courts. It is considered, however, that the situation would be judged as in the United Kingdom (see Chapter 5, page 82).

Dangerous Drugs Act

The Dangerous Drugs Ordinance creates offences relating to the trafficking, manufacture, possession, supply and consumption of dangerous drugs, these being specified in a Schedule. Registered dentist are authorized to possess and supply such drugs as are necessary for the practice of their profession.

The Pharmacy and Poisons Ordinance and the Antibiotics Ordinance control dealing with sale and supply of these substances and dentists are authorized to possess and supply those which are appropriate.

Other relevant ordinances

In addition to the ordinances already referred to the following are of importance to the dental practitioner:

The Employment Ordinance
The Occupiers Liability Ordinance
The Law Amendment and Reform (Consolidation Ordinance)
The Workmen's Compensation Ordinance (possibly to be retitled The Employee's Compensation Ordinance)
The Factories and Industrial Undertakings Ordinance
The Radiation Ordinance

THE EMPLOYMENT ORDINANCE
This requires every employer to inform a potential employee, in a manner intelligible to the latter, of the conditions with regard to wages. The employer has to notify the employee of any subsequent change and in writing, if so requested. There is no requirement to give employees written information on other terms of employment. The Ordinance is not applicable to a person employed other than by way of manual labour and whose wages exceed HK$10 500 per month.

Contract of employment. Unless otherwise agreed by both parties such a contract is treated as being on a monthly basis. Termination may be given orally or in writing and either party may do so without notice by agreeing to make payment in lieu thereof. There is the right to immediate termination without notice or payment, by either party if the behaviour of the other justifies such an action.

Severance payments. These are provided for in the ordinance, and are somewhat equivalent to the redundancy payments in the United Kingdom. Claims are filed with the Registrar of the Labour Tribunal.

THE OCCUPIERS LIABILITY ORDINANCE
This is equivalent to the Occupiers Liability Act in the United Kingdom (see page 128).

THE LAW AMENDMENT AND REFORM (CONSOLIDATION) ORDINANCE
Equivalent to the United Kingdom Law Reform (Personal Injuries) Act and renders an employer vicariously liable for injury to an employee caused by the negligence of some other employee (see page 129).

THE EMPLOYEE'S COMPENSATION ORDINANCE
This gives employees the right to claim statutory amounts of compensation for injury and disease sustained in the course of employment. No fault on the part of the employer need be proved.

Insurance against this liability has been compulsory since 1 January 1984. An employer who contravenes the requirement is liable to a fine and imprisonment.

THE FACTORIES AND INDUSTRIAL UNDERTAKINGS ORDINANCE
Some of the provisions of the Regulations under this Ordinance are similar to those in the United Kingdom Factories Act (see page 129) in that they stipulate certain requirements in places of employment.

THE RADIATION ORDINANCE
Sections 7(1)(c) and 7(2) of the Regulations under this Ordinance require all persons, including dental practitioners, who have in their possession or use, any radioactive substance or irradiating apparatus to be in possession of a licence. Any person who contravenes this requirement shall be guilty of an offence and liable to a fine of HK$10 000 and to two years imprisonment.

The Hong Kong Dental Association

Membership of the Association is recommended. The address is: Duke of Windsor Social Services Building, 8th Floor, 15 Hennessy Road, Wonchai, Hong Kong. Professional Risks Indemnity can be arranged through the association.

Singapore

The Dentists Act (Cap 76) corresponds to the Dentists Act in the United Kingdom; the Dental Council set up by that Act is more or less the equivalent of the United Kingdom General Dental Council and has similar duties and powers. Appeals against an order of the Council for removal from the Register are heard by the Singapore High Court, whose decision is final.

There is also the Registration of Dentist Regulations 1949, as amended in 1965.

The Courts

Coroner's court

This is similar in function to that in England and Wales (see page 46). Coroners have to be qualified in the law and it is generally for them to decide whether or not an inquiry is to be held. The Attorney General may also require an inquiry to be held. There is no jury. In practice, coroners are also magistrates.

Small Claims Tribunal

Claims, currently, of up to S$2000.00, can be pursued in these tribunals. There is no legal representation of the parties involved.

The District Court

Hears both civil and criminal cases. Presided over by a district judge, addressed as 'Your Honour'. There is no jury. Civil claims up to S$50 000.00 can be pursued.

In criminal cases, the maximum sentence which can be imposed is imprisonment for seven years.

The High Court

Presided over by a high court judge addressed as 'My Lord'. The court has unlimited civil and criminal jurisdiction. There are no juries. In a criminal case involving the death penalty, the trial is conducted by two judges.

The Court of Appeal

Presided over by three judges and empowered to hear appeals from any court.

Acts relevant to dental practice

Time limits for actions in negligence

These are fixed by the Limitation Act. For personal injury cases arising from negligence or breach of duty the limitation period is 3 years from date of incident or from when the plantiff became aware of a cause of action.

Age of majority

This is 21 years.

Age of consent

There is no statutory provision similar to that in the United Kingdom, and no precedents yet established in the courts. It is considered, however, that the situation would be judged as in the United Kingdom. However, the Penal Code does contain certain provisions relevant to consent in medical operations.

Misuse of Drugs Act

The Misuse of Drugs Act creates offences relating to the trafficking, manufacture, possession, supply and consumption of dangerous drugs, these being specified in a

Schedule. Registered dentists are authorized to possess and supply such drugs as are necessary for the practice of their profession.

The Poisons Act and the Medicines Act control dealing with sale and supply of poisons and medicines and dentists are authorized to possess and supply those which are appropriate.

Other relevant Acts

In addition to the Acts already referred to, the following are of importance to the dental practitioner:

The Central Provident Fund Act
The Civil Law Act
The Employment Act
The Factories Act
The Medicines (Advertisment and Sale) Act
The Patents (Compulsory Licensing) Act
The Workmen's Compensation Act

The Singapore Dental Association

The association's address is 2 College Road, Singapore 0316. Dental surgeons may join a professional indemnity protection scheme through the SDA.

Malaysia

The Dental Act 1971

The Dental Act 1971 is the Malaysian equivalent of the United Kingdom statute. The Malaysian Dental Council set up by the Act has broadly similar powers and duties as the United Kingdom Dental Council. The Malaysian Dental Council has an important role in deciding on the qualifications that are registerable and is responsible for regulating the conduct and discipline of dental practitioners. An appeal from the Council in its disciplinary jurisdiction lies to the High Court whose decision shall be final.

There are two classes of dental practitioners – dental surgeons and dentists. Dental surgeons hold tertiary qualifications. Dentists (sometimes called 'registered dentists') do not hold such qualifications. They are a relic of the times when dental surgeons were in short supply. The present policy as contained in the Act is to allow existing registered dentists to continue practising but that no new applicant may be registered as a dental practitioner unless he holds a tertiary qualification in dental surgery.

The Courts

The Coroner's Court

The coroner in Malaysia exercises the same function as a coroner in England. He is usually, but need not be, qualified in law. An inquest is conducted without a jury.

The Small Claims Court

Set up in 1987 and presided over by a Second Class Magistrate (usually a lay person), it covers claims of up to M$3000.00. The parties are not allowed to bring in legal counsel.

The Subordinate Courts

The two principal courts comprising the Subordinate Courts are the Magistrate's Court and the Sessions Court.

THE MAGISTRATE'S COURT

Magistrates are divided into two classes, the First Class and the Second Class.

In the First Class Magistrate's Court (usually presided over by a lawyer), claims of up to M$25 000.00 may be tried.

In criminal cases, a First Class Magistrate may pass any sentence allowed by law not exceeding:

(a) 5 years imprisonment;
(b) a fine of M$10 000.00;
(c) whipping up to 12 strokes; or
(d) any sentence combining any of the sentences aforesaid.

However, in certain instances and in cases covered by certain special statutes, a First Class Magistrate may impose a heavier sentence.

In his civil jurisdiction, a Second Class Magistrate presides over the Small Claims Court (see above). In criminal cases, he may pass any sentence allowed by law:

(a) not exceeding 6 months imprisonment;
(b) a fine of not more than M$1000.00; or
(c) combining either of the sentences above.

THE SESSIONS COURT

The Sessions Courts rank above the Magistrate's Courts in the hierarchy. A Sessions Court judge must hold a recognized qualification in law.

In civil cases, a Sessions Court judge may try cases involving claims of up to M$100 000.00. In his criminal jurisdiction, he may try all offences other than offences punishable with death and may pass any sentence allowed by law other than the sentence of death.

The High Court

It is presided over by a judge addressed as 'My Lord' (in the Subordinate Courts, the proper mode of address in 'Your Honour').

The High Court has original civil and criminal jurisdiction, though in practice usually only cases which cannot be tried in the Subordinate Courts are tried in the High Court. The High Court also hears appeals from the Subordinate Courts and quasi-judicial tribunals.

The Supreme Court

It is now the highest court in the land with the abolition of appeals to the Privy Council with effect from 1 January 1985.

The Supreme Court mostly hears criminal and civil appeals from the High Court. It also has a special function as a sort of constitutional court.

Statutes relevant to dental practice

Time limits for actions in negligence

These are fixed in the Limitation Act 1953. In a personal injury case arising from negligence or breach of duty, the limitation period is six years from the date that the cause of action accrued. The period may be extended in certain circumstances, for instance where the cause of action had been concealed by reason of fraud committed by the defendant or by reason of a mistake.

Age of majority

The age of majority is 18 years.

Age of consent

There is no statute providing for the age of consent to treatment. There is hardly any case law in Malaysia on the subject but it is possible that the majority decision of the House of Lords in the English case of *Gillick v. West Norfolk and Wisbech Area Health Authority [1986] A.C. 122* would be followed. The effect of the majority decision is that in the case of a minor, parental consent to treatment is not necessary where the child possesses sufficient understanding and intelligence to appreciate the treatment or procedure being proposed. However, as far as possible, parental consent should be sought, even if not necessary. And in the case of a child not possessing sufficient understanding and intelligence, parental consent is necessary save in exceptional circumstances, e.g. an emergency, parental neglect or where the parents cannot be found in time.

The Dangerous Drugs Act and related statutes

The Dangerous Drugs Act 1952 creates various offences relating to the manufacture, import and export, possession, trafficking, supply and consumption of dangerous drugs. It also provides for the treatment and rehabilitation of drug dependants. Registered dental practitioners are authorized to possess and supply drugs covered by the Act as are necessary for the practice of their profession.

The Poisons Ordinance 1952 and the Poisons Regulations 1952 provide for such matters as the control of the import, storing, transport, manufacture, possession, sale and supply of poisons. Dental practitioners are allowed to supply poisons for the purpose of treatment.

Other relevant statutes

The following statutes too are important for the dental practitioner:

The Employment Act 1955 and the subsidiary legislation made thereunder
The Employees Provident Fund Act 1951
The Employees Social Security Act 1969
The Workmen's Compensation Act 1952
The Civil Law Act 1956
The Factories and Machinery Act 1967
The Medicines (Advertisement and Sale) Act 1956

The Employment Act

The Act and its subsidiary legislation make extensive provision regarding the terms and conditions of contracts of employment, covering such matters as termination of employment; payment of wages and deductions therefrom; maternity protection; hours of work, rest days and holidays; computation of overtime payments; and termination, lay-off and retirement benefits.

The Act applies to a numbr of categories of employees, including employees earning not more than M$1000.00 a month; employees engaged in manual labour; and employees who supervise or oversee other employees engaged in manual labour.

The Employees Provident Fund Act 1951

This statute was introduced with a view to providing an employee a 'nest egg' upon retirement. Subject to certain exceptions, every employer and every employee must contribute to the Employees Provident Fund a certain sum every month, computed according to the amount of the employee's wages. In the case of the employee, his contribution must be deducted from his wages by the employer and paid to the Fund along with the employer's contribution. Where there is a private 'approved fund' set up by an employer for his employees, the Board of the Employees Provident Fund may exempt the employer and the employee from making contributions to the Employees Provident Fund.

The Employees' Social Security Act 1969

The Act set up a scheme to provide benefits to employees in cases of illness and employment injury, including occupational diseases. No fault on the part of the employer need be proven.

The Act applies to all industries other than industries employing less than five persons. The word 'industry' is given a very wide definition in the statute, covering 'any business, trade, undertaking, manufacture or calling of employers' and applies to all employees earning more than M$500.00 a month.

Both employer and employee are required to make contributions in accordance with the Act to various funds set up under the Act. The scheme is administered by the Government through the Social Security Organisation (popularly known as 'Socso').

The Workmen's Compensation Act 1952

This statute provides for the payment of compensation and expenses by employers to employees for injury suffered by *accident* in the course of their employment. The employee need not prove fault on the part of the employer.

Every employer is required to insure and keep himself insured with a Malaysian insurer in respect of any liability that he may incur under the Act to any workman employed by him.

The Civil Law Act 1956

Section 14 of this Act provides in effect that an employer shall be vicariously liable for injury caused to an employee by the negligence of another employee who is in common employment with the injured employee.

Sections 7, 8 and 28A of the Act provide for certain principles to be applied regarding entitlement to and assessment of damages in personal injury claims.

The Factories and Machinery Act 1967

Various requirements are contained in the Act for the purpose of ensuring the safety, health and welfare of employees and visitors. A personal injury action against the owner or occupier of a building may well contain an allegation of failure to comply with the statute.

The Medicines (Advertisement and Sale) Act 1956

The Act contains a prohibition against advertising any skill or service relating to any ailment, disease, disease, injury, infirmity or condition affecting the human body but such an advertisement may be published with the approval of the Minister of Health by an appropriate professional body.

It is the approved practice in Malaysia for a dental practitioner to take out through the Malaysian Dental Association a classified advertisement announcing the commencement or resumption of practice or a change of practice address.

The Malaysian Dental Association

The Association's address is No. 69–2 (2nd floor), Medan Setia 1, Plaza Damansara, Bukit Damansara, 50490, Kuala Lumpur, Malaysia. Dental Surgeons in Malaysia may join a protection scheme through the Association.

Chapter 12

Forensic dentistry

By its very nomenclature, forensic dentistry, otherwise termed 'forensic odontology', implies the involvement of dentistry with jurisprudence. The science, for it is indeed such, is highlighted in instances when, for example, the identity of a murderer is established from points of comparison between his dentition and bite marks found on the victim. These, however, are somewhat rare occurrences and fall within the scope of the expert, although the services of the general practitioner may well be utilized at some stages.

Establishing the identity of persons by dental means is certainly nothing new for as Warren Harvey states in *The Criminologist* (1973, 8.28): 'Vale (1969) recorded that about 66 AD Nero's mistress demanded to see the head of his wife, on a dish, and was satisfied by recognizing a black anterior tooth', and Elphinstone (1911) wrote that after a battle in 1193 – the taking of towns, the breaking of idols, the acquisition of treasures present so little novelty that we are left at leisure to notice the capture of a white elephant and the incident of the body of the rajah (Chei Chandra Rahtor of Canory) being recognized by his false teeth'. Cameron and Sims in *Forensic Dentistry* (1974) refer to the 'identification of Charles the Bold after his death on the Battlefield of Nancy in 1477. . . . It appeared that he had lost a number of teeth as a result of an accident during his life and this dental characteristic was enough to ensure that his followers were able to recognize and identify him among the fallen.'

Dental identification is normally only necessary when a person's general features have been destroyed by time or circumstance. The dental tissues, however, survive the effects of exposure to climate and water, fire, high impact and burial extremely well.

When a murder has been committed the starting point in an investigation by the police is normally ascertaining the identity of the victim. When major or mass disasters have occurred the identification of the individual is necessary before many legal processes, of great importance to the relatives and/or beneficiaries, can be initiated; remarriage, claims on estates, claims against insurance companies and management of businesses are examples.

The processes of identification begin where possible with the recognition of clothing, personal papers and physical features, but if these have been totally destroyed then, where suitable parts of the skeleton are available, experts may determine such matters as age and height, the sex and sometimes the race. A skull with only a few teeth in situ, can provide equally accurate material for an assessment of age and sex and, in some instances, race. Explosion and high velocity impact (aircraft crash) disasters involving many bodies create special problems, for remains and personal belongings may well be be scattered over a wide area and papers and clothing largely destroyed – especially by fire. Dental identification may then be the only means available. When such accidents occur, a list of persons involved is generally available – for example from aircraft bookings or staff known to have reported for work that day, and who theoretically should have been in the aircraft or building concerned. From such lists of persons, relatives and/or friends can usually be traced, and from these the names of dental practitioners likely to have treated the victims can be ascertained.

General dental practitioners should appreciate that their records of patients may at some time be essential in establishing identity. In this respect alone the initial charting of the mouth to show at least the basic detail is of vital importance. Failure by many dentists to do this leads to difficulties and complications when identity problems arise, also when claims are lodged against practitioners for unsatisfactory treatment or negligence. Such charting is of course a requirement in the Terms of Service of practitioners working in the General Dental Services of the National Health Service.

It is by no means unusual for dental practitioners, following a mass disaster, to be approached by the police with a request for the dental records of certain named patients. Once a practitioner is satisfied as to the reason for the request he should of course cooperate fully. Such records will, of course, be scrutinized and assessed by a forensic odontologist. However, once they are out of a practitioner's hands, he will obviously have no control over who else may see them, and as they are intended solely as an aid to identification, any clinical entry of a sensitive nature not relevant to identification should be withheld. If this is not possible due to all the entries being on one sheet, a suitably amended copy should be submitted. A check on the records may well show that charting has not been kept up to date and it is then most helpful if this can be amplified from the treatment notes; the presence of any specific items, e.g. bridges, crowns, implants, root fillings, apicectomies, retained roots, unerupted teeth etc. should be stated. All radiographs and models relevant to the patients should be included, as should references to any known attendances at hospitals. This will not normally take the practitioner long, for he will be basing a report on his own records. The same exercise, undertaken by someone else, either for transmitting information by telex, facsimile or by an investigator at the site of the accident where perhaps a hundred or more victims are involved, can indeed be a laborious process. The greatest care over detail must be exercised.

The establishment of the identity of an assailant by means of the comparison of a dentition with bite marks inflicted on the victim is a highly specialized procedure and the case of *Regina* v. *Hay* is an excellent example of the painstaking work which can be involved:

The Biggar murder*

The body of a young female, subsequently identified as Linda Peacock aged 15 years, who had not returned home the previous night, was found at 6.40 a.m. on 6 August 1967, in the church cemetery of the small market village of Biggar, midway

*Based on Harvey W., Osborne B., Furness J. and Laird R. (1968) *The Biggar Murder: Dental, Medical, Police and Legal Aspects*. London, The Forensic Science Society.

between Glasgow and Edinburgh. At the time a travelling fair was in the village and this attracted many people from neighbouring areas. Overlooking the cemetery, but some distance away, is an 'open' approved school which then housed 31 young delinquents. Linda's home was outside the village beyond the cemetery.

She had been battered and strangled; there were pronounced ligature marks round the neck and one wrist, blunt injuries to her head, a burn on one wrist and bite marks on one breast. She had been dragged along the ground, her clothing disturbed and breasts bared, but she had not been sexually assaulted.

At the scene of the crime the police took a number of photographs including some of the right breast which exhibited what appeared to be bite marks (Figure 12.1). Dental help was plainly necessary and Dr Warren Harvey, a known expert in such matters, was contacted and agreed to assist.

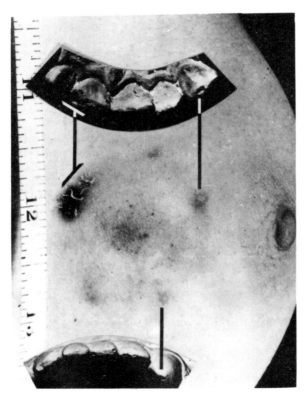

Figure 12.1 Right breast of Linda Peacock with models of suspect superimposed. Breast is shown upside down as bite marks were inflicted from above right shoulder (see text). (Photograph by courtesy of Professor Keith Simpson)

The police interviewed 3000 people but concentrated their attention on 29, including boys from the approved school nearby – for whose examination and the taking of dental impressions consent in writing was obtained from each individual. This exercise was conducted with the assistance of the Glasgow Dental Hospital. Each model was identified by a number only.

The possibility of animal bites was considered but discounted for the marks indicated the teeth were positioned in a more semi-circular arch than found in animals and also an area on the right breast showed typical effects of sucking and this is not characteristic of animal bites.

Reaction of the tissues around the marks suggested the biting took place at about the time of death. Gaps were present between the marks but it was appreciated that these did not necessarily imply certain teeth were missing, for as Keiser-Nielson (1967) wrote: 'Bite marks can never be taken to reproduce accurately the dental conditions of the originator, and represent but the remaining and fixed picture of an action, and often include only a very limited number of teeth.'

Two sets of models were of full dentures and were excluded as the teeth were set very regularly and it was considered such prostheses would not have permitted the intensity of bite indicated. A further 22 sets of models were excluded because the length and position of teeth would not have left the gaps between the bite marks or because the irregularity of teeth was such that other distinctive markings would have been occasioned. Twenty-four sets of models had been excluded and only after several re-checks, 5 remained. At this stage the problem of providing both informed opinion and evidence likely to convince a lay jury was impressed upon the police and it was agreed that the Home Office pathologist Keith Simpson, Professor of Forensic Medicine in the University of London at Guy's Hospital, be asked to cooperate as he had vast experience of the recognition and interpretation of bite marks in assault and murder cases. A meeting of Dr Warren Harvey, Detective Chief Superintendent Muncie (in charge of the case) and Chief Inspector Weir with Professor Keith Simpson and Dr (now Professor) M. N. Naylor was held and it was decided to mount models of the remaining 5 suspects on anatomical articulators following the taking of fresh impressions with face bow registrations. This was done, the models being made in acrylic resin the better to withstand fair wear and tear. Trial bites on a breast, in a mortuary, were affected and this exercise although not entirely satisfactory did in fact exclude model number 14 which previously had been considered suspect as anteriorly $\dfrac{1}{21}\bigg|\dfrac{1}{12}$ were missing and no dentures worn. The reason for exclusion was that the models could only cause the marks if the occlusal plane of the lower teeth was some 30 degrees out of horizontal! All 29 sets of models were then re-examined and the short list confirmed with the exclusion of number 14. Only at this stage was it appreciated that two circular marks on the breast were most unusual and therefore of extreme importance. These are the two marks seen nearest the nipple in Figure 12.1. No such marks were found described in previously recorded cases and it was accepted that they must be caused by teeth having uncommon characteristics. If this was a correct interpretation and the previous screening had been equally correct then one of the remaining four sets of models should show teeth capable of producing these particular marks. This proved to be so, the models concerned (number 11) showing in particular the tips of $\dfrac{3}{3}\bigg|$ flattened and those of $\bigg|\dfrac{3}{3}$ pitted but not carious.

Reference was then made again to all of the 29 sets of models to see if others exhibited similar pits but none were found. For the teeth of set 11 to have produced the marks on the breast then the assailant must have approached over the girl's right shoulder from above or behind. As this seemed unusual a further check on the other models was made but no alternative found.

The police were informed of the conclusions and warned of the scarcity of points on which identification would have to be based. Only now were the dental investigators told that number 11 represented Gordon Hay and that he was already the prime suspect.

Further impressions were taken of Hay's teeth this time using copper bands and composition for the canines and Permalastic full impressions. Face bow recordings were again made and the models mounted on an anatomical articulator. For accuracy and durability the models were plated. To assess the frequency with which pits in the tips of canines appeared in young persons 342 boys aged between 16 and 17 were examined. One tooth seen had a filling in the tip of a canine, two had pits at their tip. In no instance were two pits in canine tips found in the same mouth, thus confirming the rarity of such a situation.

Altogether 16 points of comparison between the bit marks and Hay's dentition were noted and included reference to the rotation of $\underline{2}$, a mesial cavity in $\underline{2}$, fracture of incisal edge of $\underline{1}$ and protuberances mesially and distally on the fractured surface. As a means of presenting understandable evidence to the jury transparencies of models of the anterior teeth were superimposed over a photograph of the breast.

Hay was charged with the murder and his solicitor, counsel and expert witnesses saw all material evidence and then requested similar photographs using transparencies of model number 8 which showed flattening of the tips of all incisor and canine teeth and biting edges almost level. No pits as such were present in the canines but these did exhibit saucer-shaped areas. The transparencies could not be 'fitted' to the bite marks and therefore were not superimposed on the breast photograph.

At the trial inmates of the approved school stated that Hay was missing at the relevant times and when he returned his hair was untidy, he had been sweating and the knees of his jeans were dirty. (These were washed routinely next day.) Evidence also disclosed that Hay had been in possession of a loop of string, had been in Biggar with another boy two days before the murder and they had met Linda Peacock with a girl friend.

Professor Keith Simpson was called as an expert witness for the prosecution and stated that the scaled overlay photographs and dental techniques adopted were orthodox. When asked if the comparisons between Hay's dentition and the bite marks satisfied him he replied: 'My Lord, I have looked at these with the greatest care, as I commonly have to do with instruments of any kind in relation to marks on the skin, and I see in this couple of transparencies a number of points of comparison, two of which are in my experience quite remarkable or quite unique, new to me in my work. I say that those two marks in their position and in their character, and the other mark which shows the scraping on the surface of the cuticle – for which I should require some special explanation – are 3 quite exceptional, exceptionally detailed marks; the presence of those 3 in those positions and with those details would carry me a long way towards feeling that this was an exact comparison; I could be satisfied that this set of teeth was the set that caused these marks.'

Dr Warren Harvey was also examined, being questioned over a period of 5 hours, and demonstrated how the models of Hay's right canines could cause marks on finger nail beds similar to the 'ring' marks on the victim's right breast. He stressed the abnormality of the accused's dentition and after examining 29 sets of models produced by the defence stated none could have produced the marks seen on the breast although some had flattened, or saucer-shaped depressions in the tips of canines.

Mr John Furness, a dental practitioner with considerable experience in this field, was questioned and informed the Court that he personally had produced a short list of 6 suspects from the original models and of these eventually determined that only model number 11 (Hay's) had all the necessary characteristics to produce the marks on the breast. To check on the rarity or otherwise of pits similar to those in Hay's canines he had examined 90 boys between 16 and 18 years of age and found only one such pit and this was in a lower canine. He had previously been asked by the defence to examine 32 plaster models and not one of the 120 canines included thereon had shown a pit capable of producing a 'ring' mark similar to those on Linda Peacock's breast.

Dental experts appeared for the defence but under severe questioning agreed pitted canines similar to Hay's were rare, no specific check of models against marks had been made by them and it was accepted that Hay's dentition could have caused the marks on Linda's breast but it was not beyond reasonable doubt that other mouths could have done the same.

The Jury by a majority of 14 to 1 found the case proven and Hay guilty therefore of murder. Being under 18 at the time of the crime he was sentenced to be detained during Her Majesty's pleasure.

Certainly this case was a triumph for forensic odontology for all the primary evidence was circumstantial. In Scotland a jury can bring in a verdict of Guilty, Not Guilty, or Not Proven, and in this instance the jury was satisfied by the scientific dental evidence, questioned and tested as it was by Hay's defending counsel – instructed by his own dental experts. The very experienced judge in the case indicated his approval of the verdict. It should, however, be remembered that some doubts were raised regarding the quality of bite-mark evidence in this case, and it is clear that such evidence must be viewed with complete objectivity and its possible unreliability recognized by both sides in the case.

Scope of forensic odontology

A practitioner who is requested by the police to examine a suspect dentally should explain to him, or her, the object of the exercise, stating specifically if it is intended to take photographs, radiographs and/or impressions and bite registrations, and request consent. If such consent is obtained then this should be written out and dated and the suspect's signature obtained and duly witnessed. When a person refuses consent to an examination then the practitioner should not proceed unless an appropriate judicial order is obtained.

The forensic aspect of dentistry is indeed a fascinating one and should be of interest to all dental practitioners. As time progresses so undoubtedly will the science of forensic odontology. International standards of recording, charting, storing and relaying information have been under discussion for some time. More and more national forensic odontology organizations have been formed and the *Fédération Dentaire Internationale* has established a sub-committee which obtains appropriate information from all parts of the globe and with *Inform* has compiled a library on the subject and over 1000 references; there are Chairs in Forensic Odontology, e.g. Japan and South America, and doubtless more will be established in the future.

In many instances it is on information gained from general dental practitioners that the authorities and experts must rely and this fact of necessity places a moral obligation at least on all who practise dentistry to make and maintain accurate records of patients under their care. Such records should include full names, age (or approximate age) and address – information all too frequently found to be lacking on records submitted to the protection organizations when assistance from the organization is required by a practitioner.

The full scope of forensic odontology is indeed wide for it varies from the examination of a denture and the giving of an opinion on its satisfaction or otherwise, when this is in dispute, to the identification of victims of mass disasters and of murders.

The following list, taken from *Inform* **5**, No. 2, April 1973, will indicate effectively the field covered.

1. *Criminal cases*
   (a) Bite marks in inanimate objects
   (b) Bite marks in skin
   (c) Bite wounds
   (d) Blood groups in teeth
   (e) Paternity cases
   (f) Identification problems.
       1. Mass murders – commingled remains
       2. Blasts and explosion
       3. Burned and drowned bodies

2. *Accident cases*
   (a) Identification from fragmented bodies
   (b) Identification of burned and decomposed bodies

3. *Natural deaths – Identification problems*
   (a) Techniques
       1. Dental record comparison
       2. Lip print exam (Quieloscopy)
       3. Facial restoration
       4. Montage photographs
       5. Superimposition
   (b) Special problems
       1. Age distinctions (dead and living)
       2. Sex distinctions
       3. Racial distinctions
       4. Occupational distinctions
       5. Human vs. animal distinctions
       6. Time of death lapse
       7. Hereditary aspects
       8. Blood group aspects

4. *Dental jurisprudence*
   (a) Malpractice
   (b) Medication errors
   (c) Iatrogenic problems
   (d) Rape and sexual crimes by dentists
   (e) Explosions and improperly installed equipment

5. *Injuries to teeth*

6. *Dental fraud*
   (a) Treatment
   (b) Compensation cases

7. *Ancient remains and anthropologic problems*
   (a) Activities involving teeth
   (b) Dietary influences on teeth
   (c) Cultural traits
       1. Mutilation
       2. Tattooing
   (d) Animal teeth in remote cultures

Whilst the general practitioner has his part to play in some of these applications of forensic odontology many must involve the expert in the field in cooperation with dental technicians, chemists, police and forensic laboratories having the availability of highly specialized and sophisticated equipment.

BDA recommendations

The British Dental Association in 1969 set up a Working Party, 'To make recommendations as to how the furtherance and development of forensic science within the profession might be achieved and to formulate suggestions regarding the organization by which the profession might improve its public service in this field'. As a result of the deliberations of this Working Party the following Recommendations were made.

In the light of its consideration of the evidence available, the Working Party recommends that:
1. Forensic odontology should be formally recognized in the United Kingdom.
2. The present *ad hoc* method of employing expert advice should be replaced by organized arrangements on a national scale.
3. A register of experts in forensic odontology should be established and held by the Home Office, and appropriate Government departments in Scotland, Wales and N. Ireland.
4. Arrangements for the cooperation of the dental profession in the event of mass or major disasters (including railway and other accidents) should be effected on a regional basis.
5. An internationally accepted method of charting and recording of the dentition should be introduced. As this must meet the needs of the dental profession generally, this recommendation will require to be examined in depth.
6. Air crews should be required to undergo a routine dental examination at least annually.
7. From a forensic point of view a full chart is desirable on each occasion on which a dental surgeon examines a patient for the first time.
8. From a forensic point of view dental records should be retained for at least 10 years.
9. Further research should be carried out into simple methods of marking dentures for identification.
10. A list of funeral directors capable of dealing with mass or major disasters should be compiled.
11. The Home Office and appropriate Government departments in Scotland, Wales and N. Ireland should be asked to appoint dental surgeons experienced in forensic odontology as experts in each Police Region.

12. Laboratory facilities additional to the Home Office Forensic Science Laboratory Service should be recognized as based at dental teaching hospitals where dental anatomy and oral pathology departments are experienced in forensic odontology.
13. Courses of training for professional and lay personnel should be introduced with specialized training for Police Officers.
14. The appropriate authorities should consider the inclusion of forensic odontology as a subject in the course for the Diploma in Medical Jurisprudence granted by the Society of Apothecaries, leading to a DMJ (Dent.) or alternatively the introduction of a course leading to the MSc degree or its equivalent.

Unfortunately, to date, few of these recommendations have been put into practice. However, the recently formed British Association for Forensic Odontology is seeking to promote a more formal status for the discipline. Within the past few years a taught course leading to a Diploma in Forensic Odontology has been established by the London Hospital. The ever increasing amount of litigation, worldwide, involving dental practitioners and the advent of mass transportation in larger and faster aircraft and trains has brought in its wake the necessity for dental expertise of a forensic nature. No longer can the individual practitioner remain insular; his knowledge of the dental condition of a particular patient may be needed many thousands of miles away and in a short period of time. Many problems are now international rather than national or even local and dental practitioners must therefore be prepared, for the common good, to accept in particular new methods of recording treatment and charting mouths which for effectiveness must eventually be agreed by all nations. The writing *is* on the wall, has already been noted and doubtless will be more fully acted upon in due course. In the meantime all dental practitioners should bear the problems in mind and as individuals protect their own and their patients' interests at least by the initiation and maintenance of accurate records.

Forensic odontology can raise numerous ethical and legal problems and any practitioner faced with such a problem and requiring advice and/or assistance should contact his dental association or protection organization.

Recommended reading

Cameron, J. M. and Sims, B. G. (1974) *Forensic Dentistry*. Edinburgh, Churchill Livingstone

Chapter 13

General dental practice in the National Health Service

Dentistry within the National Health Service is divisable into three categories: (1) the General Dental Services, (2) the Hospital and Specialist Services and (3) the Community Dental Service. It is the first category that is to be dealt with in this chapter.

The General Dental Services are provided by general dental practitioners as independent contractors with the Family Health Services Authority of a District Health Authority in England and Wales, the Primary Care Division of a Health Board in Scotland, or the Area Health and Social Services Board in Northern Ireland. Health authorities and boards cover all parts of these countries and each takes its name from the locality concerned: e.g. The Surrey Area Health Authority (England), The Mid-Glamorgan District Health Authority (Wales), The Western Isles Health Board (Scotland) and The Eastern Health and Social Services Board (Northern Ireland).

Who may provide 'General Dental Services'?

To provide treatment within the General Dental Services a practitioner must be included in the Dentists Register. Any practitioner whose name appears in the Medical Register but not in the Dentists register may legally practise dentistry but *not* within the General Dental Services of the National Health Service.

A registered dental practitioner desirous of providing General Dental Services must apply for inclusion in the dental list of a Family Health Services Authority or its equivalent (see above).

The remainder of this chapter, whilst relating specifically to England and Wales, is in principle equally applicable to Scotland and Northern Ireland.

The Family Health Services Authority (formerly the Family Practitioner Committee)

The purpose of this Authority is to administer the arrangements for the provision of services by individual dental and medical practitioners, pharmacists and opticians. Its work includes entering into contracts with dentists, paying them the fees authorized by the Dental Practice Board, ensuring that the arrangements for general dental services are carried out and undertaking statutory disciplinary procedures relating to dentists' terms of service. In the course of performing these functions the Committee may receive or seek information from the Dental Practice Board, the Dental Officer Service of the Department of Health and the Local Dental Committee, all of which are described later.

Every registered dental practitioner applying to have his name placed on the dental list of a Family Health Services Authority accepts the terms of the contract with the Authority and this constitutes an undertaking to act within the 'terms of service' as laid down by statutory regulations.

Renumeration

A practitioner is paid for his services by the Family Health Services Authority in accordance with a Scale of Fees negotiated on a national basis between the Department of Health and representatives of the profession. Payments are made monthly and represent the total amount due for capitation fees, and claims approved by the Dental Practice Board less payments made directly by patients in accordance with current Regulations and less certain statutory deductions (e.g. for superannuation).

It is clearly necessary that every practitioner should have a proper understanding of the contract into which he has entered and knows what he, as a professional man, has agreed to do when providing general dental services.

The nature of the contract

In the provision of general dental services three parties are involved: (1) the State, (2) the practitioner and (3) the patient.

When he applies to have his name placed on the dental list of a Family Health Services Authority the practitioner contracts with that Authority, representing the State, to provide general dental services under the National Health Service Acts. The practitioner may accept or decline to accept for treatment such patients as he chooses.

To obtain treatment a patient goes to a practitioner whose name appears on the dental list issued by the FHSA for the area and asks to be treated within the Service. After the implementation of the new NHS Contract on 1 October 1990, a patient will be able to 'sign on' with an individual practitioner on a 'continuing care' basis for an initial period of 2 years. When the patient has signed the appropriate form and has been accepted, a contract is established binding upon the practitioner to abide by the terms of service.

The requirement of the Terms of Service

Having applied for inclusion in a dental list the dental surgeon is given a Personal Number as a principal practitioner. He is then able to provide general dental services at such place, or places, and at such times (which may be 'by appointment') as he has agreed and are recorded in the dental list. At the same time he is provided with copies of the Regulations and should at once familiarize himself with his

Terms of Service. Practitioners are strongly recommended to read their Terms of Service once a year and at all times when new regulations affecting them are issued. In this manner they may be kept fresh in the memory. Practitioners are advised not to regard any commentary on the Regulations (such as this chapter) as a substitute for the authoritative text of the Regulations themselves.

A practitioner may take on as much or as little National Health Service work as he wishes and is under no obligation to accept any particular patient.

Terms of service

A new contract for general dental practitioners working within the NHS General Dental Services will come into operation on 1 October 1990. At the time of writing, the precise conditions have yet to be finally agreed, but the following is an outline of the more important provisions of the Terms of Service:

- Dental care under the NHS embraces preventive care as well as restorative treatment, and its aim is to secure and maintain the oral health of a patient.
- Adult dental patients are normally accepted by a practitioner for 'continuing care', and children (aged under 18) are accepted under a capitation arrangement. In both cases this entitles patients to:
  (a) a 'treatment plan' setting out the treatment proposed and (in the case of adults) the cost;
  (b) emergency cover (with the dentist responsible to make 'reasonable arrangements');
  (c) for those adults who pay charges, replacement free of charge of certain restorations which fail within a year;

Practitioners are required to provide 'Patient Information Leaflets' and keep their professional knowledge and skills up to date through appropriate postgraduate education.

The Local Dental Committee

This is a professional body composed of dental practitioners, elected by their colleages, representing all members of the profession within the area of the Family Health Services Authority whether or not they provide general dental services.

The formation of a local dental committee is not obligatory under the National Health Service Act 1946, but the existence of such a body is of great importance to the profession. When such a committee has been democratically elected the Secretary of State may recognize it as the body with whom the FHSA have to consult when regulations so require and, resulting from such recognition, the committee acquires statutory rights and obligations, including the right to appoint to the FHSA members of the profession within its area and to appoint members and deputy members on the Dental Service Committee.

The essential purpose of the local dental committee is to represent general dental practitioners within the District and although the members have duties connected with the National Health Service the committee remains an independent body.

Because of the statutory relationship which exists between them, not only have the FHSA to seek the views of the local committee on a number of matters and to refer others to them for consideration but the local committee may, at any time, consult with the FHSA when matters arise which involve public health and welfare, or affect the profession.

The committee members have the duty to deal with complaints made by one practitioner against another involving the efficiency of the service and must also investigate any questions referred to them of record keeping or of excessive prescribing of treatment. That matters so largely professional and clinical can be dealt with by a committee consisting of professional men rather than by a body which includes lay persons is a wise and fortunate arrangement.

The Dental Practice Board

The Dental Estimates Board, by virtue of the Health and Medicines Act 1988, changed its name on 1 April 1989 to the Dental Practice Board. Separate Boards exist for England and Wales, for Scotland and for Northern Ireland. The composition of each Board is predominately professional.

Of the nine members of the Board for England and Wales, the Chairman, Vice-Chairman and five others are dental surgeons, the remaining two being lay. The Board has four main functions:

1. The authorization of claims for payment.
2. Monitoring dental treatment.
3. The detection of fraud and abuse.
4. The provision of information on all aspects of dentistry within England and Wales.

A considerable and efficient organization is required to process the very large number of dental estimate forms submitted by practitioners. The Board for England and Wales receives, on average, over 650 000 each week. These are processed by a lay staff of between 1300 and 1400 persons, and a small group of dentally qualified advisers who are consulted when decisions of a clinical nature have to be made. Many of the Boards' activities are computerized, and the first stage of the direct transmission experiment whereby the Board receives estimate details from practitioners' computers via a telephone link has been successfully completed. Since June 1987 a new management team consisting of a part-time Chairman, Chief Executive and Chief Dental Adviser has been in post. In 1990 the Board implemented a restructuring of the management and formed eight directorates responsible to the Chief Executive, namely:

- Transaction processing.
- Dental policy.
- Investigation.
- Information services.
- Corporate secretariat.
- Dental care.
- Corporate services.
- Human resource management.

It is the Board which computes payments due to practitioners for treatment undertaken. This information, in the form of monthly schedules of claims approved, is notified to the relevant FHSA, who are responsible for paying the practitioners.

In doing their work, the Board members have to rely upon practitioners providing accurate and sufficient information. If this is not forthcoming much unnecessary misunderstanding can arise.

As a check on the correctness of treatment provided and paid for, a practitioner can expect some patients to be called for clinical examination. Such examinations are carried out by Dental Officers of the Dental Reference Service (see page 177) which, since 15 March 1990, has merged with and is administered by the Dental Practice Board. This is usually a routine matter with no other significance. If a practitioner discovers some error, either clerical or clinical, the Board should always be informed without delay and where a proper explanation is given the Board can be relied upon to be helpful. However, when Board members have reason to think that errors are occurring from a particular practitioner with greater frequency than can be accounted for by normal human fallibility, they may refer a batch of patients of that practice for examination by the Dental Reference Officer. If, as a result, it appears that there has been a possible breach of the Terms of Service, the matter is referred to the FHSA for possible investigation by the Dental Service Committee (see page 176). If, however, a suspicion of fraud arises, the matter would have to be referred by the Board to the Director of Public Prosecutions.

The Dental Service Committee

A Dental Service Committee exists for each Family Health Services Authority and is concerned solely with the investigation of complaints or other questions relating to practitioners within the District involving their Terms of Service or contract with the FHSA.

From 2 April 1990, by virtue of the National Health Service (Service Committees and Tribunal) Amendment Regulations 1990, a number of changes in the constitution of service committees and their procedures came into effect. Among the amendments is the extension from eight to 13 weeks of the time limit within which complaints may be made, and a provision for complaints to be made orally in certain circumstances. Minors of 16 and 17 may make complaints, and in certain circumstances investigations can be transfered to another FHSA. An informal conciliation procedure has been established, but in any event it is strongly recommended that practitioners facing a complaint made to the FHSA seek advice, as indicated below, at the earliest opportunity.

The committee consists of a lay Chairman, and six members, all appointed annually. Three are appointed by and from the the lay members of the FHSA, and three are professional members appointed by the local dental committee. The members elect their own Chairman and carefully drafted regulations ensure that they have one acceptable to them.

Although regulations require every FHSA to establish a service committee, such committees are in no way comparable with other sub-committees of the FHSA. Service committees are independent quasi-judicial bodies charged with specific duties and operate under regulations of their own.

The committee members' duty in any matter referred to them is to find the facts and to set these out in a report together with such inferences as, in their opinion, may properly be drawn from those facts and make recommendations for the action, if any, to be taken and to present this report to the FHSA. When this has been done the committee's duty has been discharged.

The FHSA may not question the findings of fact but may disagree with the inferences drawn from the facts and are not bound to adopt any recommendation, but it is their duty to make the decision as to what action should be recommended to the Secretary of State.

It is most important that a practitioner should attend such a hearing to answer any allegations that may be made, and although the practitioner (in respect of complaints made after 2 April 1990) has the right to be assisted in the presentation of the case by any person, it is generally better for respondant practitioners to speak for themselves.

The proceedings of a service committee should be conducted in an atmosphere which is rather more domestic than judicial. The hearing is private and the evidence is not taken on oath. This less formal approach is intended to make the parties to the investigation feel more at home and make the findings of fact easier.

It is, however, the experience of the authors that many practitioners, finding themselves in the unenviable situation of being the 'respondant' dentist, contemplate the hearing with considerable apprehension and, not without reason, find the procedure itself to be something of an ordeal. Much of this understandable apprehension is due to unfamiliarity with the committee procedure and uncertainty how to present and conduct their case. Worries of this nature can be reduced if the individual concerned seeks advice, sooner rather than later, either from the secretary of the Local Dental Committee, the British Dental Association, the General Dental Practitioners Association, or appropriate protection organization.

The Denture Conciliation Committee

Inevitably many complaints by patients arise as the result of dissatisfaction with dentures. Much of this dissatisfaction is due to a lack of knowledge on the patient's part concerning the difficulties and limitations of the prosthetic art.

An FHSA may set up a Denture Concillation Committee to deal with complaints related solely to the fit and efficiency of dentures. Such a committee is able to do a great deal to resolve problems and at the same time can often preserve a good relationship between patient and practitioner. In this way many complaints that otherwise would have to be investigated by the Service Committee can be dealt with satisfactorily and in a simple manner in an atmosphere aimed at conciliation. Practitioners' responsibilities, generally, in the provision of dentures are dealt with in Chapter 4 (see page 71).

The Dental Reference Service

A number of dental surgeons hold appointments in the Dental Reference Service. Until 15 March 1990 this service formed part of the dental division of the Department of Health. Since that date it has merged with the Dental Practice Board. Their purpose is to examine and report on the clinical condition of patients referred to them. The report given by a dental officer represents his independent professional opinion. This service is available to FHSAs the Dental Practice Board and practitioners alike.

A patient, when requesting treatment within the Service, undertakes to be examined by a dental officer if so required.

Occasions occur in general practice when it can be most helpful to have the opinion of a dental officer before, during or after the treatment of a patient.

Most of the work of the dental officers is concerned with reporting on the clinical condition of patients referred by FHSAs or the Board, either after treatment has been finished (and it is desired to know if this has been satisfactorily completed) or before treatment has been started, and information is needed to guide the Board when considering estimates for approval.

Appeals from decisions of Family Health Services Authorities

If a practitioner is aggrieved by a decision of an FHSA following an investigation by a service committee or a hearing by a concillation committee, he has four avenues open to him. He may decide, upon reflection, to accept the decision without further dispute, or he may either appeal or make representations (written or oral) to the Secretary of State within one month of the date of receipt of the decision.

If a dentist disputes either the facts found by the service committee or its decision that there has been a breach of the Terms of Service, an appeal can be made. Appeals may be decided on papers or after an oral hearing. The Secretary of State may appoint three persons to hear the appeal. The chairman is a lawyer on the staff of the Department, one member a departmental dental officer, the other a dentist from a panel nominated by the British Dental Association. Both dentist and complainant may be legally represented and evidence is taken on oath.

If the dentist accepts the facts and the finding of breach but disputes the penalities imposed by the service committee (after they have been either confirmed or varied by the FHSA), representations can be made either in writing or orally to the Secretary of State. Oral representations are heard under substantially the same conditions as an oral hearing of appeal.

Appeals from decisions of the Dental Practice Board

Any person aggrieved by a decision of the Dental Practice Board concerning the treatment of a patient or the fees payable to a dentist, may appeal under paragraph 21 of the NHS (Service Committees and Tribunal) Amendment Regulations 1990, by sending to the General Manager of the FHSA a notice of appeal within one month from the date on which notice of the decision of the Board was received by that person.

No appeal against the fee can be made where the fee offered by the Board is the maximum under the scale item.

The appeal is an informal occasion where two dentists not connected with the case hear all sides of the argument and decide whether the appeal should be allowed. The two dentists hearing the appeal are appointed by the FHSA, at least one of whom is selected from a panel of dentists practising in the General Dental Service and nominated by the Local Dental Committee. No further appeal lies against the decision of the two referees.

The Tribunal

This is a judicial body set up to deal with inquiries relating to professional people in contract with FHSAs.

The Tribunal consists of a Chairman (who must be a practising barrister or solicitor of not less than 10 years' standing) appointed by the Lord Chancellor, a member appointed by the Secretary of State and, when the matter relates to a dental surgeon, a dental practitioner appointed by the Secretary of State after consultation with the British Dental Association.

Reference to the Tribunal is a most serious matter, for the inquiry is to decide whether or not the practitioner concerned is suitable to continue to provide general dental services.

There is no appeal from a decision by an FHSA to refer a matter to the Tribunal, but a practitioner has the right of appeal to the Secretary of State against any direction by the Tribunal that his name should be removed from any dental list. Such an appeal has to be made within 14 days of receiving notice of the Tribunal's direction.

Seeking advice

The practice of dentistry, especially when conducted within a nationally organized service, cannot fail to produce many problems and a conscious effort is sometimes necessary to avoid a feeling that difficulties are purposely being made.

Experience of the workings of the Health Service suggests that there is much that practitioners can do themselves to avoid trouble and that in coping with the day-to-day problems of practice there is plenty of advice readily available to them if they wish to make use of it and know where to look.

The Family Health Services Authority

The General Manager will always be pleased to provide information or advice on any matter with which the Authority is concerned including:

- General administration of the Service.
- Superannuation.
- Retirement.
- Arrangements during sickness.
- The employment of assistants.
- Explanation of the Regulations.

The Dental Practice Board

The Board's advisers will be found most ready to provide help on any point connected with the Board's work. Practitioners are strongly advised to seek the aid of the Board whenever necessary and to assist the work of the Board by always supplying the fullest possible information.

A practitioner may communicate direct with the Dental Adviser at the Board who is dealing with the estimate form for one of his patients.

The British Dental Association

The Association's secretariat is there to provide members with information over a wide field, covering such matters as:

- The Scale of Fees and the work of the Dental Rates Study Group.
- Revision and interpretation of the Regulations.
- Superannuation.
- Practice agreements.
- Ethics.
- Advice to practitioners and patients concerning the General Dental Service.

The General Dental Practitioners Association

The GDPA will provide members with information and advice over a range of topics (see page 18).

The Local Dental Committee

The Secretary is always willing to advise and assist on any matter connected with a practitioner's work. This can be particularly helpful when a practitioner needs guidance when faced with a service committee or other disciplinary matter. The Local Dental Committee is composed of local practitioners and has behind it a wealth of experience of practice within the Service and all its problems gained since the start of the National Health Service in 1948.

The address is available from the Family Health Services Authority.

The protection organizations

If a practitioner becomes involved in some difficulty affecting his professional reputation or livelihood he should at once approach his protection society which exists to give all possible help and assistance to its members.

The National Health Service in Scotland

Separate Statutory Instruments operate in Scotland but these are very similar to those for England and Wales. They include, however, special arrangements for the provision of dental services in remote areas, i.e. certain Islands and part of the Highlands. These arrangements allow for travelling and subsistence expenses and allowances to cover loss of remunerative time in addition to the normal fees for items of service. Scotland has its own Dental Estimates Board. Service committee procedures are the same as in England and Wales with appeals going to the Secretary of State.

The country is divided into areas covered by 15 Health Boards, each subdivided into Districts. Practitioners wishing to participate in the general dental services have to apply to the Primary Care Division of the appropriate Board for inclusion in its lists. The Primary Care Division is the Scottish equivalent of the Family Health Services Authority in England and Wales.

The National Health Service in Northern Ireland

Essentially the Terms of Service and disciplinary procedures are the same as for England and Wales. There are no Family Health Services Authorities, however, their equivalents being the Area Health and Social Services Boards of which there are four. A practitioner wishing to provide general dental services applies for inclusion in the list of the Board covering the area in which he intends to practise.

Area Health Boards do not undertake the setting up of service committees. This is a function of Central Services Agency, which is, as the name implies, a central administrative body for the general medical, dental and pharmaceutical services. Recommendations of service committees are conveyed to the appropriate Board. Appeals are directed to the Department of Health who form a tribunal to hear the case and whose decision is final. Dental officers employed by the Central Services Agency examine patients and issue reports when so requested. A separate Estimates Board operates for Northern Ireland.

Chapter 14

Insurances*

Every practitioner, including the newly qualified, will understand not only the advisability but indeed the necessity of joining a protection organization before starting in practice, thus obtaining unlimited indemnity in respect of professional risks as well as experienced advice and assistance with numerous practice problems. There are, however, other forms of insurance which must receive serious consideration, some of which are essential and others so advisable as to be deemed essential in view of a practitioner's legal liabilities to staff and to all persons attending at his premises; only by adequate insurances can a practitioner avoid serious consequences to himself and his dependants in the event of his illness or death, and obtain compensation for loss of possessions. The owner of a motor vehicle, as is well known, has to have at least a third party bodily injury insurance cover, as required by the Road Traffic Act.

Numerous differing policies are obtainable from various insurance companies and practitioners are likely to receive advertisements from many sources. Expert guidance is certainly advisable and this is readily obtainable from professional insurance agencies, some of which deal exclusively with medical and/or dental practitioners and on a non-profit making basis. The Dentists' Provident Society, 9 Gayfere Street, London SW1P 3AN, the Medical Insurance Agency Ltd, Hertlands House, Primett Road, Stevenage SG1 3EE, and the Medical Sickness Society, 7/10 Chandos Street, London W1 are three such organizations whose informed services are available to members of the dental profession free of charge.

Sickness insurance

All practitioners, with the exception perhaps of those in full-time employment providing sick pay during absence through illness, should appreciate the possible financial burdens arising from any incapacity to work. Adequate insurance cover against such contingencies, therefore, should be considered. There can be no doubt that the first policy under this heading that a dentist should effect is through membership of the Dentists' Provident Society and/or the Dentists' and General Mutual Benefit Society, both of which operate on a participating basis wherein all surpluses are apportioned to members.

*The author's thanks go to Norex Insurance Brokers Ltd, formerly Harrison Horncastle Insurance Brokers Ltd, for their advice and assistance in compiling this chapter.

Membership, once effected, cannot be cancelled unilaterally by these Societies. Subscriptions, and thereby benefits obtainable, are based on the number of shares a member wishes to hold and this ranges from 1 to 25. The subscription per share varies according to the age of the applicant. At the time of writing the maximum holding, including supplementary cover, entitles a member to £90 a week sickness benefit for up to six months, £45 a week for the following six months and then £27 per week until recovery. Membership of both of the Societies can thus produce £180 a week benefit initially. Optional schemes are available under which the initial benefit can be made irreducible until recovery or the subscriber reaches the age of 65 years, whichever is the sooner.

The way in which these Societies work is that all basic share subscriptions are pooled and from this pool are paid claims for sickness benefit and the cost of management. The surplus is divided amongst the members according to the number of shares each one holds and is credited to individual 'apportionment' accounts. This procedure is followed each year and interest (which is tax-free) is also added at whatever rate is being earned on the Societies' investment. In this way each member accumulates a sum of money which becomes payable to him at age 65 (or to his dependants if death occurs before that time).

These are excellent schemes and the only snag could be the limit of benefit obtainable, since this may prove insufficient to cover the essential expenses to which a practitioner is committed. In such instances additional sickness cover for at least the balance deemed outstanding should be obtained. Basically, two types of sickness insurance are available: (1) the annual policy and (2) the permanent policy.

The *Annual Policy* provides cover for a limited period, generally only for 12 months, and it is subject to renewal each year like a motor policy. If for any reason the policy-holder contracts an incapacity that is likely to recur, the company may decide not to renew the policy at all, or perhaps only offer renewal terms which exclude benefit in respect of that particular incapacity. Because of this restriction on the annual policy it is much cheaper than the permanent contract.

The *Permanent Policy*. This is the more suitable, for so long as premiums are paid cover continues until a predetermined age, usually 60–65 years, with no question of benefit being reduced or terminated in the event of claims being made which prove adverse to the insurance company.

To reduce the premium outlay somewhat, consideration may be given to policies that do not provide benefit until the insured person has been ill for a certain agreed period, as such a contract removes claims for common ailments. Obviously there is then a premium reduction as compared to immediate benefit contracts. The amount of the premium would depend on the agreed length of the period of deferment.

It may be that a combination of immediate and deferred benefit contracts would prove most suitable, but this can only be decided in the light of the dental surgeon's personal circumstances and, of course, in accordance with any conditions of a partnership or similar type agreement. Most insurers now provide a modest escalation benefit and incorporate a waiver of premium when benefit is being paid to the policy-holder, other Accident and Sickness insurance policies are available and it is suggested contact is made with a professional insurance broker for advice and comparative prices and cover.

Clearly, so far as a practitioner's family is concerned his permanent disablement could be a disaster, and adequate provision therefore should be made.

Life assurance

The eventuality of death is one which everyone has to face and practitioners with dependants should ensure that they have adequate insurance to cover the effect of this; in most instances cover needs increasing periodically due to inflation and/or increased commitments. It is possible to provide, very inexpensively, cover for accidental death and this is the most common cause of decease of young people. Such cover can at the same time be extended to include certain disablement benefits. This form of insurance is normally of an annual nature and thus the premium may be adjusted by the company whenever due for renewal.

It is, of course, very important that the normal life policy covering death from all causes is effected. This is distinct from the accident and disablement contract mentioned above, which gives very valuable but incomplete death cover. Initially, the policy providing for payment of the policy moneys only on death will probably be of most interest although quite often practitioners prefer to consider a contract giving, in addition to death benefit, a form of enforced saving. Such policies provide that on survival to a set date, selected at the outset, the policy moneys are payable to the practitioner, but in the event of his death before that time the proceeds are payable to his family. It should also be borne in mind that a policy giving 'death only' cover without the additional maturity benefits can, within certain limits, be changed to the second type of policy.

Any of these contracts can provide for the payment to the policy-holder (or his dependants) of a sum well in excess of the total premiums paid. It has been mentioned that the basic life contract can be converted to the 'Endowment Assurance', as it is called, and indeed a number of contracts carry options showing from the outset the cost of such alteration. Furthermore, it is now possible to have a policy effected in such a way that the amount of cover (and possibly its type) can be altered and perhaps increased – as and when circumstances demand.

These are very important points, so the premium outlay should always be determined at a level which the assured can readily maintain and thus, when considering the annual amount to be expended, thought must be given to possible future commitments.

It is disadvantageous, at any time, to cancel a life assurance policy, especially if some refund of moneys is anticipated. Generally there is no surrender value at all in the first 3 years and when there is a surrender value then this is well below the total sum paid as the insurance company has had to cover the risk in the interim. If the payment of a premium proves difficult then it is advisable to arrange for an appropriate reduction in the sum assured and thereby of the premium, rather than to discontinue the policy. Provided the amount of money already paid is allowed to remain with the insurance company it is possible to avoid these adverse results, since the amount paid at maturity would be proportionately reduced.

There are various forms of temporary life policy which provide for payment on the death of the assured only within a predetermined time limit. This could be of considerable value as under these contracts it is possible to provide high cover for minimum outlay, since in the event of survival beyond the stated period there is no benefit payable.

Combinations of temporary and permanent policies can be effected and are often very suitable for the younger practitioner. He or she may commence with a policy providing a reasonable sum assured, divided between 'life' and 'temporary' cover and carrying a conversion option enabling subsequent adjustments to be made as and when money is available to meet greater premiums.

Practice insurance

All practice owners are recommended to obtain a really comprehensive practice insurance policy, and these are best obtained from organizations such as those previously referred to as they are fully congnizant of the needs of the dental profession. Adequate policies give cover against all the normal risks of burglary, fire, explosion, etc., and include cover for damage to equipment, loss of income following certain incidents which make it impossible to use the premises for professional purposes, and also for any accident that might occasion harm to a person employed at (see Employers Liability (Compulsory Insurance) Act, Chapter 9, page 128), or visiting the premises. An example is the patient who slips on a polished floor and breaks an ankle and then claims compensation (see Occupiers Liability Act, Chapter 9, page 128).

House insurance

Adquate cover for a practitioner's home is as important as for his practice premises and as inflation continues the value of a house and its contents should be increased accordingly when renewing the policy. This is an aspect, therefore, which needs to be considered annually.

Personal belongings

Whilst both house and practice policies normally include clauses relating to the loss of contents there may be certain items of value which it is advisable to nominate individually and then to cover en bloc. Any such policy involved should effect cover for loss or damage when the articles nominated are being carried on the insured's person or when in transit by other means. Such items include the more expensive types of watches, cameras, jewellery, pens, cigarette cases, lighters and other personal valuables. Practitioners should also include dental instruments likely to be conveyed from place to place. Policies to effect this type of cover are termed 'All Risks'; alternatively an 'All Risks' extension can be added to a normal household or practice policy.

Personal liability

A most useful form of insurance is one which provides cover against personal liability in the event of an accident occurring as a result of some action on the part of the policy-holder (or his family, if included in the policy) whereby some other person sustains an injury and/or is involved in certain expenses. The golfer may slice a shot and the ball break a window, damage a car, strike a person, etc; a son or daughter on a pedal cycle may knock into someone and inflict damage, the family dog may even bite the postman! Adequate insurance cover is relatively inexpensive, however, and this is a very wise investment. These days a householder's comprehensive policy will be found to provide a more than reasonable indemnity for personal liability with no extra premium. Such policies should, therefore, be carefully examined and if no such indemnity is provided then a separate policy should seriously be considered. Accidents occurring from the practice of the profession are not included in such policies.

Motor vehicle insurance

This is a necessity in law. As a general rule cheap premiums do not provide the best cover and minimal essential cover is not in the best interest of the insured. A fully comprehensive policy effected with an established company or Lloyd's of London is the best investment, and practitioners having staff or working colleagues are advised to ensure that their policy provides cover for any such colleagues or appropriate members of staff to use the vehicle for business purposes.

Saving for house purchase

With the ever increasing difficulties in obtaining a first mortgage, saving money with one of the larger building societies is to be recommended. Whilst this may not prove the most attractive form of saving from the income tax point of view, it does have two distinct advantages:

1. It establishes the depositor as a potential client with the building society and thus a subsequent application for a mortgage may be more favourably looked upon than would otherwise be the case.
2. If the building society, for any reason, is unable to offer a mortgage then the money deposited can be withdrawn speedily, and with interest.

In this way profit can be assured, a situation which by no means can be guaranteed if the money is used to purchase stocks and shares or to effect a life assurance policy purely with house purchase in mind. If such a policy has to be cancelled then only a small percentage of the premiums paid can be reclaimed, the effecting of a life policy of that type does not in any event guarantee a loan when required, and the insurance company may not consider the particular property selected by a policy-holder as a suitable proposition from their point of view. It will be appreciated, therefore, that saving through a building society with a view to house purchase has distinct advantages and should therefore be investigated and duly considered before any other avenue is decided upon. Effecting a low-cost endowment policy as a means of repaying the loan at the same time the loan is arranged, should be considered.

Self-employed pensions

The Inland Revenue encourage pension provision in respect of 'non-pensionable employment' by allowing tax relief on the premiums at the highest rate of income tax paid. Those people who are wholly self-employed or alternatively are members of the NHS and also in private practices cannot participate in the earnings-related section of the State Scheme for any income not derived from the NHS.

The premiums allowable for full tax relief are limited to 17½ per cent of 'net relevant earnings' with no upper ceiling from the tax year 1980/81 and thereafter.

Full tax relief is also available on premiums for life assurance cover affected under the plans, provided that these do not exceed 5 per cent of 'net relevant earnings' or £1000 per annum. The 5 per cent must be deducted from total allowance of 17½ per cent, thus restricting the pension premiums to 12½ per cent if the maximum 5 per cent life assurance premium is expended.

Net relevant earnings are defined as the relevant earnings from non-pensionable employment or business less certain deductions such as expenses, trading losses, capital allowances, etc. Personal charges, such as alimony, private mortgage interest and payments under a covenant need not be deducted from earnings to arrive at 'net relevant earnings'.

The benefits available under self-employed pension arrangements are as follows:

1. At retirement
   (a) A pension payable monthly throughout life,
      or
   (b) A tax free cash lump sum with reduced pension, plus a reduced pension with a widow's benefit.
2. On death before retirement
   (a) Return to dependants of all contributions paid with or without interest,
      or
   (b) A widow's pension,
      or
   (c) The sum assured under the attaching life assurance policy if applicable.

The retirement benefits need not be selected until pension age which can be any time between 60 and 75. The policy cannot be encashed prior to pension age, or assigned. It is possible to arrange a pensions mortgage by using the self-employed pension contract to build-up sufficient funds with which to repay the mortgage capital at pension age. This method can be extremely tax efficient.

The importance of adequate insurance and provision for the future cannot be overstressed and the author is well aware that he has only touched upon the fringe of this subject. It is one which should receive early, very serious and detailed consideration by every practitioner. There is no doubt it is an extremely complex field but, as previously stated, expert advisers are available to the profession, and full advantage should be taken of their expertise.

Finis

While the purpose of this book has been to create an 'awareness' it is to be hoped that not only has this been achieved but also that the reader will now realize the value of obtaining expert guidance on any matter with which he is not entirely familiar.

The authors wish all their readers good luck and a happy professional career, and trust that if problems do arise the information now gained will assist materially in their resolution.

Appendix 1

Radiation protection in dental practice

Prepared by the Standing Dental Advisory Committee, for the Secretary of State for Health and the Secretary of State for Wales*

Preface

The Ionising Radiations Regulations 1985 (Statutory Instrument 1985 No.1333) were brought into operation in two stages and were fully effective by 1 January 1986.

They are consistent with the provisions of the European Council Directives (EC Directives 80/336 and 84/467 Euratom) and lay down the basic safety standards for the health protection of the general public and workers against arising from the use of ionising radiation.

Subsequently, the Approved Code of Practice for 'The protection of persons against ionising radiation arising from any work activity' was published by the Health and Safety Commission. The general guidance contained in this document is applicable to the use of ionising radiations in dental practice and paragraphs 60 and 61 of Part I refer particularly to the identification of controlled areas in dental radiography.

The National Radiological Protection Board in conjunction with the Health Departments and the Health and Safety Executive have now prepared 'Guidance Notes for the protection of persons against ionising radiations arising from medical and dental use'. Chapters 5 and 6 refer specifically to Dental Radiology and Equipment for Dental Radiography respectively.

These notes have been prepared under the direction of the Standing Dental Advisory Committee for the convenience and guidance of those persons using ionising radiations for diagnostic purposes in general dental practice. These, and the guidance Notes referred to above, are intended only to provide general guidance on good practice. The legal requirements in respect of the use of ionising radiation are contained in the Ionising Radiations Regulations 1985 and Approved Code of Practice.

In preparing these notes the requirements of The Ionising Radiation (Protection of Persons undergoing medical examination or treatment) Regulations 1988 (Statutory Instrument 1988 No. 778) have been taken into account. The Statutory Instrument is consistent with the provisions of the EC Directive 84/466 Euratom and includes specific training requirements and a core of knowledge as to the radiation protection of patients requisite for persons directing medical exposures.

1. Introductory notes

1.1 A bibliography is included at Section 7.

*Extracts from this document are reproduced by permission of the Department of Health and the Welsh Office.

Responsibility of the dental surgeon as an employer

1.2   Under the Health and Safety at Work Act, etc, 1974 a dental surgeon has the same general responsibility as other employers for ensuring the safety, health and welfare at work of their employees and others who may be affected by his work activities.

In dentistry the employer may be the principal of a practice, a group of partners, a self-employed person such as a partner in a group practice, a registered company carrying on the business of dentistry, a National Health Service Health Authority or Board, or a visiting contractor.

The particular responsibility for providing protective measures in respect of ionising radiations is derived from the Regulations and the Approved Code of Practice. Although failure to comply with any provision of the Approved Code of Practice is not in itself an offence, such a failure may be used in criminal proceedings as evidence that a person has contravened a Regulation to which the provision relates. In such an event, however, it will be open to that person to satisfy the court that he has complied with the Regulation in some other way.

Radiation Protection Adviser

1.3   The Regulations require an employer to appoint a Radiation Protection Adviser for the purpose of advising with regard to the observance of the Regulations and other health and safety matters in connection with ionising radiation. The person appointed must be suitably qualified and experienced and the appointment notified to and acknowledged by the Health and Safety Executive.

Exemption from the appointment of a Radiation Protection Adviser

1.4   An Exemption from the appointment of a Radiation Protection Adviser (RPA) has been granted by the Health and Safety Executive (Certificate of Exemption No.1 1986) in respect of general dental practice and applies when the following conditions are met:

(i)   only the person undergoing a medical exposure enters a controlled area;
(ii) no employee is exposed to an instantaneous dose rate exceeding $7.5\,\mu Sv\,h^{-1}$ (microsieverts per hour) (see paragraph 4.4);
(iii) the limitations and conditions of use in Part I, paragraph 60 of the Approved Code of Practice are complied with; and
(iv) the X-ray equipment is properly maintained.

However, this exemption only covers the operation of standard dental X-ray units when taking intra-oral and oblique jaw views and of panoramic X-ray units using intra-oral and extra oral sources. Cephalometry should not be undertaken without the advice of a RPA.

A dental practitioner will need to appoint a RPA if any persons other than those undergoing a medical exposure enter a controlled area, or employees are exposed to an instantaneous dose rate exceeding $7.5\,\mu Sv\,h^{-1}$. Advice regarding the implications of this will be obtained from a radiation survey.

Appointment of a Radiation Protection Supervisor

1.5   The employer shall appoint a suitably qualified and trained person from within the practice to act as Radiation Protection Supervisor (RPS). The name of the person appointed should be displayed in the area for which he is responsible and in the Local Rules. The duties of the RPS are set out in Section 2.

Local Rules

1.6   Every employer who undertakes work with ionising radiation shall make and set down in writing Local Rules for the purpose of enabling the work with ionising radiation to be carried out in compliance with the Regulations and shall ensure that such of those rules as are relevant are brought to the attention of employees and other persons who may be affected by them.

2. Duties of the Radiation Protection Supervisor

2.1 A Radiation Protection Supervisor (RPS) shall be appointed in each dental practice to play a supervisory role in assisting the employer to comply with the requirements of the Regulations. The person appointed should be directly involved with the work with ionising radiations preferably in a position that will allow him to exercise close supervision and ensure that the work is done in accordance with the Local Rules. Although he need not be present at all times, in the absence of the RPS adequate supervision must be maintained.

2.2 No person should be appointed as a RPS unless he:

(i) knows and understands the requirements of the Regulations and Local Rules as they affect the work he supervises;
(ii) commands sufficient respect from the people doing the work as will allow him to exercise the necessary supervision of radiation protection;
(iii) understands the necessary precautions to be taken in the work which is being done and the extent to which these precautions will restrict exposure.

2.3 The RPS should normally be a dentally qualified member of the practice.

2.4 The employer carries the ultimate responsibility for compliance with the Regulations. This cannot be delegated to the RPS.

3. Summary of basic rules to minimise radiation dose in dental practice

3.1 Primary considerations

3.1.1 Only X-ray a patient if clinically necessary.

3.1.2 The RPS shall ensure that all staff understand and observe the Local Rules.

3.1.3 Only a trained and competent operator should use the X-ray equipment.

3.2 Equipment

3.2.1 Ensure that the equipment is of adequate tube rating – not lower than 50 kV and preferably about 70 kV.

3.2.2 The beam diameter should not exceed 60 mm measured at the patient end of the cone.

3.2.3 Ensure correct beam filtration: equivalent to at least 1.5 mm of aluminium for X-ray tube voltages up to and including 70 kV and 2.5 mm of aluminium (of which 1.5 mm is permanent) for X-ray tube voltages above 70 kV.

3.2.4 Ensure that the equipment is regularly checked and properly maintained.

3.2.5 If a fault in the equipment occurs it should be disconnected and the RPS notified.

3.3 Films and film holders

3.3.1 Use the minimum number of films consistent with adequate diagnosis.

3.3.2 Use the fastest film available consistent with good film quality. Intensifying screens must be used for extra oral and vertex occlusal views.

3.3.3 A film holder should be used if possible. The operator should never hold the film, the patient or the tube housing during exposure.

3.4 Operating technique

3.4.1 Persons whose presence is unnecessary for the examination should be excluded from the X-ray room.

3.4.2 The operator must stand outside the controlled area. This will be achieved by being at least 2.0 m from the tube and the patient, and being outside the primary beam.

3.4.3 Ensure that the exposure is correctly set and a minimum exposure time is used.

3.4.4 Ensure that the exposure is properly terminated – observe the warning signals.

3.4.5 Where it is likely that a foetus will be irradiated by the primary beam a protective apron should be used.

3.4.6 Personal monitoring of staff should be carried out if their individual workload exceeds 150 intra-oral or 50 panoral films per week.

3.4.7 Disconnect the X-ray unit from the mains supply after use in order to de-designate the controlled area and to eliminate the possibility of an inadvertent exposure.

3.4.8 All films should be correctly processed.

3.4.9 Routine checks should be made to detect if any deterioration in the quality of radiographs occurs.

3.4.10 In cases of accidental over-exposure the recommended procedures must be followed. See Local Rules.

4. The selection of equipment and accessories

Standards of X-ray equipment and accessories

4.1 Dental X-ray equipment should conform with the requirements of the Ionising Radiations Regulations 1985, The Approved Code of Practice and the detailed guidance in Chapter 6 of 'Guidance notes for the protection of persons against ionising radiations arising from medical and dental use'.

(i) Tube voltage: should not be lower than 50 kV and preferably should be about 70 kV for intra oral radiography.

(ii) Beam size: the beam diameter should not exceed 60 mm measured at the patient end of the cone.

(iii) Beam filtration: the total filtration of the beam should be equivalent to not less than: (a) 1.5 mm aluminium for voltages up to and including 70 kV, (b) 2.5 mm aluminium (of which 1.5 mm is permanent) for voltages above 70 kV. The use of significantly greater filtration may be undesirable. The total amount of filtration should be marked on the tube housing.

(iv) Distance control: field defining spacer cones should ensure a focal spot to skin distance of not less than 200 mm for equipment operating above 60 kV and not less than 100 mm for equipment operating at lower voltages.

(v) Nominal focal spot position should be marked on the tube head.

(vi) Signals and warning lights: these should coincide with 'mains on' and exposure as appropriate. If faulty the equipment should be disconnected until repaired.

(vii) Fast film: the fastest available films consistent with satisfactory diagnostic results should be used.

(viii) Intensifying screens: should be used for all extra oral and vertex occlusal views. The films should be compatible with the particular intensifying screen. Whenever practicable rare earth intensifying screens should be used.

Installation

4.2 Equipment must be installed in compliance with British Standards.

Maintenance

4.3 Equipment should be checked and maintained in accordance with the manufacturer's directions. A record of maintenance including any defects found and their repair should be kept for each item of X-ray equipment.

Radiation survey

4.4 A radiation safety assessment of all X-ray equipment must be carried out by a competent authority at intervals not exceeding three years. Any recommendations made as a result of this assessment shall be implemented within 3 months. (The radiation survey will be used to define the area where the instantaneous dose rate exceeds $7.5\,\mu\text{Sv}\,\text{h}^{-1}$.) (See paragraph 1.4.)

Electrical and mechanical faults

4.5 In cases of faulty warning lights, faulty timers or other electrical faults the equipment should be disconnected from the supply and not used again until checked and repaired if necessary.

Care of protective aprons

4.6 Protective aprons should have a minimum lead equivalent of 0.25 mm and comply with British Standard 5783. Aprons should not be folded when not in use and should be thoroughly examined at least every 14 months to ensure that the protection afforded has not been impaired.

5. Other matters relating to dental radiography

X-ray room and environment

5.1 (i)   Room size: should be large enough to provide safe accommodation for those persons who have to be in the room during exposure. This will be achieved if there is sufficient space to allow the operator to be 2.0 m or further from the tube and patient and well outside the primary beam.

(ii) Additional protective panels: these may be required if the work load exceeds 150 mA min per week for panoramic films or 30 mA min per week for intra-oral films. This is roughly equivalent to 50 panoramic or 300 intra-oral films.

(iii) A dental surgery or any other room should not be used for other work (or as a passageway) whilst radiography is in progress.

(iv) Radiation warning sign: if the room door opens directly into an area where the instantaneous dose rate is greater than $7.5\,\mu\text{Sv}\,\text{h}^{-1}$ a radiation warning sign should be displayed.

(v)   Automatic warning signal: if the controlled area extends to the room entrance an automatic warning signal indicating emission of radiation is required to warn against entry.

(vi) Persons in all occupied areas outside the X-ray room should be adequately protected.

Routine dental radiography

5.2 (i)   Training and competence: a person clinically or physically directing an exposure shall have received adequate training. ('Clinically directing' means having a clinical responsibility for the decision to effect an exposure. 'Physically directing' means effecting the exposure.)

(ii) Where it is necessary to support a small child or handicapped patient the advice of a RPA must be sought.

(iii) Where a film holder cannot be used and the patient is unable to hold the film, a person assisting must observe adequate protective measures in accordance with advice of a RPA.

(iv) Exposure values should be checked before using the X-ray machine, particularly if changing between long and short cone techniques.

(v) Attenuation of beam: since the beam is not fully absorbed by the patient it should be considered as extending beyond the patient until it has been attenuated by distance or intercepted by shielding such as a brick wall.

Panoramic radiography

5.3 (i) Automatic warning signal: where the controlled area extends to the entrance of the X-ray room an automatic warning signal indicating when the equipment is in the 'ready state' and while radiation is being emitted should be provided at the room entrance.

(ii) Rotation faults: the irradiation switch should be released immediately if the rotational movement fails to start or stops before the full arc is covered.

Cephalometry

5.4 (i) Cephalometry should not be carried out without prior consultation with a RPA.

(ii) Ordinary dental X-ray equipment operating at less than 60 kV should never be used for cephalometry. Equipment operating at or above 60 kV may be suitable if used with specially designed auxiliary equipment.

6. Processing techniques

6.1 Correctly exposed radiographs can only be achieved using the appropriate exposure setting and complete development.

6.2 Strict attention should be paid to correct and consistent film processing so as to produce good quality radiographs and to avoid the necessity for examinations to be repeated.

6.3 It is essential to avoid over-exposure as a means of compensating for under-development.

6.4 In the event of any deterioration in film quality a review of the processing conditions shall be undertaken. If such a review does not resolve the problem then the X-ray unit must be checked. An on-going quality assurance programme is advisable (see paragraph 7.6).

6.5 Basic darkroom equipment must include a suitable thermometer, an accurate timer and safelights appropriate for the film in use. All items should be checked periodically.

6.6 The temperature of the developer should be checked prior to film processing and the temperature development time adjusted in accordance with the manufacturer's instructions.

6.7 The developer should be changed at least once per month.

6.8 Where automatic processors are used an appropriate quality assurance programme is advisable (see paragraph 7.6).

7. Bibliography and references

7.1 Health and Safety at Work, etc, Act. 1974, HMSO, London.

7.2 The Ionising Radiations Regulations 1985 (S.I. 1985 No. 1333), HMSO, London.

7.3   Approved Code of Practice: The protection of persons against ionising radiation arising from any work activity. The Ionising Radiation Regulations 1985. HMSO, London.

7.4   Guidance notes for the protection of persons against ionising radiations arising from medical and dental use, HMSO, London.

7.5   The Ionising Radiation (Protection of persons undergoing Medical Examination or Treatment) Regulations 1988 (S.I. 1988 No. 778), HMSO, London.

7.6   Quality assurance: Thorogood, J., Horner, K., Smith, N.J.D. Quality Control in the processing of dental radiographs. A practical guide to sensitometry. *B.D.J.* **164**: 282–287 (1988).

Address
National Radiological Protection Board, Northern Centre, Hospital Lane, Cookridge, Leeds LS16 6RW. Telephone: 0532 679041

Guidance for clinical health care workers: protection against infection with HIV and hepatitis viruses

Recommendations of the Expert Advisory Group on AIDS, January 1990*

1. Introduction

1.1 Scope of this and other relevant guidance

1.1.1   This booklet provides guidance from the UK Health Departments on measures for the protection of health care workers† in hospital and the community against occupational infection with human immunodeficiency viruses (HIV) and hepatitis viruses. The guidance is based largely on the advice of a working group reporting to the Expert Advisory Group on AIDS (EAGA) and also draws on work done by the Advisory Committee on Dangerous Pathogens (ACDP), the Advisory Group on Hepatitis and the Microbiology Advisory Committee. It is concerned principally with personnel engaged in direct clinical contact with patients although the underlying principles may be used as a basis for drawing up guidelines for those in allied occupations, e.g. persons dealing with contaminated equipment. In addition, it contains some advice on disposal of clinical waste, and labelling and transport of specimens which has implications for the safety of other staff including voluntary workers. Although this guidance has been drawn up for the protection of health care workers, it is emphasised that adherence to the recommendations will also provide protection for patients from cross infection.

1.1.2   The advice in this booklet supersedes some of the advice previously issued by the UK Health Departments on this topic (see annex 2). It is designed to be read in conjunction with the guidance listed in annex 1 which includes that issued by the Health Services Advisory Committee (HSAC) and the Joint Committee on Vaccination and Immunisation (JCVI). **It remains the responsibility of health authorities to draw up their own detailed local guidelines for staff on prevention of spread of HIV and hepatitis viruses.** All employers (including independent contractors) have a legal obligation under the Health and Safety at Work etc. Act 1974 to ensure that all their employees are appropriately trained and proficient in the procedures necessary for working safety and they have a responsibility to protect voluntary workers. Furthermore, employers are required by the Control of Substances Hazardous to Health (COSHH) Regulations 1988, enforced on 1 October 1989, to review every procedure carried out by their employees which involves contact with a substance, hazardous to health, including pathogenic micro-organisms.

*Extracts from this document are reproduced by permission of the Controller of Her Majesty's Stationery Office. © Crown copyright 1990.

†In this context the term 'clinical health care workers' denotes any person (including students, trainees and voluntary workers) whose activities normally involve contact with patients' blood or other body fluids.

1.1.3 AIDS booklet 3 'Guide for Surgeons, Anaesthetists and Dentists and their teams in dealing with patients infected with HTLV III' was published in 1986. Since then, considerable knowledge has been acquired of the risks of transmission of HIV in the health care setting (see paras 1.3.1 and 1.3.2). Much of the knowledge derives from experience in the US where 107 308 cases of AIDS had been reported to the Centers for Disease Control (CDC) by 12 October 1989. Careful consideration has been given to the guidelines for protection of health care staff drawn up by CDC and published in their Morbidity and Mortality Weekly Report (MMWR) series.

1.1.4 'Guidance for health care personnel dealing with patients infected with hepatitis B virus (HBV)' was issued by the Health Departments in December 1984 (annex 2). However, there are practical advantages in adopting common infection control policies for prevention of transmission of both HIV and blood-borne hepatitis viruses. The present document has been drawn up to cover HBV, blood-borne, non-A non-B hepatitis, and delta hepatitis and should be regarded as superseding the above.

1.1.5 In August 1987, CDC published a MMWR supplement in which the use of 'Universal precautions' was recommended. Briefly, it advised that all patients be regarded as potentially infected with HIV and/or other blood-borne pathogens and 'all health care workers should routinely use appropriate barrier precautions to prevent skin and mucous membrane exposure when contact with blood or other body fluids of any patient is anticipated.' This guidance was amended and clarified in June 1988 in response to requests from health care professionals. Universal precautions were still recommended for blood and certain other body fluids but it was emphasised that they were unnecessary when dealing with faeces, nasal secretions, saliva except in dentistry, sputum, sweat, tears, urine and vomitus unless they contain visible blood. It also provided more information on the use of protective barriers and the circumstances in which gloves might be used for phlebotomy. In terms of recommended practice, the guidance in this report is based on the same principles as the expanded CDC guidelines.

1.2 Underlying principles

1.2.1 These guidelines are based on the following underlying principles:

(i) in general, occupational risks of transmission of HIV and hepatitis viruses to health care workers arise from the possibility of their being accidentally inoculated with blood (or exceptionally certain other body fluids – see 1.2.3 below) from an infected patient;
(ii) it is not possible to identify all patients who may be infected. Not only would it be impractical to subject all patients to an infection screen, but even if screened, those who have not yet seroconverted to HIV, and those with non-A non-B hepatitis for which no test is routinely available, would remain undetected as would patients with some other blood-borne infections;
(iii) The risk of acquiring infection with HIV or hepatitis viruses in the health care setting is proportional to the prevalence of these infections in the population served and the chance of inoculation accidents occurring during the procedures undertaken.

1.2.2 The first two principles above indicate a primary requirement for blood to be handled in a uniform manner which conforms to a standard which must be practicable for all patients. However, the third principles requires that an assessment of the need for any additional precautions be based on: the risk of operator 'exposure'* to blood associated with any individual procedure; the prevalence of HIV and hepatitis infection in the population served; and for some procedures the known or suspected infectious status of the individual patient. In the past, such assessments have commonly been the basis of decisions on whether staff should receive HBV vaccine.

---

*Where the term 'exposure' is used it should be taken to refer to needlestick or other percutaneous exposures to, or contamination of mucous membrane, conjunctiva or broken skin with, blood or blood stained body fluids.

Body fluids etc. which should be handled with the same precautions as blood:

1. Cerebrospinal fluid
   Peritoneal fluid
   Pleural fluid
   Pericardial fluid
   Amniotic fluid
   Semen
   Vaginal secretions
2. Any other body fluid containing visible blood
3. Saliva in association with dentistry

1.3 Transmission of HIV and hepatitis viruses

1.3.1 *Transmission of HIV infection.* HIV has been isolated from blood, semen, vaginal secretions, saliva, tears, urine, breastmilk, cerebrospinal, synovial and amniotic fluids. However, only blood, blood products, semen, vaginal secretions, donor organs and tissues and breastmilk have been implicated in the transmission of infection. There is good evidence from studies of household contacts of infected people, that HIV is not spread by close social contact even when this is extended, as in a family setting over long periods. There is no evidence for faecal-oral or airborne spread of HIV, nor for transmission by saliva. It is theoretically possible that the virus could be transmitted across intact mucous membranes or the conjunctiva, but like hepatitis B (see below) it appears most improbable that HIV could penetrate intact skin.

The known means of spread of HIV are:

- by unprotected penetrative sexual intercourse with an infected person (between men or between man and woman);
- by inoculation of infected blood. At present in the UK this mainly results from drug users sharing infected injecting equipment;
- from an infected mother to her baby before or during birth or via breastfeeding.

1.3.2 *Transmission of HIV in the health care setting.* Information concerning the risk of HIV transmission in the health care setting, derives from case reports in the scientific literature and the results of surveillance studies in the UK and North America. These reports and studies reveal that needlestick injuries predominate as a cause of occupationally acquired HIV infection. Furthermore, the surveillance studies provide evidence that HIV is not easily transmitted in the clinical health care setting. In the US CDC Surveillance project the risk of acquiring HIV infection as a result of a single 'sharps'* injury involving blood from a known HIV infected patient was less than 0.5%. This compares with a risk of hepatitis B virus transmission under parallel circumstances of the order of 20% (see 1.3.4 below).

1.3.3 *Transmission of viral hepatitis.* The term 'viral hepatitis' covers infection by various different viruses of which hepatitis B virus (HBV) has attracted the most concern in the health care setting. A useful classification is:

(i)   Viral hepatitis A
(ii) Viral hepatitis B
(iii) Viral hepatitis non-A non-B
(iv) Other, e.g. delta hepatitis.

(i) Hepatitis A is spread by the faecal-oral route and outbreaks result most frequently from faecal contamination of drinking water and food. Control measures are therefore the same

---

*'Sharps' in this context means needles, edged instruments, broken glassware or any other item which may be contaminated in use by blood or body fluids and which may cause laceration or puncture wounds.

as for other organisms transmitted by this route and it is outside the scope of these guidelines.

(ii) Hepatitis B is caused by the hepatitis B virus (HBV). Hepatitis B surface antigen (HBsAg) may be found in virtually all body secretions and excretions of patients with acute hepatitis B and carriers of the virus (see below) but blood, semen and vaginal fluids are mainly implicated in the transmission of infection. Transmission of HBV by human bite has been reported but saliva has not otherwise been demonstrated to be infectious through natural routes. Hepatitis B is also transmitted perinatally at or about the time of birth.

In the UK, the annual incidence of acute hepatitis B from 1985 to 1988 was 4 per 100 000 adult males and 2 per 100 000 adult females. This is an underestimate of the rate of infection since some infected people do not develop symptomatic disease.

A potentially infective carrier state (a person who is HBsAg positive for more than 6 months) develops in 5–10% of adults infected with HBV in the UK and it is estimated that the prevalence in the general adult population is about one in 500. Of these, 5–10% have persistent 'e' antigenaemia (HBeAg) which correlates with a high level of viral replication and heightened infectivity (high risk carrier). The incidence of HBV infection in some parts of Africa and in the Far East, greatly exceeds that in the UK as does the proportion of infected people from those areas in whom HBeAg persists. Moreover, there is an increased likelihood of persistent antigenaemia in those infected in early life. A patient who is in the early prodromal or acute phase of hepatitis B should also be considered 'high risk' from the point of view of risk of transmission of infection.

(iii) Non-A and non-B hepatitis (NANBH) is currently diagnosed by excluding other known causes of viral hepatitis. It accounts for some 90 per cent of cases of post-transfusion hepatitis in countries where all blood is screend for HBsAg. Epidemiologically, at least two forms of NANBH have been described. A diagnostic test for one type (now known as Hepatitis C) has recently been developed and is undergoing evaluation.

An epidemic form of NANBH which is spread by water or close personal contact is outside the scope of this guidance.

(iv) Delta hepatitis is caused by a defective transmissible virus, the hepatitis D virus or delta agent, which requires multiplication of the hepatitis B virus for its own replication. Super-infection with hepatitis D virus in a HBsAg carrier is often associated with more severe liver disease. The method of transmission of the hepatitis D virus is similar to that of hepatitis B and infection occurs especially in parenteral drug misusers and those who have multiple transfusions.

1.3.4 *Transmission of HBV in the health care setting.* The most common and important method of transmission to health care personnel is by the direct percutaneous inoculation of infected blood by needle or other sharp instrument although it is possible for the infection to be spread via spillage or splashing of blood onto mucous membranes, conjunctiva or non-intact skin.

Studies of health care workers who have sustained inoculation accidents involving HBsAg positive blood indicate the risk of transmission to be approximately 20% where the potential source of infection is a 'high risk' patient or carrier. Most carriers can be classified as 'low risk' where blood contains antibody to the 'e' antigen. The chance of transmission from these patients is approximately 0.1 per cent. Overall, the chance of transmission of infection is probably of the order of 5 per cent.

There is no evidence of transmission of HBV by inhalation of droplets, neither has faecal-oral transmission been demonstrated.

2. General counter infection measures for the clinical setting

2.1 Summary

2.1.1   This chapter provides general guidance on assessment of risks associated with clinical tasks and the level of precautions to be adopted for them. It can be used as a framework for the development of more detailed guidance for individual specialties. The chapter also contains advice on matters such as waste disposal which are common to all areas of practice.

2.1.2   It is emphasised that provision of guidelines must be accompanied by appropriate training (see 1.1.2 and 2.1.4). Training programmes should be organised to meet the needs of different staff groups especially those with high staff turnover. This is particularly important in specialties such as Accident and Emergency which are largely staffed by those in junior grades who are on short term contracts or on job rotations.

2.1.3   The primary measures for prevention of occupational 'exposure' to HIV and blood-borne hepatitis viruses in the health care setting are:

(i)   protection of existing wounds, skin lesions, conjunctivae and mucosal surfaces and the prevention of puncture wounds, cuts and abrasions in the presence of blood and body fluids;

(ii)   the application of simple protective measures designed to avoid contamination of the person or clothing with blood and good basic hygiene practices including regular hand washing;

(iii) control of work surface contamination by **blood** and body fluids by containment and disinfection;

(iv)   avoidance of sharps usage where possible but when their use is essential, the exercising of particular care in handling and disposal; and safe disposal of contaminated waste.

2.1.4   The successful implementation of these measures necessitates:

(i)   assessing the particular occupational risks and ensuring suitable measures are used to minimise exposures. This will include a consideration of the risks to others such as in the disposal of bodies, tissues, body fluids, contaminated consumables and sharps and in the maintenance of equipment;

Ways to avoid exposure to HIV and blood-borne hepatitis viruses in the health care setting:

1. Apply good basic hygiene practices with regular hand washing.
2. Cover existing wounds or skin lesions with waterproof dressings.
3. Take simple protective measures to avoid contamination of person and clothing with blood.
4. Protect mucous membrane of eyes, mouth and nose from blood splashes.
5. Prevent puncture wounds, cuts and abrasions in the presence of blood.
6. Avoid sharps usage wherever possible.
7. Institute a safe procedure for handling and disposal of sharps.
8. Clear up spillages of blood promptly and disinfect surfaces.
9. Institute a procedure for the safe disposal of contaminated waste.

Use of gloves

Gloves should be used to protect the health care worker in the following situations; the type of glove used (surgical, examination or household) will depend on the task.

1. All procedures in all patients where contamination of the health care worker with blood is probable, i.e. in categories A(i) and A(ii).
2. Venepuncture when
   • the venepuncturist is inexperienced
   • the patient is restless
   • the patient is known to be infected with HIV or blood-borne hepatitis viruses.
3. When cleaning equipment prior to sterilization or disinfection.
4. When handling chemical disinfectants.
5. When cleaning up spillages of blood.

(ii) devising safe, reasonably practicable procedures and routines for performing each task; ensuring they are followed and actively keeping them under review;

(iii) promoting an awareness of risks by providing information and training and

(iv) reviewing accidents in which an exposure occurs and considering how to prevent recurrences.

2.4 Guidance common to all areas of practice

2.4.1 Many accidental exposures to blood-borne pathogens result from failure to adhere to basic rules concerning decontamination, waste disposal etc. and the following general guidance should be drawn to the attention of **all staff** within their employment setting. Moreover, it is desirable for there to be a designated individual who has responsibility for ensuring that guidance on sterilization and disinfection and clinical waste disposal is adhered to. This is particularly important in order to protect third parties, often ancillary staff, from preventable exposure.

2.4.2 *Equipment and materials.* Wherever possible single use equipment and materials should be employed in clinical procedures. This is particularly important if a patient is known or suspected to be infected with HIV or hepatitis viruses. Any equipment which is to be reused and which has been employed for a procedure involving potential contact with a patient's blood must be sterilized or disinfected in accordance with the recommendations in annex 4. Such equipment includes items which may not necessarily be in direct contact with the patient, e.g. manual self inflating resuscitation bags and dental hand pieces. Reusable equipment must be of a type that is easily decontaminated without distortion or damage to its function and the manufacturers' instructions must be consulted to ensure compatibility of materials with the methods of decontamination employed.

When selecting suction and aspiration equipment, apparatus which will discharge directly into a waste outlet is to be preferred in order to reduce the potential for accidental spillage. High speed aspirators used for dentistry should exhaust externally in order to avoid the spread of potentially infectious material within the surgery.

2.4.3 *Decontamination.* Advice on sterilization and disinfection is available in annex 4 and in various of the publications listed in annex 1.

2.4.4 *Disposal of clinical waste (excluding sharps).* All waste which is contaminated with blood must be considered as potentially infective and treated as 'clinical waste'* in accordance with the NSAC's document 'The safe disposal of clinical waste' (see annex 1). Attention is drawn to the duties of the employer under the Health and Safety at Work etc. Act 1974 which extends to employees working in the home environment. Thus the employer must ensure that adequate arrangements are made for disposal of clinical waste in the community as well as in the hospital situation.

2.4.5 *Disposal of sharps.* **Surgical or other single use gloves cannot protect workers from sharps injuries**. This underlines the need for extreme care in both the use and disposal of sharps since the circumstances in which many such injuries are sustained are easily avoided. In particular, **other staff must not be put at risk by careless disposal of sharps** and all workers must be reminded of their responsibilities in this context.

Used needles must not be resheathed unless there is a safe means available for doing so. Needles should only be removed from syringes when essential, e.g. when transferring blood to a container and needle forceps or other suitable devices should be readily available. All disposable sharps must be promptly placed in a secure puncture-resistant bin suitable for incineration and which is sited out of reach of children. These bins must never be overfilled

*Clinical waste as defined in the NSAC document is considered to be 'waste arising from medical, nursing, dental, veterinary, pharmaceutical or similar practice, investigation, treatment, care, teaching or research which by nature of its toxic, infectious or dangerous content may prove a hazard or give offence unless previously rendered safe and inoffensive. Such waste includes human or animal tissue or excretions, drugs and medical products, swabs and dressings, instruments or similar substances and materials).

since used needles protruding from overloaded containers constitute a very significant hazard to those who have to handle them. The size of items to be disposed of in sharps bins will vary considerably and it is essential that bins of adequate capacity be provided. The Department of Health has a specification for sharps containers (see annex 1) and a British standard is in preparation. When syringes containing arterial blood are to be sent to the laboratory, needles must be removed and blind hubs attached to the syringes (HC (Hazard)(88) 16, annex 1). Intravascular guidewires and glass slides must be disposed of as sharps.

Non-disposable sharps should be placed in a suitable secure enclosure to await decontamination.

3. Management of accidental exposure to blood in the health care setting

3.1 General principles

3.1.1 Needlestick and other percutaneous exposures to blood in the health care setting are unnecessarily common at present. Many result from a failure to follow recommended procedures, the basic rules of hygiene and from careless disposal of waste (see 2.4.4). Strict adherence to this guidance should reduce the incidence of these exposures.

3.1.2 There will inevitably remain occasions where exposure occurs despite careful attention to the correct procedures. In managing such exposures the following should be borne in mind:

(i)   All available data point to a very low prevalance of hepatitis and HIV infection within the general UK population except for those people whose behaviour is recognised as high risk, or who have emigrated from an area with a known high prevalence of these infections.

(ii)   All documented cases of HIV transmission in the clinical health care setting have resulted from inoculation with blood through a sharps injury or through exposure of mucous membrane or non-intact skin to blood.

(iii) Surveillance studies of health care staff exposed to blood from known HIV infected patients show that the risk of seroconversion following a needlestick exposure is extremely low (of the order of 0.13–0.5%). This compares with a risk of acquiring hepatitis B virus from needlestick exposure to HBeAg which is estimated to be of the order of 20%.

(iv)   Although there is a low level of occupational risk of transmission of HIV, the consequences are serious. Moreover, the uncertainty of knowing whether one may have been infected may have a profound psychological effect.

(v)   Staff exposed accidentally to HBV infected blood should be offered post exposure prophylaxis where appropriate. The 1988 recommendations of the JCVI are attached in annex 6 for ease of reference. These were current at the time of publication of this guidance but reference to the most recent JCVI memorandum is recommended.

3.2 Sources of advice for staff

3.2.1 It is essential for every employer to both draw up a policy on the management of exposures and for each health authority to designate one or more doctors to whom health care staff may be referred immediately for advice if they have been exposed to potentially infected blood. Doctors in Occupational Health Departments should be considered for this role. (See also 3.3.3 below.) Independent contractors have a similar obligation to ensure that such procedures are available. If appropriate they should liaise with their local health authority in order to ensure that they are aware of to whom to refer themselves or their employees in the event of such exposure.

3.2.3 At present, there is no recognised effective means of post-exposure prophylaxis for those exposed to HIV infected blood. The PHLS Communicable Disease Surveillance Centre (CDSC) and Communicable Disease (Scotland) Unit (CD(S)U) are able to provide advice on sources of up-to-date information on the potential value of prophylactic treatment. The addresses and telephone numbers are given in annex 7.

3.3 Post-exposure procedure

3.3.1   When a health care worker is exposed to blood or blood contaminated body fluids the action taken should take account of the interests of both the worker and the source patient. The circumstances which led to the exposure should be identified and all possible steps taken to prevent repetition.

3.3.2   Immediately following any exposure, the site of exposure, i.e. wound or non-intact skin should be washed liberally with soap and water but without scrubbing. Exposed mucous membranes or conjunctivae should be irrigated copiously with water. If there has been a puncture would free bleeding should be encouraged but the wound should not be sucked.

3.3.3   Any incident must be reported promptly to the person designated to record such accidents. A full accident record must be prepared and preserved and the health care worker referred to the doctor previously designated by the health authority (see 3.2.1 above). Provision must be made for an appropriate person to be available outside normal working hours to advise and treat health care workers who sustain exposure to patients' blood. This person must be provided with a written version of the health authority's policy on management of exposures.

Annex 1   Other relevant guidance for health care workers produced by UK Health Departments and/or HSE

Avoidance of needlestick: sealing of arterial blood sample syringes. HC (HAZARD) (88) 16, September 1988.
AIDS: HIV-Infected Health Care Workers. HMSO, March 1988. ISBN 0 11 321140 6.
'AIDS Booklet 5'. AIDS and Skin piercing. November 1987.
Used sharps: disposal. SIB (87) 31, March 1987.
The safe disposal of clinical waste. HMSO, 1982. ISBN 0 11 883641 2.
Specification for containers for disposal of used needles and sharp instruments. DHSS, December 1982. TSS/S/330.015.

Copies of Department of Health Guidance can be obtained from: Health Publications Unit, No 2 Site, Heywood, Lancs OL10 2PZ.

Annex 2   Health Departments' publications containing advice for protection of health care workers and now superseded by this document

'AIDS Booklet 3'. Guidance for Surgeons, Anaesthetists, Dentists and their Teams in Dealing with Patients Infected with HTLV II. CMO (87)7, CDO (86) 1 April 1986; SHHD/CAMO (86)7; HSS (MD) 5/86; CMO (86)4; CDO (86)3.
Guidance for health care personnel dealing with patients infected with HBV. CMO (84)11; CNO (84)7. December 1984.

Annex 3   Protective clothing for use in the clinical health care setting

1.   This annex contains notes on various items of protective clothing. It is a field in which there is considerable continuing research and development and therefore this guidance is not fully prescriptive. Employers must ensure that they maintain awareness of new developments through liaison with suppliers and manufacturers and that views of relevant health care workers are taken into account when local ordering policies are formulated. In addition theoretical specifications may need to be counter balanced by practical considerations notably those of restriction of the wearer's activity and comfort.

   Protective clothing should be designed for single use or be made of materials which will withstand autoclaving or, failing that, disinfection as specified in annex 4.

Information on gloves and textile items may be obtained from DH Procurement Directorate (01-636 6811, Extension 3128).

2. Gloves

Surgeons gloves should conform to British Standard 4005.

DH has recently compiled a purchasing standard for non-sterile latex examination gloves (see annex 2), intended for use when conducting medical examinations, diagnostic and therapeutic procedures. A standard for sterile examination gloves is in preparation. In the event of users being unable to wear latex examination gloves, because of an allergic reaction for example, then either plastic or vinyl should be worn for which a purchasing standard is also in preparation.

Long latex gloves of a surgical standard are available which, if sterilized, would be suitable for tasks such as manual removal of the placenta.

3. Gowns

There are several waterproof fabrics with the ability to 'breathe' available for use and which are comfortable to wear. Research into new fabrics capable of repeated laundering is ongoing. Surgical gowns with waterproof bibs and sleeves can be made to specification on special order.

4. Protective headwear

Headware in common use by operating theatre personnel does not offer complete protection against contamination by blood splashes. Protective hoods are available as an integral part of gowns currently used by orthopaedic surgeons.

5. Aprons

Where waterproof aprons are worn for procedures where there is likely to be considerable dissemination of blood it is essential that the aprons are of sufficient length to overlap with protective footwear (see below). This is especially important for procedures carried out in the lithotomy position since it is common for blood accumulating in the worker's lap to be channelled down into boots.

6. Eye wear

Various forms of combined eye and face protection are available. Guidance on the choice of eye wear is given in BS 7028: 1988 British Standard Guide for the selection, use and maintenance of eye protection for industrial and other uses. BS 2092 1987 lays down requirements for eye protectors for industrial and non-industrial uses although the applications are mainly for industrial purposes.

The basic requirement is to give complete coverage of the eyes for health care workers when splashing of blood is likely to occur. If this risk is high, it is preferable to use disposable eye protectors, otherwise personal eye protectors may be worn. These can, if necessary be made to prescription. They should include, as a minimum, fixed eye cups and must be surface cleaned and disinfected if contaminated.

7. Footwear

Fenestrated footwear must never be worn in situations where sharps are handled. For tasks involving likely dissemination of blood it is recommended that wellington boots or calf length plastic overboots are worn rather than shoes or clogs. The need for footwear to be adequately decontaminated after use has already been stressed (paragraph 2.3.1).

Annex 4   Decontamination methods

1. General principles

(i) In clinical practice, contaminated equipment, clothing etc. may harbour a wide range of micro-organisms of varying susceptibility to inactivation. Sterilization inactivates even resistant bacterial endospores. The disinfection methods recommended here may not inactivate resistant spores but should be adequate to inactivate the range of organisms likely to be encountered. Thus although the following guidance deals specifically with HIV and HBV it is emphasised that other pathogens may be present and sterilization by heat is the preferred method of decontamination. Sterile instruments must be used to penetrate skin and to enter normally sterile body areas.

(ii) In **all** cases, thorough cleaning must precede sterilization of disinfection of instruments or equipment. Workers undertaking this should wear suitable protective clothing including household gloves.

(iii) Manufacturers' instructions must be consulted on compatibility of materials with the method of sterilization or disinfection preferred. Equipment used for sterilization or disinfection must be commissioned on installation, regularly served and maintained and tested in accordance with the manufacturers' instructions and Department of Health Advice (see HEI 185 annex 2).

2. Sterilisation

HIV and Hepatitis viruses are susceptible to heat. **Wherever possible** equipment must be sterilised by conventional procedures employing moist or dry heat (see HEI 88, 1980, annex 1). The highest sterilising temperature compatible with the equipment to be sterilised should be used. Recommended minimum temperatures and hold times for achieving sterility in steam sterilisers are 134°C for 3 minutes, or 126°C for 10 minutes, or 121°C for 15 minutes, or 115°C for 30 minutes. The correct use of hot air sterilisers requires the load to achieve and maintain a temperature of either 180°C for 30 minutes or 160°C for one hour. Whichever method is in use the recommended temperature must be achieved within the load to ensure sterilisation and thus adequate time must be allowed for the goods under treatment to heat up before timing starts. Manufactuers' instructions for effective and safe use of steam and hot air sterilisers must be followed.

3. Disinfection – physical methods

Viruses may be inactivated by immersion in boiling water although it is stressed that boiling cannot be relied upon to inactivate bacterial spores. If boiling is employed, cleaned instruments should be completely immersed in water at 100°C and any air bubbles dislodged. The water should be allowed to reboil and the item left for a minimum of 5 minutes. A purpose made instrument boiler should be used. This should incorporate an electrically heated unit, a hinged lid and a perforated shelf for raising and lowering instruments. The water should be removed at the end of each day and the boiler left empty until re-used.

4. Disinfection – chemical methods

For heat labile articles and surfaces which cannot be sterilised or boiled it will be necessary to employ methods of chemical disinfection. The use of chemical agents is restricted by many factors, including their variable effects on different micro-organisms, incompatibility with various surfaces (including, in many cases corrosive properties), reduced efficacy in the presence of organic matter, susceptibility to deterioration with storage and toxic potential. Chemical disinfection must only be undertaken in the absence of a satisfactory alternative. Recommendation of disinfectants for the purpose of inactivation of HIV and hepatitis viruses is restricted by lack of adequate data for many chemical agents. Although various publications have claimed efficacy against HIV for a wide range of disinfectants and detergents, the evidence for some claims is equivocal. Furthermore, in any clinical situation where it may be necessary to inactivate HIV it will also be necessary to inactivate HBV which is generally regarded as more resistant.

The methodology for evaluating the activity of compounds against HIV and hepatitis viruses is complex, not least because of the need to simulate 'real life' conditions where organic contamination is likely to be present. Research in this field is on-going but, pending publication of further results the following agents should be used for disinfection:

(i) *Hypochlorite*. Fresh aqueous solutions of sodium hypochlorite (bleach) or sodium dichloroisocyanurate tablets or granules are recommended for general surface disinfection. For cleaning surfaces contaminated with blood and for mopping up blood spillages the concentration used must be equivalent to 10 000 parts per million (ppm) available chlorine. In general this corresponds to a 1:10 dilution of household bleach but it is emphasised that the strength of individual proprietary brands of bleach may vary and that hypochlorite may deteriorate on storage. Granular sodium dichloroisocyanurate may be used to disinfect blood spillages (see below). Hypochlorite has the disadvantage of being corrosive to metals and of bleaching fabrics.

(ii) *Glutaraldehyde*. For non-corrosive disinfection of delicate items such as fibreoptic endoscopes freshly activated 2% alkaline glutaraldehyde may be employed following thorough washing. Endoscopes which will enter sterile body cavities must be immersed for a minimum of 3 hours and other endoscopes for a minimum of 30 minutes or one hour if the presence of *Mycobacterium tuberculosis* is suspected. Glutaraldehyde has irritant and sensitising properties and must be handled with great care.

(iii) *Alcohol*. Alcohol is not recommended for disinfecting the surfaces of equipment or work-benches. It should only be used as a final choice for materials which are incompatible with the above disinfectants. In these cases the items should be immersed in 70% Isopropanol or Industrial Methylated Spirits for a minimum of one hour.

5. Cleaning work surfaces

It is recommended that work surfaces liable to become contaminated are covered with sterilisable trays or disposable impermeable coverings. In either case, the covering must be changed at the end of each procedure and the underlying surface cleaned using a solution of 1000 ppm available chlorine. Any blood contamination of the surface must be cleaned and disinfected with a solution containing 10 000 ppm available chlorine (see above).

6. Spillages

If blood is spilled – either from a container or as a result of an operative procedure – the spillage should be dealt with as soon as possible. The spilled blood should be completely covered, either by sodium dichloroisocyanurate granules or by disposable towels which are then treated with 10 000 ppm sodium hypochlorite solution. A few minutes must elapse before the towels etc. are cleared and disposed of as clinical waste. The worker who deals with the spillage must wear appropriate protective clothing. This will include household gloves and a disposable apron and, in the case of extensive floor spillages protective footwear (see annex 3).

7. Further information

More detailed guidance on various aspects of decontamination is available in various of the documents listed in annex 1. In addition, comprehensive guidance on control of infection measures, particularly in primary care situations, has been published by the British Medical Association (see annex 5).

Annex 5   Guidance on infection control issued by professional associations

This list is provided for information; inclusion in the list should not be taken as necessarily implying that the guidance is endorsed by the UK Health Departments.

AIDS and Hepatitis B. Guidelines for Anaesthetists. Association of Anaesthetists. April 1988.
Guidance to blood borne viruses and the control of cross infection in dentistry. British Dental Association. 1986 (under revision).

Professional ethical guidance
Duties of Dentists Infected with Human Immunodeficiency Virus (HIV) or Suffering from AIDS. General Dental Council. January 1988.

Annex 6   Recommendations of Joint Committee on Vaccination and Immunisation on Hepatitis B Immunisation and Post Exposure Prophylaxis [Extracts from pages 70–77 and 114–115 of 'Immunisation against Infectious Disease. HMSO, 1988. ISBN 0 11 321136 8]

Hepatitis B immunisation for health care workers

1. Vaccination should be considered for the individuals listed in paragraph 5 below. It should be offered to those at highest risk although this list should not be regarded as exclusive. Screening for antibiodies prior to vaccination may be considered in a population where the antibody prevalence is expected to be high.

2. Immunisation takes up to six months to confer adequate protection. This should be kept in mind when considering the need for individuals to have the vaccine. It is especially relevant in the case of new students and trainees.
   Note: It is important that vaccination against hepatitis B does not encourage relaxation of good infection-control procedures. The vaccination does not prevent cross-infection with hepatitis B or protect against other blood-borne diseases such as HIV.

3. The vaccine should not be given to individuals known to be hepatitis B surface antigen (or antibody) positive, or to patients with acute hepatitis B, since in the former case it would be unnecessary and, in the latter, ineffective. Intimate contacts of individuals suffering from acute hepatitis B should be treated by passive immunisation (see para 11) followed by active immunisation (this should be commenced simultaneously).

4. Hepatitis B vaccine may be given to HIV positive individuals.

5. Doctors, dentists, nurses, midwives and others, including students and trainees, who have direct contact with patients or their body fluids, or are likely to experience frequent parenteral exposure to blood or blood-contaminated secretions and excretions should be considered for vaccination. Groups at highest risk in this category are:

1. Those health care personnel and others who are at risk because they are or may be directly involved in patient care in institutions or units for the mentally handicapped over a period of 6 months or more.
2. Those working in units treating known carriers of hepatitis B infection who are at risk because they are or may be directly involved in patient care over a period of 6 months or more.
3. Laboratory workers, mortuary technicians.
4. Health care personnel on secondment to work in areas of the world with a high prevalence of hepatitis B infection, if they are to be directly involved in patient care.

6. *Management of accidental inoculations.* In the event of accidental inoculation with infectious material from a patient with hepatitis B, health-care workers should be offered combined active immunisation with hepatitis B vaccine and passive immunisation with

hepatitis B immunoglobulin. If they have already been successfully vaccinated, they should be given a booster dose of vaccine unless they are known to have adequate protective levels of antibodies (see also para 11).

7. *Vaccine supplies.* The following hepatitis B vaccines are available:

H-B-Vax   Merck Sharp and Dohme 0992 467272
Engerix B   Smith Kline and French 0707 325111

The vaccine is effective in preventing infection in individuals who produce specific antibodies. Ten to fifteen per cent of those over the age of 40 do not respond; a smaller proportion of younger people are non-responsive and, overall, the vaccine is about 90% effective. Where it is thought necessary, post-vaccination screening for antibody response can best be done 2–4 months after the course of injections.

Non-responders should be considered for a booster dose but, as even then the response is likely to be poor, hepatitis B immunoglobulin (HBIG) may be necessary for protection if exposure to infection occurs. Patients who are immunodeficient or on immunosuppressive therapy may respond less well than healthy individuals and may require larger doses of vaccine or an additional dose.

The duration of immunity is not precisely known but is of the order of three to five years. Advice on the need for further booster doses cannot yet be formulated, but individuals who are at high risk may wish to determine their antibody level periodically. If this falls below 10 mIU/ml the need for a booster dose should be considered.

8. *Recommended dosage for primary immunisation.* The basic immunisation regimen consists of three doses of vaccine, with the first dose at the elected date, the second dose one month later and the third dose at six months after the first dose.

The recombinant vaccine has also been used where more rapid immunisation is required, for example with travellers when the third dose may be given at 2 months after the initial dose with a booster dose at twelve months.

The vaccine should normally be given intramuscularly. The injection should be given in the deltoid region, though the anterolateral thigh is the preferred site for infants. The buttock should not be used because vaccine efficacy may be reduced.

9. *Dosage schedule.* The dose is the same for each of the 3 injections. Adults and children over 10 years:

1.0 ml intramuscularly (20 micrograms)
0.1 ml intradermally (2 micrograms)

10. *Adverse reactions.* Adverse reactions to hepatitis B vaccine observed to date have been generally limited to soreness and redness at the injection site if given intramuscularly.

Injection intradermally may produce a persisting nodule at the site of the injection, sometimes with local pigmentation changes.

It is important that adverse reactions should be reported to the Committee on Safety of Medicines by the yellow card system.

Post-exposure prophylaxis: hepatitis B immunoglobulin (HBIG)

11. A specific immunoglobulin is available for passive protection against hepatitis B. Its use should be considered in persons who are accidentally inoculated or who contaminate the eye or mouth or fresh cuts or abrasions of skin with blood from a known HBsAg positive person. Individuals who sustain such accidents should wash the affected area well and seek medical advice. Advice about prophylaxis after such accidents should be obtained by telephone from the nearest Public Health Laboratory. Advice following accidental exposure may also be obtained from the Hospital Control of Infection Officer or the Occupational Health services.

12. *Supplies of HBIG.* Public Health Laboratory Service, either from the Central Public Health Laboratory (Tel: 081-200 6868) or via local Public Health Laboratories. Hepatitis B immunoglobulin is held in Scotland by the Blood Transfusion Service:

Aberdeen (0224) 681818
Dundee (0382) 645166
Edinburgh (031) 2297291
Glasgow (0698) 373315
Inverness (0463) 234151

Hepatitis B immunoglobulin is held in Northern Ireland by the Regional Virus Laboratory, Royal Victoria Hospital, Belfast. Tel: (0232) 240503)
    Note: Supplies of this product are limited and demands should be restricted to patients in whom there is a clear indication for its use.

13. *Dose.* Available in 1 ml ampoules containing 100 iu, and 5 ml ampoules containing 500 iu for intramuscular injection. Adults: 500 iu (5 ml) preferably within 48 hours and not more than 10 days after exposure. A second dose 4 weeks later is required unless:

(a) There is evidence of past HBV infection in the recipient's pre-immunoglobulin blood sample, or
(b) Tests show that the inoculum is anti-HBe positive and therefore not infective, or
(c) A course of HB vaccine is begun at the same time as the first dose of HBIG is given.

14. *Notes*
1. HBIG is not appropriate for treatment of any type of hepatitis B infection.
2. It is not available for travellers.
3. A blood sample should be collected before HBIG is given but administration should not be delayed until test result is known.
4. HBIG will NOT inhibit the antibody response when given at same time as HB vaccine.

Annex 7   Addresses of CDSC and CD(S)U

Communicable Disease Surveillance Centre, 61 Colindale Avenue, London NW9 5EQ. Tel: 081-200 6868.

Communicable Disease (Scotland) Unit, Ruchill Hospital, Glasgow G20 9NB. Tel: 041 946 7120

Glossary

ACDP   Advisory Committee on Dangerous Pathogens.
COSHH   Control of Substances Hazardous to Health Regulations 1988.
EAGA   Expert Advisory Group on AIDS.
HIV   Human Immunodeficiency Viruses (including HIV 1 and 2).
HSAC   Health Services Advisory Committee.
JCVI   Joint Committee on Vaccination and Immunisation.
MAC   Microbiology Advisory Committee.

Clinical health care workers   Any person (including students, trainees and voluntary workers) whose activities normally involve contact with patients' blood or other body fluids.
Decontamination   A general term for removal of microbial contamination to render an item safe. This will include methods of cleaning, disinfection and sterilisation.
Disinfection   A process which reduces the number of viable micro-organisms on an item but does not completely destroy or remove all bacterial spores.

Exposure   Needlestick and other percutaneous exposures to, or contamination of mucous membrane, conjunctiva or broken skin with, blood or blood stained body fluids.

Micro-organism   For the purpose of this document, the term 'micro-organism' includes viruses.

Sharps   Needles, edged instruments, broken glassware or any other item which may be contaminated in use by blood or body fluids and which may cause laceration or puncture wounds.

Sterilisation   The complete destruction or removal of micro-organisms including the most resistant bacterial endospores.

Guidelines for handling mercury

The following guidelines have been drawn up for the British Dental Association by Professor G. S. Nixon and Dr Christine Whittle of the Turner Dental School, Manchester. Originally published in *BDA News* in 1977, they were first revised and updated in 1980, and then in 1982. This latest revised version was prepared in January 1990; it is reprinted by permission of the British Dental Association.

All personnel concerned with the handling of mercury in any form should be acquainted with the potential hazards of this metal. Personnel should also receive instruction in the safe handling procedures needed to deal with any mercury spillages together with suitable methods for the disposal of contaminated materials. The need for routine personal hygiene should be appreciated to minimize the possibility of skin absorption of mercury. If care is taken during the dispensing, handling and disposal of mercury as set out in the guidelines below any potential hazards can be avoided. However, the overall risk of mercury can be minimized greatly by using pre-dispensed capsules.

Personal hygiene

Since mercury can be absorbed through the skin, it is essential for hands to be washed immediately in cold water after any handling of metallic mercury or contaminated equipment. Hand contamination can be minimized by the use of disposable plastic gloves or by the application of a barrier cream. Hand washing facilities should be readily accessible and include hot and cold water, soap, towels and nailbrushes. Ideally, a liquid soap dispenser, disposable paper towels and elbow operated taps are recommended.

Mercury vaporises readily even at room temperature and can be absorbed by inhalation. Eating, smoking, drinking and the application of cosmetics should not take place in the dental surgery, and personnel who are working with mercury should not undertake any of these actions until the hands have been washed.

Cuts in the skin must be protected before any work involving metallic mercury or amalgam is commenced.

Working environment

All dental surgeries should be efficiently ventilated, preferably by means of a mechanical exhaust ventilation system to the outside. Recycling air conditioning systems should never be used in dental surgeries unless a mercury absorbent filter system can be included.

Floor coverings in dental surgeries should be of the linoleum or polyvinyl chloride type with a smooth surface. Joints between sheets of the floor covering should be kept to a minimum and sealed and these should not be in the vicinity of the dental chair or amalgam preparation area. If possible the edges of the floor covering should extend a short distance

209

up the wall to eliminate crevices and in addition any joints should be filled. Tiled floors should be avoided and carpets should never be used.

Dust traps should be avoided, for example open shelving should be replaced by closed cupboards.

All operations involving the use of mercury should be confined to a single designated area preferably in a room other than the dental surgery. Contact with metallic mercury should be minimized and the use of disposable capsules containing amalgam alloy is to be recommended. This area should be kept free from any other equipment and away from any form of heat (heat from radiator, hot air sterilizer, hot air vent of autoclave and indirect heat from sunlight). Such an area should be well ventilated. The work surface itself should be of a smooth impervious material such as Formica. A wooden or metal bench should be avoided or, if used, covered in plastic sheeting. The wall to bench junction should be sealed and covered to prevent mercury accumulating in inaccessible areas at the back of the bench. As an additional precaution the working surfaces should be cleaned on a weekly basis with a mercury suppressant such as a 1 per cent suspension of calcium oxide/flowers of sulphur. (*Note:* care must be taken when using calcium oxide and water due to the exothermic reaction, and plastic gloves must be worn during the washing procedure.)

Cleaning equipment used in the dental surgery itself should not be used in other areas. It is preferable to use a damp mop for cleaning. A conventional vacuum cleaner should never be used as this will increase the atmospheric concentration of mercury vapour. The use of a mercury suppressant such as 1 per cent suspension of calcium oxide/flowers of sulphur once a week will also help to keep the mercury vapour at negligible levels.

Operative procedures involving the use of mercury

Any operative procedures involving mercury (such as preparation of amalgam) or amalgam (such as cleaning amalgam carriers or packing instruments) should be carried out over a suitable drip tray lined with aluminium. Amalgamators or other equipment used in conjunction with mercury should be placed in a shallow tray lined with foil which is large enough to catch any stray droplets. These will form an amalgam which is non-volatile.

If amalgam preparation requires mercury to be dispensed, such as filling reusable capsules or filling the reservoir of an automatic amalgamator, a small funnel must be used to reduce the possibility of mercury spillage. Mercury dispensers used to dispense into reusable capsules must be routinely checked for 'leakage'. The use of pre-proportioned capsules with predetermined amounts of mercury helps to reduce the possibility of mercury spillage.

Storage of metallic mercury and waste mercury material

Mercury should be stored in a well ventilated area away from the surgery.

Mercury from spillages or amalgam residues should be stored in a cool place in a well sealed, clearly labelled container under a solution of 5 per cent potassium permanganate. Waste mercury should not be poured down the sink, placed in open waste bins or kept in beakers or other open containers.

Procedure to deal with a mercury spillage

Any mercury spillage must be cleaned up immediately. In no cirumstances should a vacuum cleaner be used for cleaning up mercury spillage.

All the required equipment for dealing with a spillage should be readily available and checked routinely. Such equipment should include disposable plastic gloves, paper towels, a bulb aspirator for the collection of large drops of mercury, a suitable container fitted with a seal, and a mercury-absorbent paste (equal parts of hydrated calcium oxide, flowers of sulphur and water). Lead from X-ray packets is very useful for dealing with small spillages. Alternatively a commercial mercury spillage kit can be used (see below), though these are expensive, and are no more effective than the mercury-absorbent paste described above.

Disposal of waste and contaminated materials

All waste mercury, including pieces of amalgam and the results of spillages, should be kept in a labelled sealed container preferably under potassium permanganate until sufficient has accumulated for return to the supplier for the purpose of recovery.

Articles contaminated with mercury, e.g. squeeze cloths, cotton wool rolls and paper towels, should be kept in a labelled sealed container until disposal is possible. Polyethylene bags are suitable for this purpose. Prior to disposal the container should be stored in a safe cool place.

When aspirator bottles are cleaned the wash should be poured down an open external drain and not down the surgery sink drain.

When using preproportioned amalgam capsules the cap of the capsule should be replaced before disposal.

Monitoring for mercury exposure

If there is any reason to suspect a serious mercury spillage or atmospheric contamination by mercury, the concentration of mercury vapour in the air should be measured and compared with the threshold limit value for the eight-hour working day (presently 0.05 mg Hg per m^3).

Additionally, the personnel should undergo urine or other forms of biological monitoring. It is recommended that personnel who are routinely exposed to mercury should undergo some form of monitoring at regular intervals.

Mercury spillage kits can be purchased from Techmate Limited, 10 Bridgeturn Avenue, Wolverton, Milton Keynes (Tel: 0908 322222). Mercury collectors to deal with any minute mercury droplets remaining after a spillage can be purchased from Jencons Scientific Limited, 16 Cherry Court Way Industrial Estate, Stanbridge Road, Leighton Buzzard (Tel: 0525 372010).

Index